RECREATION: WATER AND LAND

WATER PRACTICE MANUALS

RECREATION:
WATER AND LAND

WITH A FOREWORD BY
H.R.H. THE DUKE OF EDINBURGH, KG, KT

EDITOR
Bernard J. Dangerfield

*(Deputy Secretary, The Institution of
Water Engineers and Scientists)*

Compiled and Published by
The Institution of Water Engineers and Scientists,
London, England.

©Published by The Institution of Water Engineers and Scientists,
6-8 Sackville Street, London W1X 1DD,
England.

ISBN 0 901427 11 X

First published, 1981

Text photoset in 9/10pt. Times

Printed in Great Britain
at The Lavenham Press Ltd., Lavenham, Suffolk, England.

It is difficult enough to reconcile the different and often conflicting demands on the use of land. Agriculture and industry, housing and amenity, recreation and conservation, all have to be satisfied. The problem with water is that the same stuff can be used for different purposes at successive stages of its career from the moment it falls as rain till it finally runs into the sea. As it goes from hill to river, to lake, to reservoir or canal, to domestic or industrial use, to agriculture to sewage works, back to the river and out to sea, all the conflicting demands for its use have to be reconciled with the fact that water is an absolutely vital factor - the support system of all life on earth.

This book investigates the use of water for recreational purposes. If this use of water conflicts with others, it is as nothing to the conflicting demands of the different forms of recreation. Sailing, motor boat racing, sub-aqua diving, fishing, canoeing, bird-watching, the conservation of nature and wildlife and water skiing - very few of them compatible with one another and each of them may require different qualities of water and many of them may themselves have an influence on the water as a consequence of the way they use it.

Recreation therefore poses a particularly difficult problem for water engineers and scientists as well as for the owners and managers of water resources in their various forms. As a work of reference this book should be invaluable to them.

1981

PREFACE

Both the former Institution of Water Engineers and the Society for Water Treatment and Examination held a well-earned reputation as learned societies responsible for the publication of authoritative works on water technology and science. In 1975 the common interests of these bodies led to their amalgamation and The Institution of Water Engineers and Scientists was formed. This new Institution has again entered the book-publishing field with a wide-ranging series under the general title *Water Practice Manuals.*

The books will appear, over a period of several years, as a series of separate volumes and will deal mainly with the engineering and scientific elements concerned with the water cycle. They will also focus attention on more general subjects which, in England and Wales, have now become the responsibility of the Regional Water Authorities which were set up by the Water Act 1973. In recording what has become, or is likely to become, accepted current practice the books will not be confined entirely to British experience. Where relevant, references will be made to overseas practice and, in particular, to thinking and developments within the EEC. In due course the whole series will form a basic library for those concerned with the technology and science of water.

The first book, entitled *The Structure and Management of the British Water Industry,* covers the various aspects of the water cycle which are controlled by the water authorities and the other relevant public bodies exercising responsibility for "water" in the U.K. This, the second volume, is a wide-ranging and soundly based text on the general recreational use and potential of water and associated land.

Members of the Institution have, for many years, been personally involved in their professional capacities with the recreational use of reservoirs and their catchments and, to a more limited extent, with river navigations. The Water Act 1973 embodied in legislation an increasing response, within what was to become the water industry, to meet both primary "water" functions and also to cater for specific kinds of recreation. The Institution had, primarily for the guidance of its own members, published booklets on recreation on rivers, reservoirs, and gathering grounds in 1963 and 1972 but the extended opportunities arising from the 1973 legislation increasingly called for a wider professional involvement in the detailed control and management of recreational facilities.

The organizations created by the 1973 Act continued to place overall senior responsibility for reservoir operation and water quality control with engineers and scientists, but turned increasingly to other disciplines to assist with the provision and management of recreation in its more detailed aspects. Much of this present book has been written by non-members of the Institution whose professional role has been associated with the water authorities' various involvements in recreation. The remainder has been prepared by Institution members with their own personal responsibilities in the recreational field. Its contents are thus authoritative and practical, condensing hard-won detailed experience in a field where printed guidance, keeping recreation fully within the context set by the 1973 Act, will benefit both practising managers and those serving on public bodies exercising recreational responsibilities.

The book, however, has not been prepared solely in response to the water industry's involvements in recreation. Its contents are relevant to the establishment and management of open-air recreation on water and on associated land by public authorities generally and by the private sector as well.

NOTE ON THE INSTITUTION OF WATER ENGINEERS AND SCIENTISTS

The Institution was established as The British Association of Waterworks Engineers in 1896 and was incorporated in 1911 as The Institution of Water Engineers. On 2nd January 1975 its name was changed to The Institution of Water Engineers and Scientists preliminary to the Institution and the Society for Water Treatment and Examination amalgamating on 1st September 1975. The combined Institution now has a membership of over 5500.

The *objects* of the Institution are set out in its Memorandum of Association. In summary these are:

1. To advance water engineering and science and education therein.
2. To promote study and research work in water engineering and science and to publish the results thereof for the public benefit.
"Water engineering and science" means the application of engineering or scientific knowledge or skill to the supply of water, the management of rivers, the treatment of sewage and its disposal, and the control of pollution in relation to water.

The corporate membership of the Institution comprises engineers and scientists, including chemists, bacteriologists, geologists, hydrologists and others concerned with the water cycle. Corporate members must be holders of approved first degrees in engineering or science and must satisfy the Council as to their practical knowledge and experience of water engineering and science. Persons in other disciplines who occupy senior positions in the water industry or who are engaged in support services can be admitted to non-corporate membership.

Most members of the Institution in the United Kingdom work for public or quasi-public authorities. In England and Wales, these are the National Water Council, the ten Regional Water Authorities and the statutory water companies; in Scotland, the nine Regional and three Islands Councils together with the Central Scotland Water Development Board; and in Northern Ireland, the Department of the Environment for Northern Ireland (Water Services Branch).

Other members work in central government, research and teaching establishments, or as consulting engineers. Some members are concerned with the construction of civil engineering works as contractors, or as manufacturers of equipment such as pumps or treatment plant.

About 18 per cent of the members of the Institution are overseas, either because they are citizens of overseas countries or because they are working there on secondment from the United Kingdom.

The main function of the Institution is the provision of learned society activities, i.e. the sharing of experience and the dissemination of knowledge through meetings and publications. In the United Kingdom and the Republic of Ireland there are seven Local and two Specialist Sections, each with its own programme of papers and visits to works. In addition the Institution organizes at least two conferences or symposia each year.

The publications of the Institution, besides this new range of Water Practice Manuals, include a Journal (published six times a year), proceedings of symposia, and various reports.

ACKNOWLEDGEMENTS

The Council of The Institution of Water Engineers and Scientists acknowledges the help given in the preparation of this book by those serving the many bodies and organizations involved in the water industry and related activities.

Acknowledgements for permission to reproduce extracts from published works are included, where appropriate, in the text.

The Council also acknowledges with gratitude the work of the Manuals Subcommittee, which was set up for the planning of this series of Water Practice Manuals. The members of the Subcommittee are: H. Speight (Chairman); T. W. Brandon; P. J. Gadd; T. A. Harker; J. D. Jepson; J. E. Massey; B. H. Rofe; K. H. Tattersall; and B. J. Dangerfield (Subcommittee Secretary).

CONTRIBUTORS

The Council of The Institution of Water Engineers and Scientists acknowledges the considerable debt of gratitude which is due to the following who have contributed to the writing of this book.

Book Co-ordinator

C. A. Serpell,   BEng, FICE, FIWES, formerly General Manager, Sunderland and South Shields Water Company; now retired.

Chapter Contributors and Helpers

Chapter 1: Historical and Legal Aspects

Contributed by: A. S. Hughes,   MA, FBIM, Solicitor, Secretary and Director of Administration, Northumbrian Water Authority; also, Honorary Solicitor, Association of Water Officers.

A. J. Nuttall,   LLB, MPhil, Assistant Solicitor, Northumbrian Water Authority.

Assisted by: The references to the position in Scotland were contributed by:
E. Bain,   LLB, Principal Solicitor, Department of Administration, Lothian Regional Council.

The references to the position in Northern Ireland were contributed by:
W. A. Condy,   BSc, FICE, FIWES, Director of Water Services, Northern Ireland Department of the Environment.

Chapter 2: Public Health Considerations and Pollution Control Aspects

Contributed by: M. A. Hilson,   FRSC, FIWES, Principal Scientist (Water Treatment and Supply), North West Water Authority

Assisted by: H. Speight,   BSc, FICE, FIWES, Director of Resource Planning, Southern Water Authority

Chapter 3: Activities and Supporting Requirements

Contributed by: F. G. Davy,   DSO, DFC, FRICS, Assistant Director (Estates and Recreation), Directorate of Administration, Anglian Water Authority.

A. E. Ericson,   BA, DipTP, FRTPI, MIRM, Manager, Recreation and Amenity, Southern Water Authority.

J. R. Hampson,   DFC, BSc, MIF, Assistant Director (Recreation), Welsh Water Authority.

Chapter 4: Planning and Construction of Recreational Facilities

Contributed by: J. K. D. Green,   BEng, FICE, FIWES, MBIM, Water
                                    Supply Engineer, Western Division,
                                    Yorkshire Water Authority.

Assisted by: A. E. Ericson,   BA, DipTP, FRTPI, MIRM, Manager,
                                    Recreation and Amenity, Southern Water
                                    Authority.

                 R. E. Shapland,   BSc, FIFor., Forestry Officer, North West
                                    Water Authority.

Chapter 5: The Management of Recreational Facilities

Contributed by: J. K. D. Green,   BEng, FICE, FIWES, MBIM, Water
                                    Supply Engineer, Western Division,
                                    Yorkshire Water Authority.

Assisted by: J. Chandler,   BSc, FZS, MIBiol, Fisheries Officer,
                                    Southern Water Authority.

                 R. E. Shapland,   BSc, FIFor, Forestry Officer, North West
                                    Water Authority.

Chapter 6: Safety and Protection

Contributed by: M. L. Parry,   MA, MIBiol, Assistant Director of
                                    Scientific Services (Fisheries, Amenity and
                                    Recreation), Severn-Trent Water
                                    Authority.

Assisted by: Commander R. W.   Fisheries Officer (Draycote Water),
                 Dunn,   Severn-Trent Water Authority.

                 Mrs. J. Stevenson, Technical Assistant, Operations
                                    Department, Severn-Trent Water
                                    Authority.

Chapter 7: Economic and Financial Considerations

Contributed by: C. J. Woods,   IPFA, Assistant Director of Finance
                                    (Capital), Southern Water Authority.

                 R. Banerji,   BA, MA, MBA, Chief Economist,
                                    Directorate of Resource Planning,
                                    Southern Water Authority.

Chapter 8: Public Relations

Contributed by: B. E. Parker,   MIPR, Public Relations Officer, Wessex
                                    Water Authority.

Chapter 9: Participating Bodies

Contributed by: A. Blenkharn,   Director, Water Space Amenity
                                    Commission.

Assisted by: Miss Anne Dickinson, formerly Research Assistant, Water Space
                                    Amenity Commission.

CONTENTS

Chapter 4—*continued*

Chapter 5. The Management of Recreational Facilities

Chapter 6. Safety and Protection

Chapter 7. Economic and Financial Considerations

Chapter 8. Public Relations

Chapter 8—*continued*

Chapter 9.   Participating Bodies

LIST OF ILLUSTRATIONS

*Between
pages*

44-45   Sailing on the Thames Water Authority's Queen Mother reservoir, at
Datchet
Sailing on the Derwent reservoir of the Sunderland and South Shields
Water Company

Water-skiing and power boating at the Cotswold Water Park in
Gloucestershire and Wiltshire
Henley Royal Regatta
Kielder Water, Northumbrian Water Authority

Trout fishing on Blagdon reservoir, Bristol Waterworks Company
River fishing, Wessex Water Authority
Sail-boarding at Bewl Bridge reservoir, Southern Water Authority

Hang-gliding at Rivington, North West Water Authority
Ferry Meadows Country Park, Peterborough Development Corporation

Chapter 1

HISTORICAL AND LEGAL ASPECTS

1. PREAMBLE

AIM OF BOOK

THIS, the second book in the series of Water Practice Manuals dealing with the science and technology of water-related matters, is concerned with the provision, management, and operation of recreational facilities, in all their varied forms, on the waters and land adjoining them which are administered by water undertakers and others.

In the context of this book, water undertakers are the statutory water undertakers defined in the Water Act 1945, Section 59, as any company, local authority, board, committee or other person applying water under an enactment. Currently they consist of the regional water authorities and statutory water companies in England and Wales, the regional and islands Councils in Scotland, and in Northern Ireland the Water Service of the Department of the Environment.

The book combines the extensive knowledge and experience of many of those closely associated with water-based and waterside recreation within the water industry. As a reference manual, however, the interest of the book is not limited to those charged with the day-to-day organization and management of recreational activities. It will also be valuable to all interested in the more general aspects of making water-related facilities available to the public, either on an occasional basis or as members of clubs established specifically for the purpose.

This, the first chapter, traces the historical development of the demand for recreational use, and refers to the role and legal powers and duties of the water undertakers and others in promoting and controlling these activities.

STATUTORY PROVISIONS

This chapter refers specifically to the legal position as it applies in England and Wales, but where appropriate reference is made to the chief differences which apply in Scotland and Northern Ireland.

Many of the statutes referred to have been subject to considerable amendment and judicial interpretation since they were first enacted, and it is likely that further amendments will be made from time to time. It is often difficult for anyone but a professional lawyer to discover the exact state of the law at any particular time, and the layment should keep up to date on Case Law and beware of relying on out-of-date or Queen's Printers copies of the statutes without taking professional advice.

A table of the statutes referred to in this chapter is given in Appendix A, p. 43.

2. HISTORICAL BACKGROUND

INTRODUCTION

The Industrial Revolution which this country experienced in the eighteenth and nineteenth centuries prompted a large scale exodus from the rural areas to the towns and cities in search of work. That same period also saw the rapid development of transport systems, notably the rail network and more importantly still, the canal system which features so significantly in today's water recreation scene.

Movement of population from the countryside to the towns has stabilized in this century with the vast bulk of the population now permanently centred in the large cities and industrial conurbations. Such movement as there is now is largely in the other direction, albeit of a temporary and spasmodic nature in that at weekends and holiday times the town-dwellers are increasingly flocking back to the countryside to spend their leisure hours enjoying a different environment or pursuing recreational activities. With increased affluence and improved transportation and roads, it is now comparatively easy for people to escape from their artificial urban environment to relax and enjoy themselves in more natural surroundings.

Water provides a particular fascination in the quest for recreation in two ways. The contrasting environments where land and water meet are a focal point of interest for passive enjoyment of the countryside and a variety of water sports provide an attractive and challenging alternative to land-based activities.

The wide scope of activities which are attracted to water creates problems, however, in that everyone has a different ideal form of recreation or leisure. In meeting this challenge for diversity, it becomes necessary to resolve the compatibility between different pursuits, as well as to protect the primary functions of the water concerned.

POST-WAR GROWTH IN DEMAND

It is clear that since the early 1950s there has been a growth in all forms of recreation but a particularly large increase in popularity of water-based sports.

Important elements in the demand for recreation are the increases both in incomes and in the time available for leisure. Total personal disposable incomes in the U.K. rose from £10 302 million in 1951 to £97 312 million in 1977. In real terms income almost doubled[1]. At the same time the basic working week decreased from 44.4 hr in 1951[2] to 39.9 hr in 1977[1] and whereas 97 per cent of employees were entitled to two weeks or less paid holiday in 1951, by 1977 99 per cent had obtained three weeks or more[1].

Water sports such as swimming, sailing and angling have a long history, originating in necessity and naturally flourishing on an island with a long coastline and a nautical tradition. It is estimated that there are now nearly 3¾ million anglers in Great Britain[3]. Membership of the Royal Yachting Association has increased from 1 000 in 1950 to 52 000 in 1977. Membership of canoe clubs has increased seven-fold and of the British Sub-Aqua Club over ten-fold[1], and there has been a similar growth in popularity of the use of canals for pleasure cruising[4].

The Department of the Environment has estimated that there are about six million people who regularly participate in water sports[5]. However, it is not so easy to ascertain the number of people whose passive enjoyment of the countryside is enhanced by water, whether they be casual ramblers and bird-watchers or "just-lookers". An indication of the growth in these activities can perhaps be seen in a traffic census which showed a rise of 35 per cent between 1966 and 1973 in the number of cars in rural areas on a summer weekend[6], and the fact that three-quarters of the population now make at least one trip to the countryside each year[7]. Greater awareness of the countryside is apparent from the large increases in membership of nature trusts, such as the Royal Society for the Protection of Birds and The National Trust. Recorded visits to countryside facilities are equally much more frequent since the 1950s, the huge increase in car-ownership being largely responsible for this. It is possible that the raising of oil prices in 1973 and again in 1979 may temporarily limit the continued rapid growth in water-based sports which, it has been claimed, will probably treble in popularity by the end of the century. This effect will however most likely result in a reduction of unplanned car trips around the countryside and will mean more specific visits to beauty spots or recreation centres.

THE IMPACT OF TECHNOLOGY

In many respects the effects of technology on recreation are counterbalancing. The Industrial Revolution removed people from the land to the towns with the result that about 80 per cent of the population in the U.K. live in urban areas. Urban expansion and concrete jungles have created the need for country recreation by re-awakening man's instincts and desire to return to natural environments. Yet it was technological as well as social development that enabled a shorter working week to be possible and is likely to result in further reductions. It is technology that provides the roads and the vehicles which enable man to visit the countryside so easily, and the ability to increase the resources for leisure with man-made developments such as reservoirs and wet mineral workings.

With the basic motivation for countryside recreation being escapism, it might seem somewhat surprising that technology plays an important role in the activities themselves. However, for many, the creature comforts of modern society cannot be discarded and must accompany them to the countryside. Herein lies one of the major causes of difficulty. There is conflict between preservation of the environment, encouraged by those who would deny the intrusion of the twentieth century into the countryside, and the use of the countryside as an urban playground by car-driving picnickers, caravans, power boats, cruisers and water-skiers.

Increased affluence has resulted in a desire to spend money on enjoyment, and technology has provided the answer by widening the diversity of sports. Fibre-glass and nylon have facilitated improvements to fishing rods and lines respectively, reducing the cost and undoubtedly helping to increase the popularity of angling. The fibre-glass hull, outboard motor, aqualungs, and various new methods of construction are examples of developments which have enabled different sports to become practicable such as water-skiing, sub-aqua, hydroplaning, canoeing and dinghy sailing. Thus, technology has created the need and provided the means for recreation but at the same time it has caused the management of resources to be a complex issue of resolving conflicts.

PUBLIC POLICY ON ACCESS TO THE COUNTRYSIDE

Government policy on outdoor recreation was initially limited to the provision of public parks and pleasure grounds and did not otherwise interfere with the Common Law right of landowners to control access. This *laissez-faire* attitude towards opening the countryside to the public was first modified when the Law of Property Act 1925 granted public access to commons "for air and exercise" although in rural areas this right required the owners' consents.

The Access to Mountains Act 1939 was a step forward but it was not until 1949, with the National Parks and Access to the Countryside Act, that the Government first demonstrated a real interest in responding to the need for country access and recreation. Under the 1949 Act local authorities could promote open air recreation by means of access agreements and orders. However, the definition of open air recreation excluded organized games and the powers only extended to open country and not *(inter alia)* water.

The Countryside Act 1968 (and its equivalent in Scotland, the Countryside (Scotland) Act 1967) enlarged the scope of access powers, gave water undertakers powers to provide for recreation, and authorized local authorities to create country parks. The Act also stressed the importance of protection of the countryside and established a Countryside Commission whose functions are "the conservation and enhancement of the natural beauty and amenity of the countryside, and encouraging the provision and improvement, for persons resorting to the countryside, of facilities for the enjoyment of the countryside and of open-air recreation in the countryside" Section 1(2).

THE CHALLENGE TO THE WATER INDUSTRY

The Sports Council* has reported[8] that:—

"There are certain things which private enterprise cannot do; notably, it cannot acquire large tracts of land which are in multiple ownership nor can it create or control many of the basic services, such as water and roads, needed to support recreational facilities. Public authorities already control areas of land and water, such as forests, reservoirs and transport canals, which have an essential primary function; however by careful management such facilities can play an important secondary role in providing recreation.

The growth of outdoor activities, particularly water-based sports, and the gradual involvement of local authorities in the provision of country recreation has increased pressures on other public bodies such as the water industry, to do likewise. However, the scale of facilities required for many types of water sports limits the ability of private enterprise to meet the demands, except perhaps for the exploitation of gravel workings.

In 1960 the Wolfenden Committee Report[9] urged greater access to inland waterways and reservoirs for sport. Coastal waters can satisfy some of the demand but it is becoming increasingly apparent that apart from the Lake District the principal burden of providing recreation on inland waters must lie with the water industry. The National Parks Policy Review Committee[10] stressed that "It is also important that facilities for water-based recreation should be rapidly increased outside the national parks in order to cater for the growing numbers of people who wish to participate in water sports. A secondary advantage to be obtained from the development of such facilities is that they attract also as spectators some of the casual visitors to the countryside and may thus ease pressures elsewhere."

The requirements are great and the potential exists to meet the demands. Public awareness of the countryside and the environment is now at such a level that it has become much more difficult to justify exclusive use of inland waters in public lands let alone large areas of gathering grounds. It is possible for the water industry to play an important role in coping with this leisure explosion especially since, with most resources for leisure remaining largely static, those future water requirements which are met by new reservoirs will lead to new opportunities for water-based sports.

TRADITIONAL ATTITUDES TOWARDS ACCESS TO RESERVOIRS AND GATHERING GROUNDS

Fears about water-borne diseases have long been a dominant concern of the water supply industry. In the nineteenth century the growth of industrial areas and increased risks of cholera and typhoid in particular resulted in piped water supplies being taken from sources in unpolluted upland areas. The simplest way to maintain

*See Chapter 9 for descriptions of the Sports Council and other bodies concerned with recreation.

purity was to eliminate human and animal contact from reservoirs and their gathering grounds. Large areas of moorland were thus acquired by water undertakers. In some instances public rights of access were preserved by the Local Act of Parliament establishing the gathering grounds. The Manchester Water Act 1878 for Thirlmere and the Birmingham Corporation Water Act 1892 for the Elan Valley with its much copied "Birmingham Clauses" were prime examples. However, large numbers of catchment areas did not benefit from such clauses, which did not in any case give access to the reservoirs themselves. The evidence given to the Gathering Grounds Sub-Committee of the Central Advisory Water Committee for its Report in 1948 on public access (The Heneage Report)[11] revealed the wide variety in practice over access to the two million acres of gathering grounds. Although policy frequently corresponded with the circumstances when the land was originally acquired, variations sometimes resulted solely from differences of opinion as to safety of supply.

Public use of the reservoirs themselves was even more jealously guarded against, being practically non-existent until 1904 when the Bristol Waterworks Company was the first to introduce reservoir trout fishing at Blagdon. The same Company was responsible for the first organized sailing on their Cheddar reservoir in 1947. At the time of the 1948 Report[11] on access to gathering grounds only four of the 29 water undertakers who gave evidence allowed permit fishing.

Many water undertakers relied solely on protection of the source of supply to maintain the wholesomeness of the water and where there was treatment it was only screening or basic filtration. However, the ever-growing demand for water necessitated the use of less ideal lowland sources which were less easily protected from pollution. Water treatment systems improved and the specific advantage of long storage as a means of destroying micro-organisms became recognized. Exclusion of the public from catchment areas became not quite so essential. Old traditions in the water industry died hard, however, and the Special Committee on "Footpaths and Access to the Countryside"[12] questioned the basis for the wide variations in policy in 1947.

The Croydon typhoid epidemic in 1937 highlighted the need for safe supplies of water and in 1939 the Ministry of Health issued a "Memorandum on the safeguards to be adopted in day to day administration of water undertakings".[13] The need was stressed for "careful and constant supervision of supplies of drinking water" and recommended, whenever practicable, acquisition or control of gathering grounds to prevent pollution. With respect to access the memorandum stated:

"The public should be generally excluded from the reservoir itself and its banks. Permission to boat or fish in the reservoir should be granted, if at all, only on a limited scale, as a special privilege and under such control as will effectively prevent abuse. Bathing should never be allowed."

In addition, treatment of all sources of water above ground was recommended to provide more than one line of defence against pollution. The pressures resulting from higher demand and a change in public opinion that were to become overwhelming in post-war years had not yet influenced the Government or the water undertakers sufficiently to modify their traditional approach.

A CHANGING APPROACH TO RECREATION BY WATER UNDERTAKERS

Indications of the future trend in allowing access to reservoirs can be seen in the 1948 Report of the Gathering Grounds Sub-Committee[11] which referred to the existence of four lines of defence to protect water purity:—

". . .the first line will be the efforts to eliminate potential sources of pollution of the raw water, these, as we have shown, can never be wholly reliable;

the second line is long storage; this is a defence that seldom fails in practice but is subject to uncontrollable variations;

the third line is filtration; and

the fourth chlorination (or sterilization by ozone or other means)''.

Although the Report thought that more than one line of defence was desirable it was recognized that:—

"It is a commonplace of history and of natural history that over-developed defences may stifle the life they are designed to protect, and it would not be in the national interest, if, dissatisfied with effective practical security against typhoid, the water industry were to pursue theoretical perfection in this one field of public health at the cost of seriously limiting facilities for healthy exercise. . .''.

Reliance on restricted access, storage, and chlorination was not considered adequate nor was filtration deemed to be a sufficient safeguard to be able to permit unrestricted access and heavy pollution of the water source. The Report stated:—

"A reasonably pure source, however, combined with long and secure storage and adequate treatment by both filtration and chlorination appears to be thoroughly satisfactory in practice and to provide, if normally well conducted, sufficient margin for human error or the accidental failure of any single line of defence''.

Reasonable purity, concluded the Report, need not entail rigid exclusion of the public:—

"We would therefore entirely prohibit bathing and only permit boating, fishing or access to the banks under a system of control by the water undertaker sufficiently rigid to exclude the possibility of abuse. Subject to such limitation as may be necessary for the discouragement of large crowds, we can see no justification, on grounds of water purity, for prohibiting access by walkers, cyclists, or motorists to the remainder of the gathering ground''.

Access to a reservoir and its banks was thought to be a privilege not to be abused and best associated with membership of a responsible club. Greater care would be necessary where one of the lines of defence was weak or became weak and it was also pointed out that none of these safeguards was of course necessary for regulating reservoirs where there was no public health reason why recreation should not take place "on the largest scale".

The 1948 Report marks the turning point in the approach to recreation on reservoirs. Exclusion of the public on grounds of water quality was the issue in question and a more consistent policy by water undertakers was advocated. However, the Sub-Committee saw no reason why the first line of defence need be applied too rigidly when there was adequate treatment which they directed was necessary in any case. As a result, most new reservoirs included better provision for water treatment, and, aided by technological advances, made it possible to permit varying degrees of access and recreation. The question, particularly in respect of gathering grounds, became one of degree rather than of whether or not to prohibit all access completely.

In 1963 the Report of Council of The Institution of Water Engineers (now The Institution of Water Engineers and Scientists) on the recreational use of waterworks[14] supported the 1948 Report of the Gathering Grounds Sub-Committee, paying particular attention to the need for supervision and safety. The recommendation that clubs be established as a means of control was wholeheartedly endorsed. The Committee, appointed by the Institution's Council to examine recreation, noted that various conditions affected the bacteriological quality of water. These included geographical, climatic and agricultural factors, type of fauna and incidence of birds.

Although theoretically public access would increase the risk of pollution, its practical significance would vary and depend on the type of activity and extent of treatment. Compensation reservoirs were less problematic and

"The extent of the control exercised by the undertakers in the interests of the works and of the safety of the public should depend on the number of people likely to make use of the facilities, and the number of different recreational activities which are permitted".

However, the Report was emphatic that no risks should be taken with the purity of water supplied to the public, and guidelines were provided to assist water undertakers in assessing the permissibility of recreation. The Committee approved of most activities, if controlled. Sailing and rowing could be managed by a club, fishing and birdwatching by permit, and access to surrounding areas by means of designated footpaths, picnic sites, etc. Water-skiing, canoeing, bathing, caravanning and (unless on special sites) camping, were not recommended.

In the years 1966 to 1968 the Government demonstrated a renewed interest in countryside recreation. The Water Resources Act 1963, under which River Authorities were established, had for the first time given express powers to provide facilities for water recreation. Similar powers were given by the Countryside Act 1968 to water undertakers in England and Wales and to the Scottish water boards under the Countryside (Scotland) Act 1967. The Ministry of Land and Natural Resources issued a joint circular with the Department of Education and Science in 1966 on the use of reservoirs and gathering grounds for recreation[15]. Despite financial limitations and the overriding duty to supply wholesome water, the Ministers believed plans could be made to permit easier public access particularly to new reservoirs and to those natural lakes which traditionally had been open to the public and had been acquired for water supply. Attention was drawn to the guidelines in the Memorandum on Safeguards[13] and to the Report of The Institution of Water Engineers[14]. Although the proposals were said not to exceed the recommendations in those documents, the Ministers did think that bathing would be permissible in a direct-supply reservoir where there was full treatment of the water and that some other activities might be possible for casual visitors.

In 1967 the Ministry of Housing and Local Government and the Welsh Office revised the Memorandum on safeguards in waterworks[13] under the title "Safeguards to be adopted in the operation and management of waterworks"[16]. The revised Memorandum approved the 1963 Report of The Institution of Water Engineers[14] and restated the principle that regulating reservoirs, whose development had been encouraged by the creation of river authorities, should be able to provide a wide range of recreational activities. Although representations had been made by the then British Waterworks Association (absorbed into the National Water Council in 1974), during prior consultations opposing bathing in direct-supply reservoirs, the accompanying circular re-affirmed the view expressed in 1966[15] that bathing should be permitted where the safety of bathers could be ensured and treatment was comparable to that given to water abstracted from a lowland river intake. Furthermore, the Memorandum indicated that canoeing should be allowed provided that when training involved submersion it only occurred where the treatment was of the standard required for bathers. With the exception of rescue boats, however, power-driven craft should be prohibited from supply reservoirs. The Scottish Development Department circulated similar proposals for safety on Scottish waterways.[17]

A questionnaire circulated to water undertakers in connection with the Report of The Institution of Water Engineers in 1963[14] revealed that only six water undertakers allowed sailing on direct-supply reservoirs, although most permitted angling and bird watching. The 1966 White Paper "Leisure in the Countryside" which preceded the Countryside Act 1968 pointed out that access to many reservoirs was restricted without sufficient reason.

Whilst the response to the changing climate of opinion appeared to be slow to affect existing reservoirs, newly built reservoirs were being planned with recreational facilities at the outset. The Bristol Waterworks Company were again one of the pioneers with the Chew Valley Lake, opened in 1956, accommodating sailing, trout-fishing and a nature reserve, although not at that time giving access to the general public. Grafham Water was authorized by an Act of Parliament containing individual powers to provide recreational facilities seven years in advance of the Countryside Act 1968. This reservoir, completed in 1966, included picnic areas, a nature reserve, and unrestricted public access to most of the water's edge. Problems of safety and supervision prevented swimming and casual canoeing; sailing and other boating activities were organized through a club responsible for safety precautions. Ultimate control at Grafham Water of necessity remained with the then Great Ouse Water Authority. Derwent Reservoir, managed by the Sunderland and South Shields Water Company, opened in 1967 and Draycote Water of the former Rugby Joint Water Board in 1969 are other major examples of new reservoirs planned for multiple use, including informal recreation. The Rugby Joint Water Board's recreation policy provides an indication of the changing factors governing recreation on reservoirs where complete control of the catchment areas is not feasible and better water treatment is provided[18]:—

"(1) Major decisions of the Board relating to the recreational use of reservoirs should be taken after consultation with the West Midlands Regional Sports Councils.
(2) Any development of recreational facilities should be designed to provide the maximum utilization of the water, and to avoid giving exclusive rights which might result in other interests being denied the use of water which was not being fully utilized by the monopoly holder.
(3) Any rights granted for recreational purposes should be flexible in nature, and restricted in term, so that adjustments may readily be made to meet changes in public demand.
(4) Any recreational facilities should be organized and charged so that, in the long run, no additional expense falls upon the Board. . .".

In 1972 The Institution of Water Engineers issued a revised version of their 1963 Report under the title Recreation on Reservoirs and Rivers[19], which re-affirmed the prime duty of water undertakers to provide safe water and recognized that although development of recreation should be encouraged, the availability of other resources was relevant. This factor is of particular importance in Scotland where there is an abundance of lochs and rivers and a large coastline providing sufficient water for recreation without needing to use reservoirs. In a paper presented to The Institution of Water Engineers in 1970 Little[20] remarked:—

"Because there is a high scarcity value of inland water surface areas in England, this is no reason why the pressure for the multiple-use of inland waters should automatically be transferred to Scotland."

Likewise, even in the popular tourist area of the Trossachs, within easy reach of Clydeside, careful control of access to catchment areas has enabled the purity of water abstracted from Loch Katrine to be maintained, without elaborate treatment.

The increased willingness of water undertakers to provide recreation is reflected in changes in the Institution's 1972 report[19]. After advising that:—

"Where treatment given to water abstracted from direct-supply reservoirs is minimal, prevention of any further risk of pollution at the source will be a dominant factor in any decision of the water undertaker."

The report suggested that public access to direct-supply reservoirs frequently involved no additional risks of pollution. Thus it no longer discouraged canoeing and sub-aqua activities and merely drew attention to management problems created by permitting water-skiing. After strongly emphasizing water purity in 1963 the later report demonstrates that in most cases protection of the public and avoidance of over-use and conflicts are often more relevant factors. Thus swimming is still not recommended, but pollution by bathers is no longer given as one of the reasons. This change of emphasis has resulted in the policy for regulating reservoirs being little different except that less restrictions need to be made on powered craft, camping, and caravanning.

RECREATION ON OTHER INLAND WATERS BEFORE REORGANIZATION

It was estimated in 1969 that public water supply reservoirs constituted less than one-fifth of the non-tidal waters in England and Wales[21]. Rivers form the greater part of the remainder, though the abandonment of canals for the carriage of freight has led to their being used for amenity purposes, and wet mineral workings are increasingly becoming available. River authorities were given powers under the Water Resources Act 1963 to provide recreation over the reservoirs they controlled and also over other non-tidal inland waters which were regulated by them. Excluded were tidal waters, waters within the control of a navigation authority, harbour authority or conservancy authority, and also independent lakes or groups of lakes not discharging to other inland waters.

The other public body with major powers to provide recreation in inland waters is the British Waterways Board with its network of canals and navigable rivers. Local authorities and private interests can also be involved, principally with lakes and mineral workings and to a certain extent, rivers and canals.

Rivers

Rivers have traditionally been used for angling and, where possible, boating. Sailing and rowing are generally only feasible on major navigable rivers but on most rivers canoeing is possible, subject to difficulties over rights of navigation, especially where riparian owners wish to protect valuable fishing rights against disturbance. The Tyne Recreation Study[22] recognized the value of riverside walks like the Thames towpath as a source of leisure and the Trent provides an example of the successful multiple use of a river. In addition to the rivers themselves there is recreational potential in drainage channels, flood storage and river-regulating reservoirs, and river purification lakes. Public health concerns are predominantly about the health and safety of the participants and the principal problems concern access and congestion.

The establishment of river authorities under the Water Resources Act 1963, with overall responsibilities for river management, was a step forward in the organization of the water industry and helped to develop opportunities for recreation. Regulation of the flows of rivers (whose levels varied partly as a result of water abstraction), pollution control, and a fisheries policy all assisted in obtaining the best leisure use of rivers. On navigable rivers, recreational powers were vested, under the Act, in the British Waterways Board in conjunction with their control of the canal network.

The 1972 Report of The Institution of Water Engineers[19] recognized this new unified approach to recreation made possible by the river authorities and included recreation on rivers. Attention was drawn to the pollution risk of cruising, especially where the river was a source of water supply and recommended adequate provision for the safe disposal of human and domestic waste. Comments in the report on activities in the catchment area of regulating reservoirs also applied to rivers.

Canals

The network of broad and narrow canals and navigable rivers, initially a major means of commercial transportation, is now principally used for leisure with very little commercial use of narrow canals. Canals were nationalized in 1948, and under the Transport Act 1962 control passed from the British Transport Commission to the British Waterways Board. Although canals were already being used extensively for angling and cruising, the Board now had recreational powers. It was charged, however, with making proposals for canals that were no longer viable for commercial traffic. The resultant Report[23] revealed that the revenue from pleasure craft on narrow canals was several times greater than that from commercial users, although leisure activities themselves could not be self-supporting financially.

Apart from navigation, canals frequently have other functions—land drainage and industrial water supply—and their maintenance would in any event be necessary for these purposes. Without navigation, weirs could replace locks and still permit the essential functions of the canals as well as angling, canoeing and towpath walks. If however, such a change were to be made, it was considered that the use of canals for navigation would be lost permanently since the cost of reversing such a changeover would be prohibitive.

The Government took the view[24] that the recreational potential of cruising on inland waterways was too valuable an asset to be lost and should be subsidized from public funds. Provision was made in the Transport Act 1968 for the retention of 2300 km of the Board's 3100 km of waterways for navigation. In addition, 559 km of commercial waterways, generally broad canals, were to be used primarily for the carriage of freight, though recreation would be possible. A total of 1 748 km of canals, mostly narrow, were designated cruising waterways with an annual maintenance grant.

Many of the problems of recreation on canals are similar to those on rivers, particularly congestion on narrow canals where the 6.4 km/hr speed limit, necessary to prevent bank erosion, eliminates any potential for water-skiing or power-boating. Canals are thus principally used for angling, cruising, and occasional canoeing with a greater scope sometimes possible on broad canals. After the Transport Act 1968 gave them direct powers to maintain cruising waterways, the British Waterways Board commenced an extensive programme of improvements to facilities and encouragement of clubs and commercial interest in canals[4].

Lakes and Mineral Workings

Scotland is well favoured with natural lakes but in England and Wales the only natural lakes of sufficient size to permit major recreational potential are in the Lake District and in North Wales (Lake Bala). Private owners and local authorities have developed some of the smaller lakes for fishing, informal recreation and sometimes boating, but the pressure of demand in England has led to the use of wet mineral workings for leisure purposes. Most lakes and mineral workings are in private ownership. Local authorities can purchase or offer assistance in developing leisure facilities but the ultimate decision rests with the owner. Planning permission conditions can be one of the means by which the public need for recreation can be realized and the gravel industry is now recognizing the commercial potential of its wet workings, although in urban areas it can be more profitable to infill for other development. In addition there have been larger scale schemes planned by local authorities with grants under the Countryside Act 1968. Examples are the Holme Pierrepont National Water Sports Centre, Nottinghamshire, which features an Olympic rowing course constructed from several pits, and the Cotswold Water Park in Gloucestershire and Wiltshire, with a series of lagoons accommodating different activities. Separation of water areas into lagoons makes it easier to permit power-boating and water-skiing, which so often have to be prohibited on other inland waters. Similar schemes have been planned for the Colne Valley and the Lea Valley, near London. Coal mining can also lead to new water resources when subsidence creates lakes such as the "flashes" in South Lancashire and when opencast mine-workings are landscaped into a country park.

THE NEW WATER INDUSTRY

The Water Act 1973 added what has become known as the fourth dimension of the water industry, imposing ministerial responsibility for recreation on inland waters as a part of a national policy for water in England and Wales (Section 1(2)d). The unified approach to water management through the creation of regional water authorities will help to promote recreation, which is so dependent upon the other aspects of water policy. Furthermore, there is now a positive duty on water authorities in England and Wales to provide recreation. Although an improved structure and an additional duty will not in themselves change attitudes in the water industry they will encourage the trend of reviewing the need for constraints in the light of new knowledge and technology and increasing public demand for greater access.

The differing situation in Scotland is recognized by the legislature which did not impose any duty on the regional authorities, created by the Local Government (Scotland) Act 1973 with responsibilities for water supply, to use reservoirs for recreation. In the reorganization of local government in Northern Ireland, at 1st October 1973, the responsibility for water supply and sewerage services was vested in the Ministry of Development (now the Department of the Environment for Northern Ireland). In the Water and Sewerage Services (Northern Ireland) Order 1973, Article 42 empowers the Department to provide facilities for recreation on any land vested in it for the purposes of the Order and to make charges for the use of these facilities.

The National Water Council, which was set up by the Water Act 1973, is an independent statutory body with statutory functions. Its role is that of a central co-ordinating, consultative and advisory body, and its principal duties are to advise Government Ministers on national policy for water and to promote and assist the efficient performance by the regional water authorities of their functions.

In 1979 the Council, in collaboration with the Department of the Environment, the Welsh Office, the Department of Health and Social Security and the Public Health Laboratory Service, issued a publication entitled "Water supply hygiene: safeguards in the operation and management of public waterworks in England and Wales"[25], which brought up-to-date the Memorandum issued in 1939[13] and revised in 1967[16]. This is one of a number of publications dealing with health and safety matters which have been issued by the National Water Council since the re-organization of the water industry in 1974.

The document gives advice on a wide range of safety matters and on the protection of sources of water supply. As far as public access to reservoirs and gathering grounds, etc., is concerned, it is stated that "Where water supplies derived from rivers are subjected to comprehensive treatment, recreational activities in and around regulating and compensation water reservoirs discharging solely to these rivers are unlikely to constitute a significant pollution hazard" and "decisions on public access will normally be guided more by considerations of public safety and amenity than by water quality and hygiene".

In the case of reservoirs from which water is taken directly for treatment and public supply, different considerations apply and the document reiterates the views expressed in the 1939 Memorandum and states that "Public access and recreational use may involve a risk of pollution, but the significance of the risk and the extent to which such activities can be permitted will depend upon the characteristics of the reservoir and on the treament given to the water. Restrictions and control will be needed for most kinds of recreation and they should be designed to be adequate to safeguard the water supply".

The Water Space Amenity Commission, set up under the Water Act 1973 (Section 23), is also an independent statutory body. Its function is to advise, after consultation with other parties, the Secretary of State, the National Water Council and the water authorities on the formulation, promotion and execution of the national policy for water relating to recreation and amenity in England. It also has, by statute, informal but strong links with the Welsh Water Authority.

The Commission's task is one of co-ordinating and promoting activities in connection with water space within the control of the industry as the amenity arm of the National Water Council, and as the link between the water industry and amenity and recreational interests in general.

The greatest change as far as recreation is concerned undoubtedly occurred where pressures for more leisure resources were greatest, in England and Wales. Even though inland waterways remained the responsibility of the British Waterways Board (who had already developed expertise in the leisure use of water) rather than under the aegis of the new water authorities, these changes in the water industry have gone a long way in establishing a structure capable of handling the increasing popularity of water sports.

Chapter 9 of this book is concerned with the many and varied organizations involved with recreation.

3. INCENTIVES

STATUTORY RESPONSIBILITIES

Section 20(1) of the Water Act 1973 provides that:—

> "Every water authority and all other statutory water undertakers may take steps to secure the use of water and land associated with water for the purposes of recreation and it shall be the duty of all such undertakers to take such steps as are reasonably practicable for putting their rights to the use of water and of any land associated with water to the best use for those purposes."

This is now the principal statutory provision governing recreation on water in England and Wales, but despite introducing for the first time a duty to have regard to recreational needs, it is not free from criticism. Unlike the provisions for Wales, in the following Section, there is no indication of how the duty is to be carried out. Firstly, even though Section 20(3) refers to a power to negotiate with other persons in respect of recreation only on *inland* water, the wording of Section 20(1) "water and land associated with water" would appear to be wide enough to apply to coastal waters. Secondly, after creating a duty on water operators, in response to growing public pressures, the Act also places limitations on that duty, which give water authorities in effect a discretion as to when they fulfil it. Not only is the duty confined to land and water controlled by the water authorities, but recreational use must be "reasonably practicable". Although this term is somewhat vague as to which practicalities are intended, it has been interpreted by water authorities to include a requirement that recreation should not interfere with other functions and obligations imposed on water authorities.

The 1973 Act also contains special provisions for London and Wales. The Thames Water Authority was required by Section 25 to submit proposals for the transfer of recreation and amenity functions under the Act in Greater London, to the Greater London Council. The Welsh Authority must, under Section 21, consult with the Severn-Trent Water Authority in preparing a plan for the recreational use of water and land associated with water in Wales. An additional duty in respect of Wales is contained in Subsection 5, where a reservoir is built which does not benefit inhabitants affected by its construction and operation. Under these circumstances the water authority must ". . . provide, or assist others to provide, facilities for recreation or other leisure-time occupation for the benefit of those inhabitants".

The equivalent Countryside Act powers of Scottish water authorities were not replaced in the 1975 reorganization of local government in Scotland. As a result, the new regional and island authorities to whom responsibility for water supply was transferred, inherited powers under the Countryside (Scotland) Act 1967 to provide recreational facilities. Section 63, Subsection 1, authorizes them, if it appears to them reasonable to do so, to:—

"*(a)* permit the use by members of the public, for the purposes of any form of recreation, of any waterway or land in which the Authority have an interest;

(b) provide, or otherwise make available, facilities for use by persons resorting to any such waterway or land for the purposes of any such form of recreation."

The remainder of the Section contains provisions similar to those for English water authorities, but the significant difference from the English powers is that there is no mandatory duty in Scotland as in Section 20 of the Water Act 1973. In Scotland, the reformed river purification boards whose principal responsibility was to keep rivers free from pollution were not given any express recreational powers. However, since the principal reason for pollution control in Scotland is the maintenance of public health and preservation of amenities as opposed to protecting sources of water supply, the river purification boards have an important function in promoting tourism and maintaining fisheries.

The Ministry of Development (now the Department of the Environment for Northern Ireland) became responsible for conservation of water resources and water pollution control in Northern Ireland on 1st January 1972, under the Water Act (Northern Ireland) 1972. Powers to provide recreational use of waterways in Northern Ireland under Section 16 of the Act are less extensive than those applicable to water authorities in England. This Section empowers the Department of Agriculture for Northern Ireland to execute such minor works as are considered appropriate for the purpose of promoting the recreational use of any waterway. Minor works can include landscaping, the provision of footpaths and signposting, jetties and slipways, and the execution of works for public safety. The definition of "waterway" for the purposes of Section 16 does not include a reservoir or the sea.

The Forestry Commission's duties under the Forestry Act 1967 do not extend to the provision of recreation, although the Countryside Act 1968 includes a permissive power similar to that given to water undertakers.

The British Waterways Board have a duty under the Transport Act 1968 Section 105(1)b "to maintain the cruising waterways in a suitable condition for use by cruising craft" within specified size limits. Remainder waterways are required by Section 107(2) to be ". . . dealt with in the most economic manner possible (consistent, in the case of a waterway which is retained, with the requirements of public health and the preservation of amenity and safety), whether by retaining and managing the waterway, by developing or eliminating it, or by disposing of it". Section 109 authoritizes the British Waterways Board to enter into agreements with certain public bodies for the maintenance of remainder waterways.

A further responsibility, which is relevant to informal recreation in particular, is the preservation of the amenities of the countryside. Section 11 of the Countryside Act 1968 and the Countryside (Scotland) Act 1967, Section 66, provide that:—

"In the exercise of their functions relating to land under any enactment every Minister, Government Department and Public Body shall have regard to the desirability of conserving the natural beauty and amenity of the countryside."

This general duty is reaffirmed for water authorities in England and Wales by Section 22 of the Water Act 1973, which requires water authorities to have regard to:

". . . the desirability of preserving natural beauty, of conserving flora, fauna and geological or physiographical features of special interest, and of protecting buildings and other objects of architectural, archaeological or historic interest. . .".

Section 22 also requires water authorities to have regard to the preservation of public access to places of natural beauty. Every water undertaker in England and Wales also has the duty under the 1973 Act to maintain, improve, and develop fisheries in their area, to assist both commercial and recreational fishing. The British Waterways Board have a statutory duty to preserve amenities only in respect of their remainder waterways.

Unlike the limited powers applicable in Northern Ireland or to the British Waterways Board, water authorities and water undertakings in England, Wales and Scotland have wide powers to promote recreation. The Water Act 1973 also imposed a duty on water authorities in England and Wales which, by its wording, is basically a moral duty, generally recognized as such to plan for recreation whenever possible. Thus the newer developments such as Rutland Water and Kielder Water (one a pumped-storage, the other a regulating reservoir) have been able to fulfil the new duty and from their conception envisaged substantial recreational use.

GRANT PROVISIONS

The Countryside Commission

Section 5 of the Countryside Act 1968 provided that the Commission could give financial assistance to any person other than a public body, for a project approved by the Minister which was conducive to the attainment of the purposes of that Act or the National Parks and Access to the Countryside Act 1949. The 1968 Act also authorized the Exchequer to make grants to local authorities in connection with expenditure on country parks and provision of facilities in the country. Since Section 5 did not apply to water undertakers or river authorities, schemes by these bodies to develop water recreation could only benefit indirectly through local authority assistance. However, the Local Government Act 1974 Section 9 which replaced Section 5 of the Countryside Act 1968 now empowers the Countryside Commission to give such financial assistance by way of grant or loan to any person and removes the requirement of Ministerial approval of each project, although grants are subject to the general directives of the Secretary of State. Similar powers are accorded to the Countryside Commission for Scotland.

Water authorities are thus eligible for assistance from the Countryside Commission, who have produced a pamphlet[26] which contains guidelines on grants to local authorities and other public bodies. The scope of schemes capable of qualifying for assistance is wide and so the guide indicates the priority given to different types of projects, although each case is considered on its merits with importance being attached to how the scheme relates to regional and national priorities. In particular, preference is given to land in Heritage Coasts, designated Areas of Outstanding Natural Beauty and Green Belts. Guidance is also given as to factors which will influence the Countryside Commission in making grants.

Under Section 86 of the National Parks and Access to the Countryside Act 1949 and Section 2(8) of the Countryside Act 1968, assistance can also be given in providing publicity and information services in places of beauty or interest in the countryside. The Countryside Commission will, however, only consider applications for grants under these sections where there is not a composite application for assistance which can include the provision of such services.

The Sports Council

The Physical Training and Recreation Act 1937 enables the Department of Education and Science to make grants of up to 50 per cent to voluntary organizations for the capital cost of "facilities for physical training and recreation including . . . the provision and equipment of . . . swimming baths, bathing places, holiday camps and camping sites and other buildings and premises for physical training and recreation"—(Section 3(1)*a*). In cases of special hardship a grant towards the maintenance of such facilities may be available. The Sports Council was created by Royal Charter in 1971 and receives funds from the Government each year which it allocates in accordance with priorities agreed by the Regional Councils for Sport and Recreation, to appropriate schemes. Although at least 25 per cent of the cost of a scheme must be provided from non-statutory sources, clubs who can find one-quarter of their capital costs can receive substantial assistance in setting up their facilities.

Tourist Boards

By virtue of the Development of Tourism Act 1969, Tourist Boards can provide assistance for projects which will provide or improve tourist amenities in development areas, subject to such limitations as are thought appropriate. Factors such as the extent to which tourists will be attracted, the resulting benefits to the region from additional earnings and employment, and the need for assistance are relevant. Grants are also available under the 1969 Act for the purposes of hotel development and although this may be only occasionally an ancillary facility to a water recreation scheme, it can be of importance to large reservoir schemes in remote areas such as Kielder Water, where there is great potential for recreation but only limited hotel accommodation in the area.

Local Authorities

The Education Act 1944 Section 53 provides that a local education authority with the approval of the Secretary of State may assist the establishment or maintenance of places at which there are facilities for recreation and social and physical training of persons receiving primary, secondary or further education. Section 4(4) of the Physical Training and Recreation Act 1937 enables local authorities to make grants to voluntary organizations providing facilities in their area and loans for the same purposes are possible under Section 1 of the Physical Training and Recreation Act 1958, in respect of capital expenditure by voluntary organizations. A further provision giving powers to local authorities to make grants is Section 114 of the Transport Act 1968 in respect of the maintenance or improvement of recreational facilities (including fishing) on inland waterways.

Scottish local authorities are empowered by Section 91 of the Local Government (Scotland) Act 1973 to ". . . do, or arrange for the doing of, or contribute towards the expenses of the doing of anything (whether inside or outside their area) necessary or expedient for the purpose of adequate facilities for social, cultural and recreative activities." There is also a parallel provision to Section 53 of the Education Act 1944 in Section 6 (as amended) of the Education (Scotland) Act 1962.

Other Possible Sources of Grant Aid

If the Secretary of State is of the opinion that a designated conservation area is an area of outstanding architectural or historic interest, he may provide assistance towards expenditure designed to promote the preservation or enhancement of the area (Section 10 of the Town and Country Planning (Amendment) Act 1972).

Under the Ancient Monuments and Archaeological Areas Act 1979, Section 24, the Secretary of State may contribute towards the cost of the preservation, maintenance, and management of any ancient monument or the provision by a local authority of facilities in connection with an ancient monument.

Grants are available from the European Regional Development Fund for the development of industry or infrastructure. Reservoirs are an accepted example of infrastructure even where their purpose is not wholly to provide for industry. The definition of infrastructure is generally interpreted by the EEC to exclude recreation and tourism. However, in the North West of England a local authority did succeed in obtaining a grant for a swimming pool and it is possible that infrastructure might include infrastructure to serve recreation (e.g. electricity and water supplies to a tourist centre and car parks) even if tourism itself cannot directly be supported out of the Fund. Grants are further discussed in Chapter 7.

ENCOURAGEMENT BY LOCAL AUTHORITIES OF RECREATION ON FACILITIES NOT IN THEIR OWNERSHIP

The earliest powers of local authorities to encourage recreation (as opposed to provision by themselves) were concerned with contributing towards the support of public walks and pleasure grounds (Section 45 Public Health Acts (Amendment) Act 1890 and Section 14 Open Spaces Act 1906). Later provisions concerned grants to promote the national "keep-fit" campaign in 1937 and facilities for schoolchildren under the Education Act 1944. The first major attempt, though, at involvement of local authorities in recreation on a large scale was in the National Parks and Access to the Countryside Act 1949, which created designated areas called National Parks in areas of natural beauty with opportunities for open-air recreation. This Act empowers local planning authorities to provide or secure the provision of accommodation, refreshments, car parks, etc., as appear necessary when the existing facilities in a National Park are inadequate (Section 12). They can also carry out such work and do such other things as appear necessary or expedient for facilitating the use of waterways in a National Park by the public for sailing, boating, bathing, or fishing (Section 13). Although it is possible to make a compulsory access order it has been the usual practice (if at all) for local authorities to make an access agreement under Section 64 which can include compensation and financial assistance towards the cost of permitting public access. Only Sections 15 to 26 of the 1949 Act (relating to nature conservancy) apply in Scotland.

The Countryside Act 1968 added substantially to the powers of local authorities to promote recreation by authorizing the establishments of country parks. Their purpose is to provide or improve opportunites for enjoyment of the countryside by the public, having regard to accessibility from urban areas and the adequacy of existing facilities. Powers of management for country parks are extensive, enabling a local authority, under Section 7, to erect buildings, carry out works and provide such services and facilities as are necessary, whether on land belonging to them or on other land where the agreement of the owners is obtained. Section 8 contains express provisions for water recreation. A local authority is given the power to provide facilities and services for recreation on waters in or adjoining country parks and also (Section 12) in or near National Parks. Section 10 of the Act empowers a local authority to provide picnic sites. However, local authorities must "have due regard to the needs of agricultural and forestry and to the economic and social interests of rural areas", when exercising their functions under this Act and the 1949 Act—Section 37.

Local authorities can thus provide additional motivation for landowners and other public bodies to utilize land and water for recreational purposes. They can make contributions to running costs in some cases or can undertake to provide some of the services themselves if necessary. Facilities in National Parks had, under the 1949 Act, to be for "open-air recreation" as defined, which excluded organized games. This limitation was removed in the Countryside Act 1968 and extensive facilities can now be provided in country parks and picnic sites. Exchequer grants were originally available to local authorities for these purposes, but under the Local Government Act 1974 this assistance is included in the rate support grant.

The Countryside (Scotland) Act 1967 contains similar powers to create country parks and camping sites. Scottish local authorities also have greater powers than their English counterparts to encourage provision of accommodation, meals, and refreshments on land not in their ownership which may include water (Section 50). Under Section 61, a local planning authority may on any waterway in its areas "carry out such work and do such other things as may appear to them expedient for facilitating the use of the waterway by the public for sailing, boating, bathing, fishing or other water sport or recreation, but in doing so shall take into consideration the disturbance of any fishing rights over the waterway which may be caused thereby." These powers can be delegated by the local planning authority to any public body responsible for the waterway in question. This would include local water authorities. Powers under Section 61 are subject to the consent of the appropriate local water authority, and any other body having functions relating to the waterway, subject to an appeal to the Secretary of State.

In practice, local authorities everywhere can play a very important role in the development of recreation. The local planning officer may well produce a report on the recreational potential of a new reservoir, identifying suitable sites and suggesting developments. Councils often undertake to provide informal recreation, constructing lay-bys and car parks, or even purchasing or leasing land to set up country parks with grants under the Countryside Act 1968. It is in the spheres of general planning and provision of facilities for informal recreation that local authorities can be of the greatest assistance. Informal recreation requiring subsidies cannot technically be debited to the general water charges account (see Section on the Ability of Participants to Meet the Costs (p. 33) of this chapter) but local authorities do not face this handicap.

PROVISION FOR RECREATION AS A PREREQUISITE OF WATER DEVELOPMENT

Planning permission for the building of a new reservoir or extraction of sand or gravel can include conditions concerning landscaping and amenities. Likewise, legislation authorizing works may contain a requirement that public access and recreation be permitted. In this way, public pressures for recreation can manifest themselves in respect of new developments. In particular, where large areas of land are to be acquired for a reservoir or mineral workings, recreation is sometimes regarded as a quid pro quo for any loss of agricultural land or visual amenity.

Government concern that new reservoirs be planned to include recreation is evident from Circular 3/66, Ministry of Land and Natural Resources[15]:—

"Attention to the potential of new reservoirs for recreation often enables facilities to be provided more economically from the beginning. Such facilities may include, among other things, access roads and car parks, fish hatcheries, fish passes and jetties. The current practice of giving full treatment to the water taken into supply from new reservoirs enables the maximum use to be made of them for recreation."

Section 20(5) of the Water Act 1973 expressly provides that where works or the acquisition of land by a water authority are authorized, and they are likely to have a permanent effect on the inhabitants of an area which is not primarily intended to benefit from the works, the Secretary of State may include in the authorizing order provision for the recreation of those inhabitants. A similar provision (Section 21(5)) applies to Wales. It is more frequent however for the recreational requirements of a wider area of inhabitants to be considered.

Local planning authorities in preparing their Structure Plans and Local Plans may include details of their proposals for recreation and leisure. Their general strategy for recreation in an area can be facilitated through negotiations with those seeking permission for development, particularly where water recreation with its very limited available resources is concerned. Although planning permission can be deemed to be given when a government department authorizes a reservoir project (Section 40 Town and Country Planning Act 1971), such deemed consent is subject to any conditions that the Minister shall specify. Consultations will in any event take place with local authorities by virtue of Section 24(8) Water Act 1973, during the preparation of the water authorities' periodic reports and plans which must have regard to the relevant Structure Plans and Local Plans. Gravel or sand extraction requires planning permission, and it can be made a condition for wet workings that the worked pits are landscaped into lagoons[27], although the need to fill in for agricultural or building purposes will be taken into account.

ENABLING POWERS

Although Section 20 of the Water Act 1973 creates a duty for water authorities to provide recreation, it does not contain powers authorizing the discharge of that duty. Paragraph 2 of the 3rd Schedule contains general authority to do anything which ". . . is calculated to facilitate or is conducive or incidental to, the discharge of any of their functions", but recourse must be made to inherited powers from water undertakers and river authorities for specific authority to construct works or acquire any land.

Water undertakers were first given powers concerning recreation in the

Countryside Act 1968, Section 22. Paragraph 92 of the Eighth Schedule of the Water Act 1973 amends this Section so that it may apply to water authorities. Subsection 2 of Section 2 states that they may, for the purposes of providing recreational facilities; "set apart any land held by them and may provide, improve, alter, renew and maintain such buildings and other works and do such other things as may be necessary or expedient." This power can however only be exercised, in respect of waterways which are not owned by a water authority, with the consent of the owners—Subsection (5). Authority is also contained in Subsections (3) and (4) to make reasonable charges for the use of facilities provided and to let to any person, works constructed to provide recreation, authorizing them to make reasonable charges for use. There would appear, however, to have been no inherited powers to acquire land for recreation, since the general provisions of the Water Act 1945 related to acquisition for the purposes of the functions of a water undertaker and the Countryside Act 1968 merely created a power and did not make recreation a function, although Section 24(2) of the earlier Act enabled land to be acquired for an employees' recreation ground.

A water authority, under Section 20(3) of the Water Act 1973:—

". . .may, with the consent of the owner of an inland water which they have no right to use for the purposes of recreation or of land associated therewith and of any other person having a right to use the water or an estate or interest in the land, use the water or land for those purposes."

This subsection gives water authorities a power to negotiate for the use of water and associated land but not to acquire it for the purposes of recreation. Paragraph 2 of the Third Schedule includes acquisition of any property or rights, but this does not encompass compulsory purchase.

The powers of compulsory acquisition of water undertakers in Section 24 of the Water Act 1945 and of river authorities in Section 65 and Section 66 of the Water Resources Act 1963 were exercisable in pursuance of the functions of water undertakers and river authorities respectively. Recreation was not a function of water undertakers and it is not clear whether the river authorities' powers of acquisition extended to recreation. However, the Water Act 1973 expressly applies Section 22(2)-(5) of the Countryside Act 1968. Section 20(3) gives express powers of negotiation which will enable water authorities to "secure the use of water and land associated with water", in accordance with their powers under Section 20(1) of the Water Act 1973, in respect of land over which they exercise no rights. It is therefore improbable that any power to acquire land exists other than as may be envisaged by the Third Schedule, paragraph 2.

The Department of Agriculture for Northern Ireland which is empowered to act under Section 16 of the Water Act (Northern Ireland) 1972 can undertake minor works and acquire land by agreement or take on lease any land. It cannot, however, acquire land compulsorily for recreational purposes as the provisions of Section 17 (relating to the Department of the Environment) are confined to the latter Department's functions for the conservation of water resources and water pollution control. Article 42 of the Water and Sewerage Services (Northern Ireland) Order 1973, empowers the Department of the Environment for Northern Ireland to provide facilities for recreation on lands vested in it for water supply and sewerage purposes. The Department has no powers under the Order to acquire land by agreement or acquire land compulsorily for recreational purposes.

In Scotland, the Countryside (Scotland) Act 1967 contains powers to provide facilities for recreation on land owned by local water authorities and also with the permission of owners on other such land in which they have an interest (Section 63). There are, equally, powers to make reasonable charges and permit other persons to provide similar facilities. However, probably in view of the powers of local planning authorities (see Sections on Grant Provisions (p. 14) and Encouragement by Local Authorities of Recreation on Facilities Not in Their Ownership (p. 16) of this Chapter) there is no power in Scotland for the water authorities to acquire land for the purposes of recreation.

4. INHIBITING ASPECTS

CONFLICT WITH PRIMARY FUNCTIONS

Inland waters of all kinds have a function for which they were created, whether artificially or naturally, and recreation on those waters is almost always an afterthought. Rivers are the natural carriers of surplus water and waste from inland to the sea, and lakes are often a part of the natural drainage system. Canals and their feeder-reservoirs were constructed for transportation, whilst quarrying and peat extraction are responsible respectively for wet mineral workings and the Broads. Reservoirs, the major man-made areas of water, supplement the ancillary purpose of natural inland water, the supply of water for human consumption. Leisure is unlikely to be sufficiently vital for there to be large new water developments solely for this purpose. Nevertheless, in recent years, planned multi-purpose usage has made recreation less of an afterthought and more of a secondary function with particularly significant value in public relations.

The phrase "reasonably practicable" in Section 20 of the Water Act 1973 is of great relevance to the water industry, as it is most probably a reference to the secondary function of recreation in the use of water resources in England and Wales. Multi-functional water authorities will inevitably meet conflicts between their various duties and "reasonably practicable" is perhaps to be seen as the authority for giving recreation second place. In Northern Ireland and Scotland where the duty does not exist and there is merely a power to promote recreation, a subsidiary role is generally given to leisure use, although in Scotland, plentiful availability of alternative water facilities is such as to make the issue usually one of access to catchment areas rather than the water itself.

Canals have become, to a certain extent, an exception to these general principles after the Transport Act 1968 categorized canals into commercial, cruising and remainder waterways. Section 104(1)(b) stated that the primary purpose of "cruising waterways" is "to be principally available for cruising, fishing and other recreational purposes." On these canals, land drainage and industrial water supply, whilst being of sufficient value to ensure the retention of the non-commercial canal network, are of secondary importance in its functioning. Similarly, where wet mineral workings have exhausted their primary purpose and are developed for recreation, their original function has no major inhibiting effect on recreation, except insofar as the ownership of land may be divided and the physical characteristics of the lake created.

Where a river or canal is used primarily for navigation the only probable conflict is with other boats, as angling and the use of towpaths or river walks are not likely to interfere with those on the water itself. The question thus becomes one of controlling navigation by the different users.

Public Health Requirements

The duty to provide a supply of wholesome water, now embodied in Section 11 of the Water Act 1973 (and Section 8 of the Water (Scotland) Act 1946), is the predominant aspect governing the use of reservoirs. Only relatively recently has recreation become generally compatible with this duty. Although the pressures of public opinion and needs were undoubtedly responsible for the change in attitude towards recreation, only greater knowledge of health dangers and more effective treatment of the water enabled water undertakers to comply with some of the demands for leisure facilities on reservoirs. Public health requirements are discussed in further detail in Chapter 2.

A policy document (see Chapter 2, p. 52) has been published by the North West Water Authority[28] on reconciliation of responsibilities for water supply and recreation in particular cases. Although this is the policy of only one water authority and circumstances differ throughout the U.K., the general tendency is to judge the possibilities for recreation against the characteristics of the particular reservoir and its treatment plant, when considering the duty to supply wholesome water.

Pollution Control

Water authorities, Scottish river purification boards, and the Water Service of the Department of the Environment in Northern Ireland became responsible for the control of pollution in the reorganizations of 1972-73 and can make regulations for this purpose. Where an inland water is used for water supply, pollution control aims to ensure a safe source of supply for drinking water. On other inland waters, the concern is primarily for the protection of fisheries and the environment.

It is an offence under the Rivers (Prevention of Pollution) Act 1951 to permit pollution of a stream, or any lake discharging into a stream, without the consent of the appropriate water authority. Byelaws can be made under this Act in England and Wales to prevent litter and rubbish being put into streams and to control the discharge of untreated sewage from boats. Similar responsibilities rest on the river purification authorities in Scotland under the Rivers (Prevention of Pollution) (Scotland) Act 1951. These provisions will eventually be replaced by Part II of the Control of Pollution Act 1974 when it becomes operative. This latter Act will in addition prohibit the use of sanitary appliances designed for direct discharge of sewage from boats, unless sealed. Part II of the Water Act (Northern Ireland) 1972 contains provisions relevant to Northern Ireland.

The Salmon and Freshwater Fisheries Act 1975, applicable to England and Wales, makes it an offence to put into any water containing fish any matter which will be injurious to fish. As a result of the EEC Directive of 18th July 1978[29] Member States must, by 1980, have designated stretches of freshwater which they will within five years bring into conformity with the quality standards in the Directive for the protection of fish life. This is not thought to involve water authorities in any additional duties, since there is a discretion as to which waters to designate.

Apart from discharge of sewage and the possibilities of oil leakage from powered craft, recreational activities themselves are unlikely to conflict with pollution control legislation and in fact are more likely to benefit from the reduction in pollution on waterways from other sources.

Land Drainage

A river that is efficient as a means of land drainage is not necessarily the most attractive from the point of view of recreation. The straightening of a meandering river or the construction of possibly unsightly embankments can detract from the visual amenities of the landscape. Although the effects of construction works themselves may only be temporary, long term damage can be suffered by fisheries resources as a result of changes in levels and flow patterns and increased problems of erosion and siltation. Rivers would naturally have the task of alleviating flooding but the work of the water engineers in improving the drainage of fields and minor watercourses only increases the pressures on rivers. Although some canals are used for surface water drainage, excessive flows usually occur only during winter months when recreational use is minimal, and thus hardly affected.

Two advisory publications on conservation and land drainage were issued by the Water Space Amenity Commission in 1980[30,31], aimed at demonstrating how essential works of land drainage and sea defence can be achieved not only with least harm to wildlife and nature conservation but even to enhance them wherever possible.

Operational Requirements

Because recreation is generally a secondary function, particularly on reservoirs, it is inevitable that it will be restricted by the use of the water for its principal purpose. Thus, it is frequently necessary to restrict access near plant and machinery or where a hydro-electricity generation scheme is in operation. Injuries to fish may occur where water is abstracted from rivers or diverted to power turbines. When a river inhabited by anadromous fish, such as salmon, is dammed to provide hydro-electric power, the movement of fish to their upstream spawning grounds will be impeded unless it is possible to incorporate an adequate series of leaps or a fishpass. The banks of canals and the Broads have to be protected against erosion by imposing speed limits on boats. The location of a reservoir can sometimes necessitate steep embankments which preclude safe or easy access to the water's edge. The most serious conflict between primary and recreational uses, however, concerns variations in the level of the water.

Most recreational activities would ideally require a steady level, whether on a river or reservoir. Fluctuations in level can also affect the aquatic environment with detrimental effects on fisheries and their food sources as well as the flora at the water's edge. However, if reservoirs were always maintained at the level most suitable for recreation and visual appearance, then they would be rendered incapable of fulfilling their primary purpose. Canal-feeder and water-supply reservoirs may need to be substantially drawn down on occasions. Power generation requires the level of a reservoir to vary, especially where surplus off-peak generating capacity from the National Grid is used to pump water to higher levels for release when demand is high. Where a reservoir is used for flood control it should be kept at a low level prior to the possible incidence of flooding and the flood water should be released as soon as possible afterwards. Even on rivers, abstraction will on occasions severely hamper leisure use. As far as possible, and in practice for most of the time, water levels are maintained to facilitate recreation and the use of river-regulating reservoirs actually improves river levels in dry periods but it is inevitable that recreation will have to take second place in the demands placed upon water resources as a result of the costs involved to modify the ideal operational régime to suit recreation and amenities.

RESTRICTIONS ON THE RIGHTS OF ACCESS AND USE

When land is acquired which may later be used for recreation, or leisure activities are planned for a river, difficulties can be encountered when the right to use the water or associated land is not absolute or the means of access are restricted. The duty of water authorities in England and Wales is limited to their rights in respect of water and associated land and the authorization to negotiate recreational use greater than these rights, in Section 20(3) of the Water Act 1973, is merely a permissive power.

Access Difficulties

A major restriction on rivers and canals is the existence of riparian owners who control access to the water. Access is frequently only possible where roads or footpaths cross or run alongside the water or where riparian land is in public ownership. Towpaths border canals and some rivers, but where they are merely leased from riparian owners, use may be restricted to that incidental to navigation on the river or canal unless they have subsequently been scheduled as a right of way.

Various degrees of access are required for different activities. The canoeist may need only to be able to walk across fields carrying a canoe from a suitable road. A club house, car parking and mooring or launching facilities are probable requirements for boat owners. Anglers usually obtain their means of access together with fishing rights and require the least facilities.

The rights of access to enclosed waters are usually found in the title deeds, whether for a reservoir, lake or gravel pit. Reservoirs not adjoining an existing public right of way will often contain a restriction on those permitted to cross neighbouring land for access to the reservoir, frequently requiring written authorization by specified persons for specified purposes. A restricted right of way, however, might be construed to allow access for recreational purposes if, for example, the right is "for the purposes of the undertaking" or "in connection with its functions" which now include recreation even if they did not at the time of the grant. However, such a right must not interfere with any other persons who also have the benefit of the same right of way, and in order to prevent congestion, unlimited public access might not be possible although access by authorized club members probably would.

Under certain circumstances, if the facilities required cannot be negotiated, a local planning authority may be able to assist with an access order which, by virtue of the Countryside Act 1968, Section 16, can apply to rivers, canals or lakes and reservoirs through which a river or part of it flows. However, canals operated by the British Waterways Board and reservoirs owned or managed by a statutory undertaker or a water authority are expressly excluded. This Section 16 power, which would only be used as a last resort on the failure to obtain agreement, is invariably subject to the consent of the appropriate water authority, and has not yet in fact been exercised. In Scotland the appropriate powers are contained in Section 14 of the Countryside (Scotland) Act 1967.

Sporting Rights and Rights of Adjoining Owners

Where the original land, on which a canal or reservoir was constructed, was conveyed by a vendor who retained adjoining land, then various rights may have been reserved by the vendor and in some instances these rights are capable of transfer to third persons. A survey[32] showed that sporting rights had been either totally or partially retained in 70 reservoirs in England and Wales. These were mostly small reservoirs comprising 5 per cent of the total area of water, although some are of significance for water sports.

Restrictive covenants can impose limitations on the use of land in such a way that recreation could be hindered. In these circumstances it would be necessary to seek a release by the beneficiaries of the covenants or through an application to the Lands Tribunal under Section 84(1) of the Law of Property Act 1925. The Scottish equivalents of restrictive covenants are conditions of title or land obligations and these can be varied or discharged by application to the Lands Tribunal for Scotland.

The factors affecting modification are slightly different from those in England and Wales.

Where an owner of land has the right to use some other land not belonging to him, in a particularly way, such right is known as an "easement" and in Scotland a "servitude". Easements exist for the benefit of land known as the "dominant tenement" and the most relevant easements relating to land purchased for water development are rights of way, which can be for specific purposes such as the right of a farmer to cross the land with cattle. If such a right exists, then the " servient tenement" over which the right exists must not be used in such a manner as to derogate from the original grant. In other words, unless the right of way is extinguished by purchase and subsequent merger with the servient tenement, it must not be interfered with. Similar precautions are probably necessary to those needed where a public right of way adjoins the land to be used for recreation (see Section on the Impact of Recreation on Adjoining Areas (p. 29) of this chapter). Other easements can exist, including the right to enjoy land as a pleasure ground[33] (probably the only right to recreation other than field sports capable of existence in law) but these are very unlikely to be met.

Sporting rights are a form of profit à prendre, being a right to enter upon another person's land in order to take something away from it. Profits à prendre can exist with or without a dominant tenement and can be exclusive ("several" profits à prendre) or in common, but are unknown to Scots Law. Thus, sporting rights such as angling and fowling can be enjoyed by riparian owners but are also capable of being possessed by clubs or individuals without a relevant interest in land. As with easements, the owner of a profit à prendre can bring an action in nuisance if he is disturbed in the enjoyment of his rights, although he also has an additional remedy in an action for trespass. In Scotland, only salmon fishing can exist as a separate interest in land.

It is frequent, particularly in the case of older reservoirs, for land to have been purchased with a reservation of "sporting rights", occasionally with an express right to use a boat on the reservoir. Whilst a recreational right can exceptionally exist as an easement, the only sporting rights that can be the subject of a grant are profits à prendre—field sports. Thus, the right to use a boat, which in any event cannot be an exclusive right, can only be for the purposes of fishing or wildfowling.

Those clubs and individuals who have leased fishing rights from riparian owners of rivers and canals are naturally unwilling to enlarge the numbers who share their privilege or to see their rights diminish in value due to the incidence of other water-based activities. Although the legal position of the owner of sporting rights is only such as to enable him to prevent interference with his right, in practice, on rivers where there is no public right of navigation the riparian owners will themselves frequently seek to exclude any possible threat to the value of the leased fishing rights. It may therefore be necessary to seek a release or assignment of such rights in order to proceed with the development of recreation.

Private Ownership of River Banks Affecting Activities on the Water

On tidal waters there is presumed to be a public right of navigation. On non-tidal waters, however, riparian owners own the river bed and a right of navigation only exists where it can be shown to have been acquired by the public either by immemorial user, by statute, or by express or implied dedication. Thus the owners of river banks will be able to prevent any recreation on a river if there is no public right of navigation.

Even where such a right of navigation does exist, it is primarily a right of passage although, by analogy with rights of way on land, this does not prevent stopping for short periods, and passing along a river can be for pleasure. Navigation does not include any rights to fish or to cross another person's land to obtain access to the river, and similarly there is no resultant right to land or moor on the banks of a river. Such rights must be separately negotiated. Once a public right of navigation can be demonstrated there are, prima facie, no limitations on its extent beyond the capacity of the river and its exercise in a reasonable manner. There are no classes of rights of way as there are on land. The degree of reasonableness will be determined by the size of the river and on the interference with other rights. Thus, boats of excessive size or speed could be unreasonable in their exercise of the right of navigation, especially where there is undue congestion, interference with anglers, and bank erosion. As a result, it is probable that many of the proposals for recreation on rivers will require the co-operation of riparian owners, even if there is a public right of navigation.

THE INFLUENCE OF LOCAL AUTHORITIES

When exercising their planning functions, local authorities do not act solely as proponents of recreation in their areas. The concern of the local planning authority is with the formulation of plans for recreation that are compatible with the overall development of the locality. There are also various other controls which a local authority exercises over developments which apply equally to recreational proposals. The influence of local authorities, in addition to providing incentives, manifests itself as a moderating force on any excessively enthusiastic plans, and sometimes as a dampening factor reflecting public attitudes and concern about the possible effect of proposals.

The first stage in the planning programme for an area is the preparation of a County Structure Plan under the Town and Country Planning Act 1971. A survey is first made which must encompass various matters including the physical and economic characteristics of the area, the size, composition and distribution of the population and the transport system. The purpose of a structure plan is to formulate general policies for the development and use of land as appear justified by the survey. The proposed uses must be related to proposals for adjoining areas and plans for the region as a whole. Land use, included in the plan, can be for recreational and leisure purposes. Before the structure plan is finally drawn up, the proposals and the survey must be publicized and the opportunity given for interested persons to make representations which will be taken into consideration in the final plan. Copies of the structure plan are always available to the public, who should also be informed of their right to make objections to the Secretary of State and the time-limits for so doing. The Secretary of State is required to consider all written objections and, should he feel it necessary, he may require a public examination into specific matters dealt with by the plan. However, only those persons invited by the Secretary of State or the person appointed to hold the examination are entitled to be heard at such an inquiry.

Local plans, prepared generally by the district planning authority, must conform with the wider outlines of the appropriate structure plan, for they provide finer details missing from structure plans. Local plans can be based on the county survey or on an additional one in the district itself and proposals must likewise receive adequate publicity. Objections can be made by the public to the local planning authority prior to adoption of the local plan and the Secretary of State will only intervene if he is not satisfied that the procedures have been properly followed. A public hearing or inquiry will be held to consider objections to the local plan, after which the local planning authority adopts the plan with or without modifications.

The statutory requirements for the two types of development plans ensure that the public is given ample opportunity to put their views to the local authorities, who are required to take such views into consideration. Regulations governing the preparation of the plans add further requirements of consultation, generally with such other authorities or bodies as the local planning authorities think appropriate. There are also directions that any Government body or public body likely to be affected, including water authorities, public utilities, the Nature Conservancy Council, the Countryside Commission and the Regional Councils for Sport and Recreation, should be approached. Where recreation and access may affect agricultural land, it is also necessary to consult the Ministry of Agriculture, Fisheries and Food.

Although development plans play an important part in the future development of an area, in themselves they have very little legal force. They demonstrate the guidelines to be followed by local planning authorities in exercising development control, but despite their practical importance they have no legally binding effect. Where a recreational proposal is contrary to the development plan, however, and a grant of permission would be a substantial departure from the plan, the local authority must advertise the proposals in a local newspaper and allow objections to be made. If the proposals would prejudice the implementation of either a structure plan or a local plan modification introduced by the Secretary of State, details of the variation must be sent to the Secretary of State who may then restrict the permission or require the matter to be referred to him. A development plan is not always precise enough to enable it to be followed to the letter, but in practice it is one of the most important considerations in the determination of a planning application.

Development control (deciding planning applications) is exercised by local planning authorities in respect of building operations, engineering operations, mining operations or other operations, in, on or under land or the making of any material change in the use of any buildings or other land. Land includes land covered with water.

Building and engineering operations include the erection of clubhouses, moorings, jetties, slipways, and access roads. The introduction of large-scale sports or leisure activities on water or land adjoining water probably constitutes a material change of use needing planning permission. However, ancillary uses do not require consent and can be of a completely different nature to the existing use provided that they do not constitute a material change—a question of fact and degree of intensification. Thus, whilst some quiet waterside activities might not need planning permission, the greater the effect of the changed use of the land and water, the more likely it is that planning consent should be sought. In 1972 the Secretary of State for the Environment decided on an application by a local authority for planning permission that the commercial use of land for sailing and fishing does require planning permission.[34] This suggests that recreational developments are prima facie material changes of use unless they can be shown to be not material (i.e. ancillary) or non-commercial (which does not apparently mean publicly organized).

When a water authority introduces recreation as a part of its functions under Section 20(1) of the Water Act 1973, it may be possible to argue that the proposals constitute a "permitted development" being required for the purposes of a water undertaking "carried out in, on, over or under the operational land of the undertaking except:—

(a) ... the erection ... of buildings;

(b) . . . any structures . . . exceeding 15 metres in height or the height of the . . . structure . . . replaced," (Class XVIIIC para. (vi) Schedule 1 of the Town and Country Planning General Development Order 1977 and Class XV(C) of the Scottish equivalent Order in 1975).

Buildings are defined in Article 2(1) of the Order as any structure or erection *except* plant or machinery, or a structure or erection in the nature of plant or machinery, or a means of enclosure (fences, walls, etc). This class of permitted developments will, if it can be applied to recreation, cover all changes of use and structures in the nature of plant or machinery less than 15 m high.

Local authorities are also allowed "permitted developments", under Class X111 of the 1977 Order. No change of use is permitted, merely the construction of "small ancillary buildings, works and equipment as are required on land belonging to or maintained by them for the purposes of any functions . . . otherwise than as statutory undertakers". This will enable limited developments on council-owned or maintained lakes and mineral workings subject to the general principles on change of use.

These two classes of permitted developments are not absolute however, for the Secretary of State or the appropriate local planning authority, with the Secretary of State's approval, may suspend their application in respect of particular developments and/or particular areas. Adequate notice of such a decision must be given and the direction will not take effect before such notice.

Where planning permission by the local planning authority is required, it can be subject to such conditions as they think fit. Conditions may restrict the use of the development. By this means a local authority could control even activities which would not constitute a material change of use, or which would otherwise be permitted by the 1977 Order (Article 3(2)) where there was some construction or engineering operation involved such as slipways for boats. Restrictions could be placed on the periods when new activities may take place and the entire permission may be of a limited duration. The discretion in imposing conditions is wide but not unlimited for they must not be vague or ambiguous and should reasonably relate to local planning considerations.

A developer can appeal to the Secretary of State against planning conditions or a refusal to grant permission. Notice of appeal must normally be within six months of the decision and will result in the Secretary of State referring the appeal to an inspector for a public or private inquiry unless both parties to the appeal request that it be determined by written representations. The Secretary of State generally makes the final decision without being bound by any inspector's report, and he can either reverse the planning authority's decision or vary any of it in any way, even where only one condition was appealed against.

In addition to their planning control functions, local authorities have various other powers with which they can, to varying degrees, influence proposals for recreation. Tree preservation orders can be made, whether in respect of individual trees, groups of trees, or woodland areas. Such an order will prohibit the felling, topping, lopping or wilful destruction of the protected trees without the consent of the local planning authority, except in the case of dead or dangerous trees, trees causing a nuisance, or action in accordance with a statutory obligation. This last defence is unlikely to avail a water authority in view of the wording of Section 20 of the Water Act 1973 and the express requirement in Section 22 to pay due regard to the need for conservation of flora, although it may be applicable to the exercise of other water authority functions. Further control exists over the construction of certain buildings through building regulations, the designation of conservation areas and areas of archaeological importance and the protection of buildings listed as of special architectural or historic interest (see also Section on The Compatibility of Recreational Activities (p. 34) of this chapter). The licensing power of a local authority may need to be exercised for club houses. Caravan sites may need a site licence; signs would need to comply with the Advertising Regulations and if public footpaths are affected, Highways Acts powers would be exercisable by the local authority.

Local authorities thus have fairly extensive powers to control recreational proposals as well as to encourage them. For the most part, however, these powers may not need to be formally used since the development of a plan for recreation, particularly when proposed by a public body such as a water authority, usually starts on the basis of various informal consultations in which the local authorities play a major part.

ASSURANCES AND UNDERTAKINGS GIVEN DURING THE COURSE OF PROMOTIONAL PROCEEDINGS

There is no legal obligation for promoters of recreation to give any assurances or undertakings, but in practice the preparation of a major scheme for water development inevitably involves a large number of consultations with various bodies. Consultations are not always a one-way process of seeking views and advice, but can involve the provision of information and promises to interested parties.

Perhaps the most important consultations are with local authorities from whom it may be necessary to seek planning permission or assistance in the provision of facilities. Local authorities will have drawn up plans for the area and will generally be very aware of the demand for recreation and the adequacy of existing facilities. They will also have carried out an extensive survey and consultation in the preparation of their development plans and will be directly responsible for the provision of recreation and leisure services. Informal negotiations and consultations can therefore be of the greatest benefit to a water authority or other body promoting recreation. Various undertakings may be given to the local authority concerning the landscaping of any buildings and the control or limitation of potential activities. These undertakings may or may not be incorporated as conditions of planning permission. Alternatively, an agreement may be entered into under Section 52 of the Town and Country Planning Act 1971 or Section 50 of the Town and Country Planning (Scotland) Act 1972.

Section 52 of the 1971 Act enables the planning authority to enter into agreements for the purpose of restricting or regulating the development or use of land, whether or not it is the subject of the application. This procedure could be used to avoid the imposition of unwelcome planning conditions and to enable planning requirements to be settled relatively informally. Although the planning authority is not restricted in the exercise of its powers by such an agreement, the person making the undertakings is bound by them. Another example of undertakings replacing the more formal procedure is an agreement to guarantee public rights of access to footpaths on the perimeter of a reservoir which obviates the need for the local authority to declare the footpaths public rights of way under the National Parks and Access to the Countryside Act 1949.

Assurances may also be given to local residents or groups. Residents can influence proposals indirectly through the effect of their views on the local planning authority. It may be necessary to purchase land from individual landowners or bodies such as the Forestry Commission. Whilst compulsory purchase powers may be available if the scheme is by a water authority and includes non-recreation purposes (see Section on Enabling Powers (p. 18) of this chapter) and is not in respect of Crown lands (including the Forestry Commission), common land and certain nationalized industries' land, it is considered preferable to negotiate purchase by agreement. This may again involve giving assurances to satisfy the requirements of landowners who retain land affected by the proposals and where restrictive covenants in the conveyance are considered unnecessary. Similarly, in the course of consultation with local parish councils and interested groups such as sports clubs, naturalist societies, farming representatives and residents associations, undertakings may be given concerning the availability or non-availability of types of recreation.

Where an organization such as the Countryside Commission, a Regional Council for Sport and Recreation or a Regional Tourist Board is involved in providing grant aid for a recreation project, then it is not unreasonable to suppose that various conditions may need to be satisfied to ensure that the aid is put to good use and is not spent on a facility which may only be temporary. Assurances may be needed for this purpose and also, in the general development of a major project, to such other national bodies as the Nature Conservancy and government departments whose approval might be necessary or desirable in obtaining authorization for the scheme.

One can categorize undertakings into three classes although the classes overlap and are not clearly defined. The differences lie in the binding effect they have and so it is only when a dispute arises concerning an assurance or undertaking that the categories become of any importance.

(1) *A promise*, whether oral or in writing, can be a contractual legally binding obligation where it is made for a valuable consideration which in this case could mean an act or undertaking by the promisee (although consideration is not necessary in Scotland). Thus, if land subject to restrictive covenants is being purchased or developed, a waived objection, amounting to acquiescence to the modification of the covenants, may be sufficient consideration. Likewise, the withdrawal of enforceable objections to planning permission, or the permission by a riparian owner for sportsmen to have access to the water or to sail where there is no public right of navigation, may be considered acts which can make an undertaking or assurance a binding obligation.

(2) *There are assurances*, the consideration for which is not legally adequate, or which are clearly more of a voluntary nature. These are merely undertakings which the promisor intends to keep, regarded as binding in the interests of maintaining friendly relations with the person or body concerned and keeping a good public image.

(3) *There remain assurances* which are not intended to be any more than statements of opinion, given when there is no obligation to do so, for guidance and general assistance. Their accuracy cannot be guaranteed either for practical reasons or because they concern policy issues which have not yet been finally determined.

The distinction between these last two types of assurances (one intended to be a definite binding undertaking, the other merely an assurance which is no more than an opinion), is important. Although neither is legally binding it is vital to make it clear when giving an assurance whether or not it is a firm undertaking. This is not only for good public relations but, in the case of a water authority, because of the possibility of a complaint by an aggrieved person to a Local Commissioner under the Local Government Act 1974, for an alleged maladministration causing an injustice.

The Impact of Recreation on Adjoining Areas

Recreation will have an effect on the locality in various ways. The impact may be minimal if it involves no more than the admission of a few anglers to a reservoir. Where, however, a wide range of activities and attractions are to be introduced, the area would be faced with a potential influx of sportsmen and casual visitors. There could be problems of noise, traffic congestion and disturbance to the countryside. Balancing this is the possibility of increased trade and employment, frequently in a rural area where unemployment and population drift may be a particular problem. Resolving this balance to advantage is primarily the task of the local authorities involved in the preparation of development plans and in general consultations on the desirability of a scheme.

A major consideration for a plan to develop recreation is the ability of visitors to reach the location and the numbers that are likely to do so. Indeed, the remoteness of a reservoir from major conurbations and the ease of access by private car and public transport will be very important in determining the probable success of the proposals. Unfortunately, this results in the dilemma so often faced by proponents of countryside recreation. The attraction of rural surroundings stems from their tranquillity and pastoral beauty. The more successful any development is in attracting visitors the greater the probability that these advantages will gradually disappear as a rural area becomes threatened with transformation into an "urban playground".

Analogous to the disturbance caused by visitors travelling to the area are the problems caused by them when they arrive. Complaints are frequently heard in farming districts that car parks and improved access roads will only encourage more people to come into the country, leaving gates open, discarding litter and trespassing on fields, causing damage to crops. However, to a large degree town-dwellers intend to make their trips to the country anyway and the provision of specific destination points where some control can be exercised will probably reduce trespass on agricultural land. Adjacent residential areas—usually small rural communities—may suffer problems of noise particularly if powered craft are used, and there may be some dangers if sports were to be permitted too close to public rights of way or adjoining property. Furthermore, it may be necessary to consider the need to prevent trespassers—principally young children—from being attracted onto the property and being injured as a result.

Care would need to be taken in the management of a site where recreation was permitted to ensure that the activities did not constitute a legal nuisance. A Common Law action in nuisance, for an injunction or damages, can be maintained if it can be shown that there has been an unreasonable interference with a neighbour's enjoyment of his land. The character of the neighbourhood is relevant to the degree of interference considered unreasonable and thus a nuisance. In a quiet rural setting it is possible that the noise produced by motorboats could be an unreasonable disturbance to local residents very close to the water. An action could be brought against the persons directly responsible for the disturbance or against the operators of the site who permitted the nuisance. In extreme circumstances it is also conceivable that the presence of large numbers of people taking part in various activities and intruding physically, aurally or visually on adjoining premises or land could constitute an actionable nuisance. It is, however, improbable that such circumstances should ever be allowed to occur either by the promoters of recreation or the local authorities.

Although public authorities, such as the British Waterways Board and the regional water authorities, will have a defence to such actions on the grounds of statutory authority, this defence is now somewhat limited in its effect. The defence has never applied where the statutory power can be shown to have been exercised negligently, and a new remedy may now be available in all other instances under the Land Compensation Act 1973 (and the Land Compensation (Scotland) Act 1973).

This Act provides for compensation to be payable for depreciation in the value of property caused by public works which are otherwise immune from an action in nuisance. It should be noted that, unlike the situation where there is no statutory authority, an action can be brought only for compensation but not to prohibit or abate the nuisance. The type of damage under the Act is more restrictive in that it is limited to physical factors such as smell, noise, and vibrations and although a claim may be brought where there is a change of use, no compensation will be payable for an intensification of an existing use. The limitation period, within which an action must be initiated, commences one year after the introduction of the activities for a compensation claim under the Act. However, a Common Law nuisance can be a continuing offence and so the limitation period might not commence until the nuisance abates.

If the alleged nuisance is one of noise there is also a possibility that summary proceedings might be brought either by the local authority or an aggrieved occupier in the Magistrates' court, under Part III of the Control of Pollution Act 1974. The court can issue an abatement order or a prohibition and each can be accompanied with a requirement to execute necessary works. This Act, in addition, contains provision in Section 71 for the Secretary of State to approve and issue codes of conduct.

There also exists a Common Law duty to take reasonable care to ensure that use of one's premises does not cause injury to persons outside. This duty extends not just to adjoining occupiers but also to members of the public using adjoining rights of way. Thus, if there is any possibility of sports activities impinging upon adjoining property, roads or footpaths, reasonable precautions must be taken to minimize the hazards. If the recreation is to take place near to a residential area, it may also be necessary to consider precautions to prevent the site acting as an allurement to young children. Ensuring that they have no easy means of access would probably suffice in these circumstances, for otherwise there may be the same duty of care as to persons legitimately on the premises.

HEALTH AND SAFETY OBLIGATIONS TO STAFF AND VISITORS

Safety factors can be responsible for preventing a recreational activity altogether, such as bathing in polluted or otherwise dangerous waters. They can also result in the need to exercise a degree of control over activities so as to avoid the possibility of persons injured bringing an action or the prospect of prosecution for breach of a statutory duty.*

In some instances it will be necessary to employ staff to supervise activities. An employer owes a Common Law duty of care to provide a safe place and system of work with safe equipment and plant. To a large extent these duties are superseded by the Health and Safety at Work etc. Act 1974 and regulations made under it. This Act, as did its predecessors, codified much of the Common Law duty of care providing criminal sanctions to enforce the responsibilities of the employer to take all reasonable precautions. Actions for compensation by employees, however, must be brought for breach of Common Law duties, for the right to bring civil proceedings for breach of the duty imposed by the Act is expressly excluded.

In practice these responsibilities are not likely to be unduly onerous as far as recreation staff are concerned. Simple instruction on safety and the provision of outdoor protective clothing might be all that is necessary. Where recreation is not the prime purpose of the premises, then some of the employees whose functions include recreation would probably have been employed in any event. Thus, the introduction of

*See Chapter 6 for a more detailed analysis.

recreation may not necessarily involve additional safety responsibilities in respect of employees.

More serious consideration has to be given to the responsibilities involved in inviting persons on to land for the purposes of recreation. The Health and Safety at Work Act 1974 Section 3(1) provides that:—

"It shall be the duty of every employer to conduct his undertaking in such a way as to ensure, so far as is reasonably practicable, that persons not in his employment who may be affected thereby are not exposed to risks to their health or safety."

This is a very widely phrased duty, being applicable to any person who may be affected. One would, however, expect this to entail principally protection of visitors and trespassers on the premises, but it could conceivably cover persons near to the premises. The scope of the duty requires that there be an undertaking and it may be possible to interpret this in such a way that only where some active "business" is being or has been undertaken. The duty clearly extends to the locks and weirs of the British Waterways Board but does it extend to ordinary stretches of canals, even to the extent of requiring fencing? Likewise the operational parts of a reservoir, the dams, overflows and draw-offs, etc., and possibly the whole of the reservoir could be within the duty. However, it is unclear whether ownership of land, by itself, amounts to "conducting" an undertaking and this argument might be applicable to the passive parts of canals, lakes, and reservoirs. One could argue that it is not conducting an undertaking to possess responsibilities concerning a river. Contrary to these arguments would be the contention that the introduction of recreation would in itself constitute an undertaking so bringing into effect the statutory duty.

There is, of course, an alternative statutory duty which is more normally applied to such situations, viz. the Occupiers' Liability Act 1957. This Act creates a duty to take reasonable care to see that visitors to premises are safe from "dangers due to the state of the premises or things done or omitted to be done on them". An occupier who invites persons on to his land must not be negligent in taking precautions for their protection. Measures required are to protect against dangers caused by the physical condition of the land and the way in which it is used. The Act also expressly provides that greater care will be necessary for the protection of children, but it does not extend to trespassers who must rely on the general principles of Common Law. The Occupiers' Liability (Scotland) Act 1960 contains similar provisions but a number of differences exist as a result of the separate development in England and Scotland of the law in regard to negligence and duty of care.

Where there is a contractual relationship between the visitor to the premises and the occupier, in addition to the Occupiers Liability Act responsibilities, there may be an implied contractual warranty, for example that equipment hired is fit for its purpose and thus reasonably safe and properly maintained.

The quality of bathing water is also a relevant safety factor but the only current legal obligations in this respect are to comply with any local authority byelaws made under the Public Health Acts. A new responsibility could arise as a result of the EEC Directive of December 1978 concerning the quality of bathing water[35]. Regional water authorities will be the "competent authorities" within the Directive whose duty will be to achieve compliance within ten years of specified quality requirements. The Directive applies to bathing expressly authorized by the competent authorities or traditionally practised by a large number of bathers where there is no express prohibition. It may be necessary to have regard to this Directive in determining whether or not to allow bathing. Moreover, severe pollution of rivers would not only inhibit the availability of bathing facilities but could also affect most other activities, including angling when fish are affected.

The Ability of Participants to Meet the Costs

It has long been the policy of water undertakers that, if possible, recreation should not be a subsidized activity. The 1963 Report of The Institution of Water Engineers[14] emphasized that:—

"Participants in the various sports should pay subscriptions which ensure that their activities are financially self-supporting."

Similarly, private operators, although they may receive grant aid, will inevitably only develop recreation if it can be profitable.

By contrast, the British Waterways Board receives Government grants to keep the waterways open, in effect subsidizing pleasure cruising, although some subsidies would be necessary even if there were no boats on the canals. Recreation facilities provided by local authorities are partially paid for through general rates and partially from direct charges made on the actual users of facilities. Individual users therefore do receive a subsidy and do not pay the full costs of recreation.

The position of the public water industry was first formulated in the Water Resources Act 1963 which limited expenditure by river authorities on recreation to the total receipts from registration fees and charges from users. This requirement is effectively repeated in the Water Act 1973. Section 29 (1) states that:

"It shall be the duty of every water authority so to discharge their functions as to secure that, taking one year with another, their revenue is not less than sufficient to meet their total outgoings properly chargeable to revenue account."

Section 30(5) further enacts that it must be ensured by 1st April 1981 that ". . . charges are such as not to show undue preference to, or discriminate unduly against, any class of persons."

The Water Act 1973 and the Water Charges Act 1976 together emphasize the duty imposed upon water authorities to charge costs incurred to the users of facilities. Thus it can be argued that general landscaping, access roads, and basic facilities for casual visitors benefit the general public and should be financed out of the environmental services charge assessable on the community at large. The specific costs of individual sports should, however, be financed by the participants. This would mean that the cost of facilities such as ski-ramps, landing stages, and drying facilities should be charged to users by means of permit charges or club rents, etc.

It is not immediately clear however what self-financing entails and how practicable it is. On a reservoir, various costs arise which cannot always be separated easily to calculate the precise cost of a leisure activity. Further policy problems arise when the "fair" economic rent or charge exceeds that which the user is able or willing to pay.

It is possible in some instances to enable recreation to utilize facilities already provided for other purposes such as constructional access roads and contractors' huts. Indeed, it may even be feasible to position or design such provisions in such a way as to be more suitable for subsequent conversion. This would be one means of minimizing the cost which ought to be charged to the sportsmen. In other instances it can be difficult to ascertain whether a cost is attributable directly to a particular sport. If it is necessary to operate a warden patrol or safety boat is this a service to the general public or to the sailing club? If improved treatment facilities become desirable in order to permit recreation, should this cost be borne by the general public, in other words the ratepayer, or by the users of the reservoir? Cost assessment problems are also faced with administration and management services.

Grant aid can reduce the amount of the costs that must be passed on to the user, as can franchise revenue. On some lakes or reservoirs, it may be feasible for the right to sell light refreshments to be leased. It would also be possible to raise revenue from the direct sales of food, drink, and sports equipment in the case of major projects.

Willingness or ability to pay revolves around various factors. Some sports, such as angling, are used to paying relatively large sums for the privilege of using water. Others, sailing and cruising in particular, traditionally have not been accustomed to high licence fees even though the capital costs of providing facilities for them can be greater and the fees proportional to the cost of running a boat are relatively low. Schemes for vastly improved boating facilities (e.g. on the Broads) can be inhibited by the large increase in licence fees which it is claimed could not be afforded by boat owners.

The location of the resource will also be relevant to the demand and charge that can be made for recreation. The further a reservoir is from the conurbation it serves, the more a pricing scheme must take account of the cost of transport in order to attract visitors. Equally, the availability and cost of alternative facilities will also affect the financial feasibility of a price structure.

There is no common policy to resolve these problems, perhaps because it is desirable, in any event, to examine the individual requirements of each project. In some reservoirs, where access is easy, a charge is made for car parking. At others, perhaps more remote, car parking will be free. Invariably some form of compromise is reached. Although recreation is a general need for the public, it is not reasonable to expect the water rate payer to meet all the expenses, but neither is it practicable to charge the entire costs to the user who would simply become less interested in water sports compared with other forms of sport and leisure. The compromises vary from accepting partial recovery of costs to adjustment of the expenditure attributable to recreation or perhaps the waiving of loan charges.

There is however a promising future as far as the ability to pay for recreation is concerned. Leisure and tourism is one of the fastest growing industries, and it is anticipated that the end of this century will see a large increase in the amount of leisure time available. Water resources are more finite than those for other sports and so demand should increase sufficiently to enable water authorities to make the fullest use of those resources.

The economic and financial aspects of recreational development are discussed in Chapter 7.

THE COMPATIBILITY OF RECREATIONAL ACTIVITIES

The demand for water sports and the relative shortage of water resources result in potential congestion caused by multiple use of reservoirs and other waters. Different activities have their own requirements, which can frequently conflict when they compete for the same water space. An additional compatibility which must be sought is between the sporting and leisure activities and the duties to wildlife and conservation. Clearly, the size of the water will be relevant to the degree of use permissible, and the greatest difficulties will occur on rivers and canals. Future planning of multiple use of water requires careful consideration of these problems, and the sports themselves need to be controlled to minimize conflict.

Angling tends to be very affected by interruptions and disturbances from other sports and even has problems of conflict between game and coarse fish.

On rivers and canals there is frequent conflict between fishermen and boats of all kinds, causing angling interests to oppose any proposals for navigation in private waters where there are fishing rights. Canoeists in particular seek to use the more challenging conditions of shallow, fast-flowing white waters on the upper reaches of rivers where game fishing is to be found. Other conflicts can occur when boats disturb fish, dislodge sediment or catch lines, and conversely where anglers fish at mooring places. It appears preferable to avoid the latter form of conflict by arranging, wherever possible, for moorings to be off the river, at the same time increasing navigational space. This problem is obviously less important on large lakes or reservoirs where it may be possible to restrict boats from operating too near the water's edge. A further disturbance is simply the noise created by powered boats and its effect on peace and quiet—an integral part of the attraction of angling.

There is also much concern expressed by game fishermen when coarse and game fish are present in the same waters. It is contended that the breeding and feeding habits of coarse and game fish are incompatible. This particular problem is avoided on reservoirs by selective stocking, and proposals are sometimes made to relieve the conflict on rivers by means of weirs incorporating fish passes, thereby restricting coarse fish to the lower reaches.

Boats, in addition to competing with anglers, compete with each other. High speed power boats create a wake which may cause a hazard to other boats. Oarsmen and water-skiers are particularly susceptible to interference from wake. There is obviously also a collision danger, particularly on rivers and canals, if rules of navigation are not obeyed, and clearly any areas set aside for bathing must be well separated from those for boats.

Water-skiing and power boats, even though spectator sports, invariably raise cries of protest from conservationists and other sportsmen. There will also be pressures from adjoining land owners or members of the public wishing to preserve the quiet of the countryside and objecting to any such sports. On rivers, riparian owners may actually suffer damage to their banks from erosion caused by the wake of high speed craft. It is for this reason that there is a permanent speed limit of 6.4 km/hr on all the narrow canals, where this problem would be even greater than on rivers.

Informal recreation on lakesides or land adjoining reservoirs is not in itself in conflict with other users. Portable radios could however disturb the character of the setting, as might noisy ball games or overactive dogs. The greatest problem would come simply from any large influx of visitors causing overcrowding.

The Department of the Environment has advised[36] that natural inland waters contain habitats that are particularly vulnerable to change, including developments within catchment areas. Special care must be taken to protect such areas. Some will already be listed as national nature reserves or sites of special scientific interest under the National Parks and Access to the Countryside Act 1949, or as local nature reserves under the 1949 Act as amended by the Local Government Act 1972. Certain locations are also designated under the Ramsar Convention on Wetlands of International Importance[37]. As a result there will be some waters where recreation will not be possible at all.

Moreover, in fulfilling its duties towards nature conservation and amenities, a water authority must consider the potential damage when permitting recreation on its waters. Equally, other operators will need to have regard to these considerations to meet public concern and planning requirements. Thus, some activities may need to be prohibited or controlled and landscaping would be necessary to preserve the appearance of surroundings. The latter requirement should not be too difficult, bearing in mind the type of works and buildings required by recreation, although in some areas of high scenic value it may be necessary to restrict development on the shoreline. It is the former aspect of conservation which causes the most serious problems.

It is argued by the Wildfowl Trust[38] that modern civilization has robbed ducks and geese of much of their natural habitat and that it was only right that gravel pits and reservoirs produced as a result of the needs of our civilization should come to the help of wildfowl. In practice, conflicts occur mostly with sailing, for powered boats are often considered completely incompatible near a nature reserve. Reservoirs already support a substantial proportion of the duck population in Britain during the winter, when recreation is minimal. However, increased sailing on reservoirs is a serious threat to wildfowl, according to the Wildfowl Trust[38] who emphasize two main arguments. Firstly, wildfowl are in themselves a source of recreation. Secondly, their specialized requirements restrict the choice of site and make them especially sensitive to disturbance. Measures must as a result be taken principally to reduce the conflicts with sailing and other boating activities. By properly controlling bird watching and the exclusion of casual visitors there should be no undue disturbance to birds. Seasonal fishing only causes minor upset to birds and, within reason, can be compatible.

In addition to protecting wildfowl, it may be desirable (and a water authority's responsibilities require this), to consider a wider ecological spectrum. Pollution from boats, discarded rubbish, and excessive noise can damage the countryside and affect wildlife. Flora near and on the shoreline may need to be protected from the effects of boats and land activities. One possible solution is to create nature reserves on sections of reservoirs, partly meeting these responsibilities, by preserving some of the flora and providing a sanctuary for animal life.

Clashes of interests can often be avoided at the planning stage by adequate consultation and liaison with interested parties. Sports organizations, potential clubs, and conservation interests can more easily resolve their problems if brought together on a single committee established for this purpose by the controlling body, usually the water authority or (for river developments) the local authority. Prior planning of multiple use of water resources will increase the potential success of such developments.

Recreational activities and their compatibility are discussed in more detail in Chapter 3.

5. CONTROL OF ACTIVITIES

NECESSARY MEASURES

The solution to those inhibiting aspects which are not concerned solely with the planning of a development is often to exercise adequate control over recreation once it is established. Measures are necessary to protect the basic functions of the development, neighbours, wildlife, safety considerations and to resolve any conflicts that arise.

It is vital that public health is not prejudiced, particularly when recreation is permitted on direct water supply reservoirs. However it is accepted that, with more effective treatment facilities currently in use, far fewer limitations are necessary. Naturally, great care must be taken over the disposal of sewage generated by residential developments, clubs and campers, and sanitation must be provided for casual visitors. Care needs to be taken in the use of fuel oils and extra precautions may be needed to prevent spillage. On direct-supply reservoirs, powered boats might present too great a risk of contamination to be permitted at all. The 1972 Report of The Institution of Water Engineers[19] also recommended that, except with river-regulating reservoirs, camping and caravanning in the catchment area should be very carefully supervised and appropriate arrangements made for the disposal of effluents and the collection of litter.

It will of course also be essential to ensure the security of works and equipment, and exclusion of the public from such areas is equally essential for their own safety. Because of the danger to operational works, the British Waterways Board has considered that it would be almost impossible to control the use of power-driven craft on their reservoirs.

The dangers of congestion and collision on canals and rivers may make it desirable that some form of registration of boats be adopted, so that craft can be identified when they infringe regulations or codes of conduct. Speed limits may also be desirable, depending upon the capacity of the canal or river.

At popular places of recreation there will be need for control of traffic and visitors. Cars should be directed to suitable parking places. Damage to the landscape adjoining the reservoir and on neighbouring property can be avoided by the provision of suitable paths and signposting and the maintenance, where appropriate, of a warden system. Fencing could also be a means of protecting nearby agricultural land, although ditches may be more appropriate for preventing access by motor vehicles.

Water safety is the most important reason for controlling activities near water. Codes of conduct, publicity pamphlets, and notices will all help, but may not be sufficient. Clubs can play an important role in educating members and enforcing safety provisions, but where large numbers of the public have access to the water's edge it may be essential to provide a water safety service, often with a rescue boat. The problems related to such service are so great that bathing and unorganized canoeing and sailing may have to be prohibited altogether on some reservoirs due to a belief that to allow such activities in a limited controllable area would encourage the public to think it was permitted anywhere on the reservoir. Partitioning of reservoirs to keep sailors away from dangerous areas and from fishermen's lines is a general solution which may be possible. Such are the statutory safety responsibilities of an operator of a water recreation centre that this is probably one of the most important factors in assessing the degree of permissible activities.

Safety implications themselves feature the conflicts between different users of the water. The increased danger of a water activity requires that it be more carefully controlled than land-based activities. Many sports conflict with each other and frequently it may be expedient to ban one particular sport altogether. Power-boating and water-skiing cause many problems of conflict and, to meet demand, the policy in some areas is to prohibit them entirely from certain areas of water and to set aside other waters solely for these activities—usually where the noise will not affect the surroundings and where other sports are less attracted to the particular location. Where motor-driven boats are permitted on a reservoir it could well be necessary to operate some form of noise regulation. In some circumstances a fixed maximum throttle may be an acceptable solution, although such a restriction on the power of a boat is only suitable for wind-free calm conditions such as on a canal or small sheltered reservoir. On large unsheltered reservoirs this control could actually be dangerous in adverse weather conditions. Designation of approved engine types and capacities and careful monitoring of their use in accordance with maximum noise levels is probably more appropriate.

Separation of activities to different locations is not always the only solution, for the most common means of resolving conflicts between activities is through zoning and time-tabling arrangements, both of which have proved to be successful in practice. Sailing will need to be restricted in certain areas for safety purposes, and further zoning to segregate activities will generally not be difficult to implement on large reservoirs. Time-tabling has the disadvantage that the most popular times are usually common to all activities. Overall control of the numbers of casual visitors may be desirable in some circumstances and can usually only be achieved to any degree by control over the numbers of cars admitted and by a pricing policy designed to reduce the attractiveness of the site compared with other sources of country recreation. Frequently the simplest form of charge would be for car parking.

Apart from complete exclusion of all other activities an effective measure to protect wildlife is a form of zoning, with the establishment of a nature reserve, preferably at one end of the reservoir. Ducks generally require a shallow protected end of the reservoir with a large area of bank and screened from disturbance by other activities wherever possible. They further need a continuity of tenure involving no change to their boundaries over as long a period of time as possible. The nature reserve at Rutland Water closely meets these requirements, being situated in the sheltered upper arm of the reservoir and separated from the other activities. Visitors are also strictly controlled in access to the reserve. A further means of protecting a nature reserve can be seen at the new Kielder Water reservoir, where the upper shallower end of the reservoir is protected from a drop in the water level by an additional dam at Bakethin.

Measures are also needed for the protection of fisheries from fish disease (U.D.N.). On many reservoirs, fishermen and sailors are required to disinfect all their boats and equipment before taking them onto the reservoir. Preservation of fish stocks is also facilitated by controlling the number of fishing permits issued, regulating the means of fishing, requiring anglers, in many cases, to record their catch in order to be able to keep records for the purpose of determining stocking policy in the following year.

IMPLEMENTATION

Byelaws

Various statutory powers exist which enable byelaws regulating recreation to be created. Under the Countryside Act 1968 Section 22(6), water authorities have inherited statutory water undertakers' powers to make byelaws:—

"For the preservation of order, for the prevention of damage to land held with the waterway, or anything on or in the waterway or such land, and for securing that persons resorting to the waterway or such land will so behave themselves as to avoid undue interference with the enjoyment of the waterway or land by other persons, including (without prejudice to the to the generality of the foregoing provisions of this subsection) byelaws—

(a) regulating sailing, boating, bathing and fishing and other forms of recreation,

(b) prohibiting the use of the waterway by boats which are not for the time being registered with the undertakers in such manner as the byelaws may provide,

(c) preventing the passing into the water of any sewage or other offensive or injurious matter, whether solid or fluid.

(d) requiring the provision of such sanitary appliances as may be necessary for the purpose of preventing pollution,

and the byelaws may authorize the making of reasonable charges in respect of the registration of boats in pursuance of the byelaws."

Statutory water undertakers could also make byelaws to protect water against pollution under Section 18 of the Water Act 1945 and that power was extended to river authorities by Section 79 of the Water Resources Act 1963. That Section of the 1963 Act gives further powers which water authorities inherited under Section 9 of the Water Act 1973:

"Where it appears . . . to be necessary or expedient to do so for the purposes of their new functions or of their functions relating to land drainage or fisheries (subsection three)."

Byelaws under this Section may prohibit boating, swimming or other recreational purposes, or regulate such activities that cannot apply to tidal waters, waters within the jurisdiction of a navigation authority, harbour authority or conservation authority, and certain reservoirs and independent lakes. The probability that recreation was not one of the river authority's functions (but merely a power) has already been noted. If this is so, the power of a water authority to make byelaws for the purposes of recreation is limited to the powers contained in the Countryside Act which certainly includes all reservoirs previously owned by water undertakers and would probably also apply to reservoirs previously managed by a river authority. The power to create river and lake byelaws extends only to purposes relating to river authority functions. Thus, there is no power to create a byelaw controlling the speed of river boats to avoid congestion, but there is a power to create fishery byelaws for rivers. Water companies, as statutory water undertakers, will of course have the full powers to make recreation byelaws contained in the Countryside Act. A water authority in Scotland can make byelaws for preventing water pollution by virtue of Section 61 of the Water (Scotland) Act 1946.

Section 36(3) of the Water Act 1973 enacts that the procedure for making byelaws by water authorities, other statutory water undertakers and internal drainage boards under any enactment shall be that set out in Part II of Schedule 7 of that Act. The requirements are that prior notice of the byelaw shall be published at least one month in advance and copies must also be served on any public authorities who appear to be concerned. A copy should also be deposited in the offices of the water authority with provisions for inspection and any person on application is entitled to a copy free of charge. The byelaw must then be confirmed by the appropriate Minister or Ministers. A local inquiry might be instituted. The Minister or Ministers may confirm, refuse to confirm, or (if the water authority consent) confirm with modifications. A similar procedure is followed when the Secretary of State or Minister makes byelaws himself, and there are similar procedural requirements in all of the various undermentioned powers.

Local authorities may create a wide range of byelaws under Section 41 of the Countryside Act 1968 in respect of country parks, picnic sites and common land over which they have exercised powers under the Act. If the byelaws relate to a National Park or an area of outstanding natural beauty, the Countyside Commission shall be consulted first, and byelaws must not interfere with any statutory functions of any other authority. County councils can enforce all byelaws made by local authorities under Section 41 in their area. Where a country park is bounded by a waterway and facilities are provided by the local authority under Section 8 of the 1968 Act, byelaws can be made under Subsection 5 provided that the Countryside Commission is consulted and that the statutory functions of any other authority are not affected. Local planning authorities have byelaw-making powers under Section 13 of the Countryside Act 1968 for lakes in National Parks which are not owned or managed by water authorities or statutory water undertakers and byelaws can also be created by local authorities for local nature reserves (Sections 20 and 21 of the National Parks and Access to the Countryside Act 1949).

The Countryside Commission can create byelaws under Section 41 of the Countryside Act 1968 relating to land held by or managed by them and the Nature Conservancy may, as a result of Section 20 of the National Parks and Access to the Countryside Act 1949 make byelaws to apply in nature reserves.

In Scotland, Section 54 of the Countryside (Scotland) Act 1967 contains a byelaw-making power for a local authority as regards land in their area belonging to them in the countryside, and for a local planning authority as regards a country park provided by them or land or a waterway subject to access agreement or order.

Such byelaws may be:—

"... for the preservation of order, for the prevention of damage to the land, park or waterway, or anything thereon or therein, and for securing that persons resorting thereto will so behave themselves as to avoid undue interference with the enjoyment of the land, park or waterway by other persons."

They must not, however, interfere with the exercise of any public right of way or navigation or of any functions of statutory undertakers or any port authority.

The Department of Agriculture for Northern Ireland is empowered by Section 16(3) of the Water Act (Northern Ireland) 1972, to regularize the way in which any waterway may be used for any recreational purpose. The Department of the Environment for Northern Ireland is empowered by Article 42(2) of the Water and Sewerage Services (Northern Ireland) Order 1973, to make regulations as to the use, for recreational purposes, of any land or facilities on such land vested in it for the purposes of the Order.

The Transport Act 1968 provides that the Minister, on the application of any navigation authority (this includes the British Waterways Board) which owns or manages an inland waterway, after consultation with the appropriate water authority, may confer on such body power to make byelaws for such purposes as may be specified. Interested persons must be given the opportunity of making representations to the Minister. Powers of this nature are usually given to port authorities. The provision empowering the British Waterways Board to make byelaws for canals is contained in Section 16 of the British Transport Commission Act 1954 as amended by the British Waterways Act 1971 and the British Waterways Act 1975. There are powers to register pleasure craft navigating the waterways or to exclude any vessels from the canal or to regulate how such vessels shall be operated. This has been applied, for example, to water-skiing, as well as to the introduction of an overall speed limit on narrow canals. Byelaws under this section must not interfere with any of the powers or obligations of a water authority.

Direct Management

The 1972 Report of The Institution of Water Engineers[19] stated that "Those who own and manage reservoirs and other works of water supply must have the final decision in all matters concerning the quality of the water and the safety of the works", and concluded that "Effective supervision of all recreational activity is essential; competitive events attracting large numbers of spectators may require special arrangements". These views were reiterated in the 1980 publication from the National Water Council entitled "Water supply hygiene"[25].

Although encouragement of clubs reduces the burden on water authorities, final responsibility and control cannot be delegated. Thus, it is common for overall control of a sailing club to be maintained by the water authority with the club having exclusive sailing rights but required to provide facilities to such other organizations and clubs as the water authority may approve. In many cases a Recreation Manager will be appointed by the water authority to control activities and determine priorities between different users.

An important aspect in the control of angling is the issue of rod licences under the Salmon and Freshwater Fisheries Act 1975 by water authorities. This is a prerequisite to legitimate angling and can provide a control of overall numbers. It does not however, authorize fishing at any particular location, for which permission must also be sought. An analagous means to control numbers is the use of a charging policy.

Management of visitors who are allowed on a site is achieved by three means:—
— the use of wardens and rangers,
— signposting and guiding paths, and
— the provision of strict codes of conduct for different classes of users.

Wardens, in addition to their supervisory role to ensure safety and prevent pollution, can also be responsible for the maintenance of facilities and the guidance of visitors. On some reservoirs the emphasis is on site management through wardening rather than by means of fences and prohibitory notices. Despite their secondary importance, warning notices are useful and codes of conduct are valuable in promoting water safety and preventing pollution.

The British Waterways Board equally have a need to control activities, but the nature of their canal network is such that wardening is hardly practicable except at locks. Notices are used and they have, for example, introduced one standard warning notice, recommended by the Inland Waterways Amenity Advisory Council in 1970. This notice asks boaters to proceed with caution during an angling match.

Indirect Control

In many instances the day-to-day running of a sporting activity can be satisfactorily delegated to a club. This enables the club to be responsible for the safety of its members and their supervision. Where there is no primary function, as on wet mineral workings and lakes, an even greater degree of control may be exercised by clubs (who may sometimes even own the land), subject only to the responsibilities of the water authorities to prevent pollution. The 1972 Report of The Institution of Water Engineers[19] recommended ". . . that sailing should be administered by a club and that a legal document should be drawn up clearly defining the rights of and restrictions on both parties. Club rules and byelaws should also be made to the approval of the undertakers." The Report included examples of suitable safety rules which may be incorporated in to the club's rules.

It may be thought that the inclusion in a club lease of a clause excluding liability for accidents will be effective, but this must now be considered subject to the Unfair Contract Terms Act 1977. The clause itself cannot exclude liability where personal injuries are concerned, but the overall delegation to clubs and other measures might itself be sufficient precaution.

A further advantage of encouraging an activity to be organized by a club arises with control of numbers and charging policy. As collection costs from individual visitors can be extremely high, a lease with a club provides a much more convenient solution. The Tyne Recreation Study[22] recommended the use of clubs as a means of effectively controlling activities, particularly water-skiing, and of avoiding conflicts with other users. It cited the Trent Power Boat and Ski Club as a good example of sensible club collaboration between the club, water authority and county council. In this particular case the use of a club enabled the byelaws relating to speed of vessels to be relaxed for club members at particular times and dates. The disadvantage of exclusive clubs is that they prevent the public at large from having access to the water. It is often the policy of a water authority to try, wherever possible, to maintain some facilities for casual users, perhaps by issuing day permits for non-member visitors.

An additional means of indirect control is through the use of volunteers. This has been achieved on some reservoir sites in the removal of litter. Sometimes, with suitable supervision, some of the wardening duties can also be delegated. Volunteers can be particularly useful at times of peak demand, such as weekends and holidays, when they themselves will be most available for such duties.

The necessity and ability to control sports and casual visitors is a vital part of any recreational development on water. Where indirect control can effectively be exercised through clubs and volunteers (subject to the requirements and overall direction of the managing body where other functions have to be protected) this is probably the most suitable solution for all concerned.

The management and control of recreational activities are discussed in detail in Chapters 4 and 5.

6. REFERENCES

1. Central Statistical Office, 1979, "Social trends", HMSO.
2. Countryside Commission, 1974, "Digest of countryside recreation statistics".
3. Water Space Amenity Commission, 1980, "National angling survey 1980". (Main report and summary report.)
4. Inland Waterways Amenity Advisory Council, 1975, "Priorities for action on the waterways of the British Waterways Board".
5. Department of the Environment, The Welsh Office, 1973, "A background to water reorganization in England and Wales", HMSO.
6. Countryside Review Committee, 1976, "The countryside—problems and policies", HMSO.
7. Countryside Commission, 1979, "Leisure in the countryside" (CCP 124), Cheltenham.
8. The Sports Council, 1969, "A review 1966-69".
9. Wolfenden Committee Report, 1960, "Sport and the community".
10. Department of the Environment, 1974, "Report of the National Park Policies Review Committee", HMSO.
11. Ministry of Health, 1948, "Gathering grounds: Report of the Gathering Grounds Sub-Committee of the Central Advisory Water Committee" (Heneage Report), HMSO.
12. Ministry of Town and Country Planning, 1947, "Footpaths and access to the countryside", Report of the Special Committee, Cmnd. 7207, HMSO.
13. Ministry of Health, 1939 (revised 1948), Memo. 221, "Memorandum on the safeguards to be adopted in day to day administration of water undertakings", HMSO.
14. The Institution of Water Engineers, 1963 Journ. I.W.E., 17, 71, "Draft report of the Council on the recreational use of waterworks" (Final Report as separate publication in 1963 under title "Recreational use of waterworks".) Revised Report issued 1972, see reference 19.
15. Ministry of Land and Natural Resources, 3/66, Department of Education and Science, 19/66, 1966, "Use of reservoirs and gathering grounds for recreation", HMSO.
16. Ministry of Housing and Local Government, Welsh Office, circulars 1/67 and 45/67, 1967, "Safeguards to be adopted in the operation and management of waterworks", HMSO.
17. Scottish Development Department Circular 32, 1968, "Safeguards in waterworks".
18. Johnson, T. 1970, Journ. I.W.E., 24, 384, "Recreational facilities at Draycote reservoir",. Rugby Joint Water Board.
19. The Institution of Water Engineers, 1972, Report on "Recreation on reservoirs and rivers".
20. Little, G. 1971, Journ. I.W.E., 25, 102, "Recreational use of reservoirs in Scotland".
21. Drummond, I. 1969, Association of River Authorities Year Book, 174, "Water recreation and amenities".
22. Thomas, D. J., and Roberts, J. T. 1969, University of Manchester, Department of Town and Country Planning, "Tyne recreation study".
23. British Waterways Board, 1965, "The facts about the waterways".
24. Ministry of Transport, 1967, "British Waterways: recreation and amenity", Cmnd. 3401, HMSO.
25. National Water Council, 1979, Occasional Technical Paper No. 2, "Water supply hygiene: safeguards in the operation and management of public waterworks in England and Wales".
26. Countryside Commission for England and Wales, 1974, "Grants to local authorities and other public bodies for conservation and recreation in the countryside", CCP 78.
27. Cowan, R. J. 1978, Journ Planning and Environment, Law Occasional Papers, Planning and mineral workings p. 60, Conditions attached to mineral working permissions, including restoration practice and after-use problems.
28. North West Water Authority, 1977, "Recreational access to reservoirs and gathering grounds", Paper presented by North West Water Authority for Minister of State's meeting with chairman and directors of Government Agencies.

29. European Economic Community, 1978, 659, OJ L222/1, "Directive on the quality requirements for waters capable of supporting freshwater fish".
30. Water Space Amenity Commission, 1980, "Conservation and land drainage guidelines".
31. Water Space Amenity Commission, 1980, "Conservation and land drainage Working Party Report".
32. Tanner, M. F. 1977, Water Space Amenity Commission, "The recreational use of water supply reservoirs in England and Wales".
33. The decision of the Court of Appeal in re Ellenborough Park [1956], 1 Ch. 131.
34. *Journ Planning and Property Law*, 1972, 395, "Notes of planning decisions".
35. European Economic Community, 1976, 160, OJ L31/1, "Directive concerning the quality of bathing water".
36. Department of Environment, 1977, Circular 108, "Nature conservancy and planning", HMSO.
37. Convention on Wetlands of International Importance Especially as Waterfowl Habitat 1976, Cmnd. 6465, HMSO.
38. Atkinson-Willes, G. The Wildfowl Trust, 1969 *British Water Supply*, 11, 5, "Wildfowl and recreation: a balance of requirements".

Additional reading

39. Sports Council and Water Space Amenity Commission and RoSPA's National Water Safety Committee, 1976, "Water safety provision in inland areas: an advisory note".
40. Miles, C. W. N., and Seabrooke, W. 1977, "Recreation land management", E. & F. N. Spon, Ltd., London.
41. Roddis, R. J. 1974, "The law of parks and recreation grounds", Shaw & Sons Ltd., London.
42. Countryside Commission and Water Resources Board, 1973, "Recreation at reservoirs".
43. Soutar, R. 1969, *British Water Supply*, 4, 11, "Amenity use of waterworks".
44. Seeley, I. H. 1973, "Outdoor recreation and the urban environment", Macmillan, London.
45. Tanner, M. F. 1973, The Sports Council, "Water resources and recreation".
46. British Waterways Board, 1965, "The facts about the waterways", HMSO.
47. Alabaster, J. S. (Ed.) 1978, "Recreational freshwater fisheries, their conservation, management and development", Water Research Centre, Stevenage.

APPENDIX A: Table of Statutes

1878	Manchester Water Act
1890	Public Health Acts (Amendment) Act, c. 59
1892	Birmingham Corporation Water Act, c. clxxiii
1906	Open Spaces Act, c. 25
1925	Law of Property Act, c. 16
1937	Physical Training and Recreation Act, c. 46
1939	Access to Mountains Act, c. 30
1944	Education Act, c. 26
1945	Water Act, c. 42
1946	Water (Scotland) Act, c. 42
1949	National Parks and Access to Countryside Act, c. 74
1951	Rivers (Prevention of Pollution) Act, c. 64
1951	Rivers (Prevention of Pollution) Scotland Act, c. 66
1954	British Transport Commission Act, c. lv
1957	Occupiers' Liability Act, c. 31
1958	Physical Training and Recreation Act, c. 36
1960	Occupiers' Liability (Scotland) Act, c. 30
1962	Transport Act, c. 46
1962	Education (Scotland) Act, c. 47
1963	Water Resources Act, c. 38
1967	Forestry Act, c. 10
1967	Countryside (Scotland) Act, c. 86
1968	Countryside Act, c. 41
1968	Transport Act, c. 73
1969	Development of Tourism Act, c. 51
1971	British Waterways Act, c. 18
1971	Town and Country Planning Act, c. 78
1972	Local Government Act, c. 70
1972	Town and Country Planning (Scotland) Act, c. 52
1972	Town and Country Planning (Amendment) Act, c. 42

1972   Water Act (Northern Ireland), c. 5
1973   Local Government (Scotland) Act, c. 65
1973   Water Act, c. 37
1973   Land Compensation Act, c. 26
1973   Land Compensation (Scotland) Act, c. 56
1974   Local Government Act, c. 7
1974   Control of Pollution Act, c. 40
1974   Health and Safety at Work etc Act, c. 37
1975   British Waterways Act, c. 23
1975   Salmon and Freshwater Fisheries Act, c. 51
1976   Water Charges Act, c. 9
1977   Unfair Contract Terms Act, c. 50
1979   Ancient Monuments and Archaeological Areas Act, c. 46

The growth in popularity of sailing has been considerable: membership of the Royal Yachting Association increased from 1000 in 1950 to 52000 in 1977. Organized sailing on a water supply reservoir was first started by the Bristol Waterworks Company in 1947.

Right. Sailing on the Thames Water Authority's Queen Mother reservoir, at Datchet *(H. McKnight).*

Below. The Derwent reservoir of the Sunderland and South Shields Water Company, showing the clubhouse, dinghy and car parks and the launching slipways.

Above. The Cotswold Water Park in Gloucestershire and Wiltshire, where a series of lagoons makes it easier to accommodate water-skiing and power-boating which so often have to be prohibited on other inland waters. (H. McKnight).
Right. Henley Royal Regatta on the River Thames (H. McKnight).

Left. The newly completed K Water (Northumbrian Water Auth will be Western Europe's largest made lake, with a capacity of 2 megalitres. It will ensure the supplies to the North East int next century. The reservoir will h surface area of 1087 hectares will provide extensive recrea opportunities. In the upper sha end of the reservoir is a nature re which will be protected from a d water level by the additional d Bakethin.

Above. "Tackling-up" at the Blagdon reservoir of the Bristol Waterworks Company. In 1904 the Company was the first to introduce reservoir trout fishing.

Left centre. River fishing in Wessex — a particularly popular pastime (Wessex Water Authority).

Left. Bewl Bridge reservoir, Southern Water Authority: the fast-growing sport of wind-surfing or sail-boarding.

Left. Hang-gliding at Rivin(
(North West Water Author(
(H. McKnight).
Below. Children's play are(
Ferry Meadows Country (
(Peterborough Development
poration).

Chapter 2

PUBLIC HEALTH CONSIDERATIONS
AND POLLUTION CONTROL ASPECTS

1. INTRODUCTION

CHAPTER 1 of this book includes references in outline to public health aspects of allowing access to reservoirs and the land adjoining them. In this Chapter attention is focused on factors of particular importance when water is abstracted more or less directly from such reservoirs for public water supply purposes. Public health considerations of some sort arise whether a recreational water is a river, lake, or reservoir, but they are of immediate relevance to the statutory maintenance of a wholesome water supply for public use where a direct supply reservoir is concerned. The primary functions of a public water supply authority can be regarded as:—

(1) Providing an adequate supply of safe and suitable water.
(2) Managing their reservoirs and other works for water supply in a manner which leaves with them both the final decision and the final responsibility for all matters affecting the safety of that supply in regard to quality and to quantity.

The provision of recreational facilities on water and water catchments need not conflict with these functions, provided that they do not prejudice the application of adequate arrangements and operating procedures to protect the quality of the water passing into the public supply system.

The engineers and scientists responsible for designing and operating water supply systems are well aware of the public health responsibilities which they exercise. In the U.K. the wholesomeness of the public water supply is accepted without question; a commendable state of affairs arising because of long experience and the constant vigilance which is exercised on the public's behalf. Members of the public, however, including in this context both the managers of recreational facilities and the participants in water-related activities, may not so readily appreciate the impact made by increased public access to water and, in particular, to reservoirs and lakes used for public water supply. This chapter therefore commences with a short historical review of developments over the last 150 years, and then indicates the general nature of modern water treatment processes and the vital role they play in protecting the quality of water passing into supply. Reference is then made to the effects of recreational activities on the quality of water in reservoirs and the influence of such activities on water treatment plant and equipment. This is followed by a section on the reconciliation of the various responsibilities of a water supply authority and a suggested means of rationalizing what, of necessity, must be subjective judgements about particular levels of recreational activity. The necessary provisions required to minimize the impact on water quality of recreational activities on and around reservoirs are then set out.

2. HISTORICAL REVIEW

The growth and concentration of population and industry in many parts of the U.K. during the nineteenth century resulted in the provision of piped water supplies on a rapidly increasing scale, so bringing under control the explosive growth of diseases such as cholera and typhoid which had become an everyday feature of life in cities and industrial conurbations in the middle of the century. Water clarification and disinfection by chemical means had not then been introduced, and where water treatment was practised it was confined to the simple process of slow sand filtration. Great reliance was, therefore, placed upon the selection of sources of water from unpolluted upland areas and on the remoteness of reservoir gathering grounds and headworks to provide protection from contamination by human activities.

As the science of bacteriology developed it was realized that the storage of water in large reservoirs for long periods was in itself an important protective measure, because intestinal micro-organisms die off rapidly after they leave their warm-blooded hosts. So it was that the nineteenth century campaign for production of urban water supplies from remote and unpolluted catchments, albeit with minimal or no treatment of the water, coupled with the corresponding development of urban sewerage systems, dramatically reduced the incidence of water-borne diseases. These developments paved the way for the twentieth century work which has, in this country, eradicated the most serious water-borne diseases and vastly reduced the risk of less serious diseases such as paratyphoid. Waterworks development in the nineteenth century has had a considerable influence on the practices of the water supply industry up to the present day, and it was accepted by both the public and the water undertakers alike that keeping the sourceworks free of the risk of human pollution was a good and highly desirable practice.

However, with the introduction of motor transport the public became more mobile and as more leisure time became available the desire developed for access to remote and peaceful areas of the countryside. This greater mobility, however, also increased the risk of contamination of, what had originally been, remote water gathering grounds and reservoirs. As the twentieth century progressed, public water undertakers became more concerned to protect water supplies by reinforcing the traditional "lines of defence".

Stresses inevitably developed between water undertakers and the more active sections of the public interested in gaining access to reservoirs and gathering grounds. Believing that their statutory responsibilities required them to be steadfast towards attitudes derived from nineteenth century practices, some water undertakers remained adamant in the face of mounting criticism. This attitude was endorsed by the Ministry of Health in the 1939 "Memorandum on the safeguards to be adopted in day-to-day administration of water undertakings" (Memo. 221)[1]:—

"Whatever the source of supply may be, and whether or not purification treatment is given to the water before it is brought into service, every effort should be made to secure that so far as is practicable the raw water is protected from pollution."

That same document, however, also drew attention to the desirability of maintaining several "lines of defence" between the raw water source and the consumer, i.e.:—

"It cannot be sufficiently stressed that a policy of reliance on a single line of defence between the consumer and a polluted source of water is fraught with danger. Not only should all reasonable steps be taken, as has been suggested above, to keep the source as free as possible from pollution, but the water should, after collection, be subjected also to more than one line of defence, for example, filtration, as well as sterilization by chlorination or otherwise."

Chapter 1 describes how other official reports followed after the Second World War and pointed the way towards greater public access to reservoirs and gathering grounds. As a result new reservoir schemes have been provided with suitably elaborate water treatment plant and in recent years most schemes, and the associated water treatment arrangements, have been planned from their inception to accommodate recreational use as well as greater general access by the public.

Reservoirs, however, have long operating lives and the ability fully to accommodate changed attitudes to public access and recreation is having to wait until opportunities arise for the installation of new treatment plant, often in connection with entirely new non-recreational risks which have changed the circumstances at individual sites. Many reservoirs remain, therefore, at which the water treatment facilities are somewhat rudimentary. In such cases risks to the public supply may be low as long as public access to the reservoirs and gathering grounds remains negligible.

The earlier reservoirs were mainly for direct supply, i.e. reservoirs from which water is taken, after treatment, directly into the piped distribution system (these are called direct-supply reservoirs). Some, however, were built, or later re-allocated, specifically to provide compensation water to river systems, and these are termed compensation reservoirs. Developments in water treatment and supply during the mid-twentieth century led to the introduction of river-regulating reservoirs from which water is released to flow down a river system, often for many miles, before it is abstracted and treated to form part of the public supply. This development received further encouragement as a result of the Water Resources Act 1963, and the regional planning processes it initiated. A revised edition of Memorandum 221, issued by the Ministry of Housing and Local Government and the Welsh Office in 1967 under the title "Safeguards to be Adopted in the Operation and Management of Waterworks"[2], contained the following paragraph in connection with public access to reservoirs and gathering grounds and regulating and compensation reservoirs:

"There is no reason, save in wholly exceptional circumstances, why river regulating and compensation reservoirs, i.e. those which discharge into rivers, should not under suitable control be used for all the recreational purposes, including bathing, for which their siting and physical characteristics make them suitable."

The same document reserved the position in respect of direct-supply reservoirs in the following way:—

"Where however the reservoir is one from which water is taken after treatment direct into public supply, different considerations apply. Public access and recreational use involve a risk of pollution, but the significance of the risk and the extent to which such activities can be permitted will depend upon the characteristics of the reservoir and its surroundings, on the size of the reservoir and on the treatment given to the water. Restrictions and control will be needed for most kinds of recreation, but they need not be greater than are required to safeguard the water supply."

Reference is made elsewhere to the Reports of The Institution of Water Engineers and Scientists (formerly The Institution of Water Engineers) on "Recreational Use of Waterworks" (1963)[3] and "Recreation on Reservoirs and Rivers" (1972)[4]. These publications recognized that greater access to reservoirs and to the land associated with them could be accommodated provided that suitable control procedures were followed and that due, and constant, regard was paid to the treatment given to the water before it passed into public supply. The 1972 Report[4] advised that:—

"Where treatment given to water abstracted from direct-supply reservoirs is minimal, prevention of any further risk of pollution at the source will be a dominant factor in any decision of the water undertaker.

"Where water is subsequently to be fully treated it should be possible to allow the public to enjoy whatever recreational facilities can be provided. The criterion should always be to minimize the risk of pollution."

Since the reorganization of the water industry in 1974 a number of publications dealing with health and safety matters have been issued. The most recent successor to Memorandum 221 was published in 1979 by the National Water Council entitled "Water supply hygiene: safeguards in the operation and management of public waterworks in England and Wales"[5]. This document was prepared within the water industry and issued in collaboration with, and with the approval of, the Department of the Environment, the Welsh Office, the Department of Health and Social Security, and the Public Health Laboratory Service. The following quotations from the document are pertinent:—

> "Where water supplies derived from rivers are subjected to comprehensive treatment, recreational activities in and around regulating and compensation water reservoirs discharging solely to these rivers are unlikely to constitute a significant additional pollution hazard. In such circumstances, decisions on public access will normally be guided more by considerations of public safety and amenity than by water quality and hygiene."

As far as direct-supply reservoirs are concerned, the document reiterates almost verbatim the views contained in Memorandum 221 which are reproduced on p. 47 of this Chapter.

Whilst this historical review has referred particularly to raw water resevoirs (i.e. where water is stored before treatment for public supply) it should also be appreciated that treated water is generally subjected to further short-term storage before it reaches the consumer. After the water has been treated and before it is introduced into the distribution system, the water is stored for a short time in service reservoirs. These reservoirs, which are located within, or close to, urban areas, are covered as a protection against contamination, and they are often grassed over. Access to these grassed areas by the public introduces the risk of pollution arising at a stage where no further treatment of the water is normally possible before it passes into supply. Access to some service reservoir roof areas is allowed on a restricted basis but the incidence of vandalism and acts against public property preclude any general relaxation of long prevailing attitudes towards this type of reservoir.

3. OBJECT OF WATER TREATMENT

In view of the emphasis given above to the provision of adequate treatment of water supplies it is necessary to examine briefly the objectives of water treatment and to refer to the various unit treatment processes available and the contribution that they make towards the provision of an adequate number of "lines of defence" between the reservoir water and the consumers' taps.

The object of water treatment is to produce a treated water free from visible suspended matter, colour, odour and taste, and from all bacteria indicative of the possible presence of disease-producing organisms. The treated water should contain no dissolved matter, either of mineral or organic origin, which would render it dangerous to health. Further it should not, during its passage to the consumer, dissolve substances injurious to health.

4. TREATMENT PROCESSES

In order to attain this demanding specification a combination of the following processes is necessary:—

Clarification	Stabilization
Disinfection	Taste and odour control

The actual combination adopted and their individual complexity will depend on the nature of the raw water and on possible future changes in its quality resulting from changed circumstances and operational procedures on both reservoirs and gathering grounds. Of the above four processes clarification, and taste and odour control, affect the aesthetic quality of the treated water by the removal, during treatment, of objectionable materials of natural or synthetic origin.

The other two processes (disinfection and stabilization) normally have little or no effect on the appearance or palatability of the treated water, but are necessary to ensure protection of the public against harmful bacteria and the taking into solution of material from the pipework of the distribution and domestic plumbing systems.

Whilst it has been convenient here to consider water treatment processes under the above separate headings they cannot normally be considered in isolation, particularly when dealing with raw waters of doubtful quality. The clarification process for instance can, depending on the method used, make a significant contribution towards the disinfection of the water by the removal of bacteria. At the same time, it can considerably affect the efficiency of the subsequent disinfection process. Some methods of taste and odour control may also be inextricably bound up with the disinfection process.

It cannot be emphasized too strongly that water treatment is a field in which a little knowledge can be a very dangerous thing. Expert advice and knowledge is required to design and control the operation of treatment plant and should be sought by anyone likely to have the combined responsibility of the management of a recreational and a water supply facility. Within the water supply industry, whose primary task is procuring, treating, and distributing a public water supply, the necessary expertise is available and the recreational interest has no opportunity to prevail over operational requirements. Situations may arise elsewhere, however, where the reverse may apply if suitable advice is not sought and heeded. Such advice applies not only the methods and processes needed to protect the health of the public, but to the precautions necessary, when using the recognized water treatment chemicals, to protect the operatives themselves.

5. COMBINATIONS OF TREATMENT PROCESSES REQUIRED FOR A PARTICULAR WATER

Combinations of the various treatment processes can be tailored to provide safe and adequate treatment for raw waters of wide-ranging qualities.

Surface-derived waters can, to a greater or lesser degree, be subject to bacterial pollution by either animals, birds, or humans, and it is necessary to secure "defence in depth" against the possibility of harmful bacteria reaching and persisting in the supply mains. All surface-derived waters should thus be subjected to a combination of treatment processes arranged so that reliance is not placed on a single disinfection process. If the water comes from a river or stream (or from any source known to contain effluent from a centre of population), then specific attention needs to be paid to the combination of processes and the provision of a spread of chlorination points to ensure disinfection throughout the treatment sequence.

6. POSSIBLE EFFECTS OF RECREATIONAL USE OF RESERVOIRS AND GATHERING GROUNDS

Having reviewed the general nature of the water treatment processes necessary to secure a consistent and reliable standard of quality for public supply, it becomes necessary to consider what increased pollution risks have to be anticipated as a direct result of increased recreational activity on reservoirs and gathering grounds.

The possible effects of recreational use of reservoirs and gathering grounds can conveniently be considered under three headings:—

Bacteriological effects
Chemical effects
Operational problems

BACTERIOLOGICAL EFFECTS

In order to visualize the possible magnitude of any bacteriological pollution it is interesting to consider that the introduction of 1 gramme of faecal matter into 1 million gallons (4.5 Ml) of water, would, assuming that the faecal matter was evenly distributed throughout the volume of water, result in an increase in coliform count of about 1 per 100 ml.

In practice, however, such faecal pollution would be localized and the coliform organisms would be in high concentration in a small volume of water, but as the pollution became diffused into a larger volume of water with the passage of time, the result would be a considerable reduction in numbers. The full effect would not be apparent at the reservoir outlet unless the pollution occurred very near to the outlet.

Even in upland reservoirs, which are not at present used for recreational purposes and which can be regarded as well protected and virtually unpolluted, coliform organisms counts of several hundreds per 100 ml are quite normal, and presumably arise from natural causes such as wild animals and farming activities. From this it can be seen that, with the possible exception of very small reservoirs, there is a great capacity for absorption of faecal pollution before any significant deterioration in the bacteriological quality becomes apparent at the reservoir outlet.

Having examined the possible magnitude of any deterioration in the bacteriological quality of water in a reservoir, it is necessary to consider how such deterioration due to the introduction of faecal matter might occur. Pollution could arise due to recreational activities either at the water's edge (including feeder streams) and on surrounding land, or on the water surface itself. There is at present undoubtedly a certain amount of illicit access to reservoirs and catchment areas which are supposedly closed to public access. These activities may or may not affect the present bacteriological quality of the reservoir water. Opening up of reservoirs for recreational purposes would lead to a greater number of people being present in the vicinity of the water's edge and, at certain times of the day at least, this would tend to discourage acts leading to increased pollution. Any additional pollution which might occur, due to the presence of the public, within a few yards of the water's edge, behind bushes, etc., whether such additional pollution were due to the activities of humans or domestic animals, would not make a significant direct contribution to a deterioration in bacteriological quality of the reservoir water. Similarly, pollution on the catchment area in the vicinity of feeder streams to the reservoir could be expected to have little effect on the bacteriological quality of the water leaving the reservoir, except possibly where a directly polluted feeder stream entered the reservoir near its outlet.

As far as activities on the water surface of a reservoir are concerned it is likely that swimming and related direct body contact activities would generally be banned, either on aesthetic grounds or in the interest of the safety of the bathers themselves. The 1972 Report of The Institution of Water Engineers[4] mentioned the dangers associated with swimming, and recommended that bathing should not be permitted in reservoirs. These dangers were also referred to in the Second Biennial Report of the Standing Technical Advisory Committee on Water Quality[6].

Generally, the only other activities on the water surface would involve the use of boats. In this case it would obviously be preferable if such boats were kept at or on the reservoir itself and not regularly brought by trailer from unknown points of origin. When, however, boats are imported, then consideration could be given to introducing a simple disinfection process, swabbing both boat and trailer with a suitable disinfectant, at a properly organized launching site. Given proper supervision any bacteriological pollution resulting from activities on the water surface would be less than that occurring from activities at the water's edge, which in itself would be relatively insignificant.

The significance of any bacteriological pollution arising from activities near the water's edge would be considerably reduced by the provision of adequate toilet facilities.

CHEMICAL EFFECTS

The main chemical effect of increased recreational activity on or near a reservoir, which could have a direct influence on the treatability of the water by virtue of a slight increase in concentration, would be the levels of nitrogen and phosphorus. Increased concentrations of either or both of these elements could lead to increased algal growth, and hence to an increased load of suspended matter to be removed by a clarification treatment process. It is highly unlikely, however, that recreational activity even on an intensive scale when compared with agricultural activities would lead to an increase in the concentrations of these elements to levels which would give rise to any significant treatment problems.

Recreational activity at a reservoir would undoubtedly increase the risk of pollution of the reservoir water by hydrocarbon oil products. This pollution could arise as a result of leakages or spillages from power boats and from vehicles parked in the vicinity of the reservoir. The major portion of the hydrocarbons present in oils and fuels used for internal combustion engines do not in themselves present any significant health hazard. They may, however, contain a small fraction of polyaromatic hydrocarbons which do have a health significance. Normal treatment processes incorporating chemical coagulation are fairly effective in removing polyaromatic hydrocarbons from water but, nevertheless, it would undoubtedly be prudent to take all reasonable precautions to protect the reservoir water against the ingress of such compounds. To this end the use of powerboats should be restricted to a reasonable number of safety patrol boats and workboats on direct-supply reservoirs. If water-skiing is to be permitted on direct-supply reservoirs then it would be preferable for the towing boats to be powered by a liquified hydrocarbon, such as propane, which does not present any such hazard. Car parking areas in the vicinity of a reservoir should be equipped with drainage systems designed in such a way as to prevent any accidental spillage or leakage of oil products gaining access to the reservoir.

OPERATIONAL PROBLEMS

Problems liable to arise as a result of increased recreational activity at and around reservoirs are those which may pose operational difficulties or constraints. Difficulties may arise due to litter, vandalism, or just sheer interference with installations by the general public. Security precautions are featured in Chapter 6, and some provision to this end will minimize the chance of problems of this kind occurring and causing pollution of the water. Litter may present a serious problem, particularly as plastic bags and packaging materials are notorious in the water industry for causing malfunctions in valves and other mechanical apparatus.

Recreationalists may not always be aware of the elementary fact that reservoirs are designed to empty as well as to fill. There is a danger in these circumstances that a well established recreational activity may find itself without the water on which it depends, a particularly frustrating situation when the cause of the depletion of the water level would be the prolonged fine weather rendering a recreational outlet so enjoyable. Instances have been noted where recreational interests have sought constraints on reservoir operation, such as requests to maintain specific water levels at particular times of the year. Quite apart from the effect which this would have on the ability to maintain water supplies, it may even be necessary for the water undertaker to restrict recreational access because of anticipated treatment problems arising in a drought situation. Recreational requirements must remain subservient to the operational requirements of the water undertaker and this situation should be reflected in the terms within which recreation and public access takes place.

7. RECONCILIATION OF RESPONSIBILITIES FOR WATER SUPPLY AND RECREATION

The public water supply responsibilities of any water undertaker must, of necessity, impose constraints on the recreational use of direct-supply reservoirs and their catchment areas to safeguard public health. Less stringent constraints need, as already indicated, apply to other types of reservoirs, such as compensation water and regulation reservoirs discharging to rivers. Similarly, different constraints must apply to different forms of recreational activity, depending on whether these would involve access to the water surface, the shoreline, or the feeder streams.

Each supply source has to be considered on its merits, having regard to the nature and extent of the treatment facilities available and the effectiveness of their operation. In the case of a direct-supply source, there must also be regard to the size and nature of any lake or reservoir involved; the nature and characteristics of the gathering grounds; and the degree of control of the gathering grounds exercised by ownership or other means. All these factors will differ from source to source. In order to ensure the requisite quality of the water supply the treatment plant must provide a comprehensive disinfection system in combination with a clarification process, both being adequate to deal with any increased requirements occasioned by the proposed recreational activity.

Water undertakers will differ as regards the age, type, and number of reservoirs they own or operate. A single universal attitude towards recreation, capable of taking into account all permutations of circumstances, would thus be impracticable. However, the attitudes and approach to the problems created by recreation and public access which have been developed by one of the regional water authorities in England (the North West Water Authority[7]) provide a useful illustration.

The statutory obligations on this water Authority, as indeed on all other similar bodies, include the duty:—

To supply wholesome water for domestic purposes.
To take such steps as are reasonably practicable for putting to the best use for recreation purposes its rights to the use of water and of any land associated with water.

These obligations are, as already indicated, likely to be in conflict with one another, but the need to comply with both statutory requirements is important. On the one hand, the Authority is responsible for supplying safe potable water to several million people, and no unreasonable risks can therefore be countenanced. This demands constant vigilance in the operational procedures at sources of water, as well as considerable capital investment on water treatment plant. The possible consequences of failure include loss of public confidence, illness, possibly even death due to water-borne diseases.

On the other hand, there is the duty to accommodate recreation on land and waters. Clearly, an appropriate and practical middle course must be found and the key to it lies in the statutory wording "such steps as are reasonably practicable . . ." (Water Act 1973, Section 20(1)). The problem of reconciling these statutory obligations is always likely to be complex, but it is of special magnitude where a water supply authority operates a large number of small reservoirs. Any policy adopted has to be capable of consistent application across the whole range of practical requirements, and application of the policy to actual cases must promote credibility in the eyes of the lay public, whether they be interested in the suitability of the water supply for drinking or in the use of land and water space for recreation, or both.

The North West Water Authority[7] has formally adopted the following procedure for solving the problems of applying its policy to actual cases:—

It has codified its attitude towards the requisite standards for water treatment and the facilities for providing them, so that the unavoidable subjective judgement of its engineering and scientific specialists may be both consistent and in line with up-to-date and acceptable expert opinion.

It has established a method for rating the effectiveness of water treatment plants according to the technical features they possess.

It has specified the minimum ratings with which water treatment plants should conform in order to ensure adequate "lines of defence" for the general protection of the water supply at the types of water sources encountered in practice, taking into account any protective effects of storage that can be relied upon at those sources.

Believing that the additional pollution arising from public access for recreational purposes is likely to be relatively small, and by its nature easily dealt with by efficiently operated treatment plant installed in compliance with those minimum requirements for general protection of the water supply, the kinds of recreational activities that would be permissible (having regard only to water quality considerations) are considered to be directly related to the rating of the water treatment plant provided in any particular case.

This procedure emphasizes that a logical and consistent approach to the formation of a detailed recreation development programme at direct-supply reservoirs is, in essence, a critical appraisal of the water treatment processes in use at present.

The ratings of treatment plants are assessed by considering how many out of six desirable features are in existence at the treatment plant (Table 2.I). Each of these features provides a contribution to the defence against contamination of the water supplies, though some carry more weight than others.

The specification adopted for the required minimum ratings of treatment plants for particular types of water sources is given in Table 2.II.

A comparison between the required rating in any particular case and the rating of the plant already provided reveals whether it is considered that there are an adequate number of "lines of defence" for the protection of the water supply. Indeed, the application of such a system may show up deficiencies which require to be made good, irrespective of any proposals for recreational use. It is inevitable that where there are known deficiencies in the lines of defence there cannot be expectation of greater public access for recreation until the deficiencies have been removed. On the other hand, where it happens that the existing treatment plant is rated higher than the minimum required for the source concerned, the permissible recreational activities would be rather less constrained than in other cases.

TABLE 2.I.   Method of Assessing Plant Rating

Feature	Assessment of rating								
1. Adequate clarification process	X	X	X	X	X	X	X		
2. Adequate disinfection process	X	X	X	X	X	X	X	X	X
3. Clarification process contributes to disinfection by removal of bacteria	X		X	X			X		
4. Chlorine residual automatically adjusted after contact period	X	X					X		
5. Chlorine residual continually measured after contact period			X		X				X
6. Adequate contact period, but no automatic chlorine residual control or continual measurement				X		X			
Treatment plant rating	A	B	B	C	C	D	D	E	E

Any plant failing to achieve an "E" rating is classified "F".

Notes to Table 2.I:
(1) An adequate clarification process implies that the installed process is capable of producing an aesthetically acceptable water at all times whatever the seasonal variations in the particular raw water.
(2) An adequate disinfection process implies that duplicate chlorinators and motive water pumps or pressure water systems are provided, and that the chlorinators are fed from a gas header pipe system connected to at least two cylinders or drums which are equipped with an automatic changeover panel to ensure continuity of gas supply.
(3) Clarification process contributing to disinfection by removal of bacteria generally means that the process incorporates either slow sand filtration or chemical coagulation.

TABLE 2.II

Type of water source	Minimum rating of treatment plant required
Direct abstraction from a lowland river subject to pollution	A
Lake or reservoir on catchment not owned by authority	B
Lake or reservoir on catchment not owned by authority but with no potential pollution hazards	C
Lake or reservoir on catchment owned by authority, with only moderate agriculture and habitation	C
Lake or reservoir on catchment owned by authority, with no potential pollution hazards	D
Remote catchment with no potential pollution hazards and long storage of raw water	E

Recalling that the permissible kinds of recreational activities in any particular case are to be considered as directly related to the rating of the water treatment plant, the Authority has defined its guidelines as set out in Table 2.III, subject to the following three fundamental assumptions:—

(a) That the existing treatment plant in any particular case is not inadequate for the protection of the supply in the general circumstances of that case, i.e. it has at least the rating specified for the type of water source concerned.

(b) If, in any particular case, it is desired to permit recreational activities beyond those permissible against the treatment plant rating specified for that case, additional capital investment and operating costs would be required to up-rate the treatment process appropriately. (There might then be a sound argument for charging the whole of these additional costs to the recreational beneficiaries.)

(c) That any recreational activities would be effectively managed and supervised, and that all necessary car parks, toilets, and similar facilities would be provided.

TABLE 2.III

Rating of treatment plant provided	Recreational activities that may be allowed, having regard to water quality considerations only	
	On gathering grounds	At or on reservoirs
A	No constraint	No constraint
B	No constraint	Selected
C	Selected	Limited
D	Incidental	Limited but shoreline only
E	Incidental	None
F	None	None

The following are definitions of the terms used in Table 2.III:—

No constraints.—No overriding constraint on the types of recreational activity which would be allowed, subject to this being found practicable and safe at the places concerned.

Selected.—Selected activities, e.g. angling and sailing, but without limitation on numbers.

Limited.—Limited numbers of participants in selected activities, e.g. a maximum number of anglers or boats at any particular time.

Incidental.—No organized activity, but freedom for quite casual activities, e.g. walking, climbing, and ornithology. Suitable picnic areas would be allowed.

It is to be noted that the description of the policy and its application has been concerned with reconciliation of the conflicting statutory duties, having regard only to water quality considerations. The question of whether particular sites are safe and suitable for particular recreational activities is a separate matter.

8. SUMMARY OF PRECAUTIONS NECESSARY TO CONTROL POLLUTION OF RECREATIONAL WATERS

The precautions listed below will particularly apply to the recreational development of direct-supply reservoirs, i.e. those reservoirs from which water is drawn directly through a suitable treatment works and passed by pipeline into the public water supply system. Nevertheless, some of the precautions can be regarded as applying equally to compensation and river-regulation reservoirs as they are in general simply "good housekeeping" measures designed to protect the natural environment.

(i) Serious consideration should be given to the type and number of power-driven boats allowed on reservoirs in view of the possible harmful effects which might arise due to leakage or spillage of fuel and oil products. It is suggested that, particularly on direct-supply reservoirs, the numbers of boats be kept to a minimum and on smaller reservoirs be limited to safety and work boats.

(ii) Car parking areas and roadways adjacent to the reservoir shorelines should be designed with the possibility of the leakage and spillage of oil products in mind.

(iii) Any oil storage installations associated with buildings provided as part of the recreational development should be so arranged as to contain any leakage.

(iv) Illicit dumping of unwanted materials or objects by the public should be guarded against.

(v) Whilst it is not within the scope of this book to deal with agricultural practices, it is important that care be taken in the use of agricultural or horticultural chemicals on any areas adjacent to a reservoir which have been landscaped as part of the recreational development, in order to ensure that excessive amounts of such chemicals do not gain access to the reservoir.

(vi) Adequate toilet facilities should be provided for visitors to the area.

(vii) Adequate and appropriate sewage disposal facilities should be provided for all premises and these should be properly maintained. The question of the discharge of effluent from such sewage disposal facilities will require attention, and each case will probably require individual consideration. The seasonal and intermittent use of facilities must be borne in mind when deciding on methods of treatment, together with the size and topography of the reservoir and nature of the water therein. Consideration of the proximity of any existing public sewerage system is a further point to be borne in mind when deciding on the method of effluent disposal.

(viii) Recreational activities on land and water must be adequately supervised and any necessary works carried out to minimize the possibility of interference with water supply apparatus by the general public.

(ix) Arrangements must be made for the collection and disposal of litter from areas accessible to the public.

(x) Facilities should be provided at suitable points on the reservoir shore for the disinfection of recreational equipment such as boats, trailers, diving equipment, etc., brought to the reservoir from other locations. The facilities can be relatively simple, consisting of means of swabbing the equipment with a suitable disinfectant solution such as sodium hypochlorite. On no account should phenol-based disinfectants be used in the vicinity of a water supply reservoir, because of the taste problems likely to arise as the water is chlorinated before being passed into supply.

(xi) If chemical toilets are to be provided then only proprietary products based on formaldehyde should be used.

9. ADMINISTRATION OF CONTROL MEASURES

Administration of control measures on catchment areas wholly owned by the water undertaker is relatively simple. Where land is not owned the situation becomes more difficult; much will depend upon the goodwill of owners and occupiers. The somewhat higher risks associated with land not owned by the water undertaker should be matched by the adequacy and efficiency of operation of the water treatment plant concerned. On the other hand, full ownership and control of gathering grounds should not be regarded as reason for making savings in the provision of adequate treatment plant.

10. CONCLUSIONS

The use of reservoirs and associated gathering grounds for recreational purposes and for regulated access by the public should not significantly increase the pollution load arising from natural causes already carried by the reservoir. Some precautions need, however, be taken. These include the provision of services to minimize the possibility of additional pollution, however slight, and to prevent the recreational use from interfering with the statutory operational responsibilities of the water undertaker.

  The level of recreational activity which can be permitted at any particular reservoir site depends on the standard of treatment provided to render the water suitable and safe for public supply purposes. It is not possible to base judgements of the relative water treatment requirements on a fully objective basis, but a system of codification of water treatment plant characteristics and requirements is a valuable aid towards making the necessary subjective judgements on a sound and consistent footing.

  Because the primary duty of any water undertaker is to provide safe and suitable water, final decisions in all matters concerning the quality of the water and the protection and safety of the associated works must lie therefore with the water undertaker. Developments in recent years indicate that those concerned with water supply, both officers and members, have adopted a constructive attitude towards accommodating recreational use and public access wherever this can be accomplished without prejudicing that primary duty.

11. REFERENCES

1. Ministry of Health, 1939 (revised 1948). "Memorandum on the safeguards to be adopted in day to day administration of water undertakings", Memo. 221, HMSO.
2. Ministry of Housing and Local Government and Welsh Office, 1967, Circulars 1/67 and 45/67, "Safeguards to be adopted in the operation and management of waterworks".
3. The Institution of Water Engineers, 1963, *Journ. I.W.E.*, vol. 17, p. 71, "Draft report of the Council on the recreational use of waterworks" (Final Report as separate publication in 1963 under title "Recreational use of waterworks"). Revised Report issued 1972, see reference 4.
4. The Institution of Water Engineers, 1972, Report on "Recreation on reservoirs and rivers".
5. National Water Council 1979, Tech. Paper No. 2, "Water supply hygiene: safeguards in the operation and management of public waterworks in England and Wales".
6. Department of the Environment/National Water Council, Report No. 22, "Second biennial report, February 1977-January 1979, of the Standing Technical Advisory Committee on Water Quality".
7. North West Water Authority, 1977, "Recreational access to reservoirs and gathering grounds", Paper presented by the Authority for Minister of State's meeting with chairmen and directors of Government Agencies.

Chapter 3

ACTIVITIES AND SUPPORTING REQUIREMENTS

1. GENERAL CONSIDERATIONS

THE primary concern of public bodies administering water resources, sewage disposal, land drainage, and water supply functions involving a body of water and associated land will be the provision of one or more of those services. Any recreational activities which are permitted on the water or land must generally be subject to the constraints which the provision of the services imposes, as has been clearly shown in Chapters 1 and 2 of this book. This Chapter is concerned with the many kinds of recreational activities and with their general supporting requirements. The actual planning and management of the various activities is covered in Chapters 4 and 5. More detailed information on many of the recreational bodies referred to in this Chapter is given in Chapter 9.

The apparent ambiguity in this Chapter title is not accidental. Recreational activities require varying degrees of "support" by way of buildings, works, or facilities; they also vary considerably in the nature of the demands which they make on water resources and in their degree of compatibility with other users of water and associated land. These special requirements are dealt with later in the Chapter when the individual activities are discussed in detail. The most important consideration common to every activity must, however, be of the elements—the water, the land, and the air—which lend, literally, the physical support to the participant and/or his equipment. The suitability of the elements at a particular site for a particular activity is of paramount importance.

It is not possible to decide *in vacuo* that a certain recreational activity is the right thing to cater for on a particular site possibly because a neighbouring authority has that activity on a reservoir or a river. This is no suggestion, however, that would-be providers should not draw extensively on the experience of others in similar situations and seek advice from the many established bodies such as the Sports Council, the Regional Councils for Sport and Recreation, and the Water Space Amenity Commission. In addition, further help can be obtained from the governing bodies for particular sports and pastimes. Having weighed the evidence and analysed the advice a decision must be taken as to whether the proposed activity fits the particular environment.

Where a body of water is being newly created or its character is to be changed in connection with the provision of one of the primary services referred to earlier, much can be achieved by forward planning to ensure that preferred recreational activities are compatible with the requirements of the particular service. Facilities for recreation can often be built into the works and, equally importantly, the engineering requirements might be modified to enhance rather than detract from the potential for recreational activity. For example, a trapezoidal river channel with a constant fall may be ideal for land drainage purposes, but a "shallows and holes" bottom may well be acceptable and would be infinitely preferred by fish and, consequently, by anglers; or a fen drain may be constructed with a berm, where anglers may stand, without prejudicing the land drainage function.

The philosophy of conservation is frequently in tune with certain recreational activities such as looking at the countryside and angling, but there are pursuits (for example, those which involve crowds of people trampling over areas supporting delicate flora and fauna, or those which are excessively noisy), where there is likely to be direct conflict with the general philosophy. Planning must therefore embrace not only compatibility between a recreational activity and the primary service, but also compatibility with conservation interests.

When considering an extension of recreational activity on an established body of water the flexibility inherent in good forward planning is to some extent lost. However, the objective of compatibility is constant and in such circumstances consideration will be concentrated on how recreational requirements and the existing water facility can be modified to meet the essential needs of the new activity without undue disturbance of the *status quo* and the needs of the established primary service.

In the case of a local authority which has responsibility for recreation but which does not have the duty for any of the primary services mentioned, it is possible to design new water developments and land associated with them, or to adapt existing situations (provided that the rights and duties of others are not adversely affected), solely for a specific recreational purpose. In these cases, some of the constraints inherent in providing a primary service are removed. Opportunities are being taken to an increasing degree to create such recreational waters and land as part of the restoration of derelict industrial sites, notably those arising from the mining of coal, gravel, slate, clay, and iron ore.

WATER—THE PHYSICAL SUPPORT FOR RECREATIONAL ACTIVITY

Is the Element Suited to the Activity?

Each recreational activity will demand special inherent features of the water element which are often critical but which are not always apparent. For example, an operator considering whether or not to provide a fleet of motor cruisers for hire on a river or canal system must assess whether the system is large enough to sustain interest and enjoyment during a typical 14-day cruising holiday; whether there are sufficient interesting places to be visited; and what are the falls in the river and the number of locks. (Locks, if there are too many of them, can present a daunting prospect to some users of the river.) There are also a host of other points to be considered, including depth of water, type of bottom, banks and foreshore, flow velocity, water quality, and weather.

The demands will vary from activity to activity and are related to many factors including population centres, social status of participants, competition from others providing a similar facility, the attraction of people to the area for other reasons such as holidays, the existence of enthusiasts in the vicinity prepared to teach or run a club, and last but not least the current popularity of the particular activity.

Is the Activity Suited to the Element?

The first consideration must be the effect of the activity on the quality of the water, and on reservoirs used for public water supply this is of fundamental importance. In the past certain recreational activities have been regarded as quite unacceptable on such reservoirs, but in recent years there has been some change of attitude, particularly where the stored water is in a regulating reservoir or is pumped from rivers already receiving effluents and surface water run-off. Many regulating and some direct-supply reservoirs in Great Britain now have motorized fishing boats and some have water ski-ing and power boats. In some other countries the attitude to the use of mechanically propelled recreation craft on storage reservoirs is more liberal than in the U.K. Results of research carried out in the United States of

America have indicated that the effect on the chemical quality of the water of conventional outboard petrol motors, as commonly used on recreation boats, is insignificant. The effect of oil and exhaust discharges should be kept in perspective when assessing the suitability of engined boats in relation to the quality of a body of water.

Waste from boats has an effect on water quality, and the Control of Pollution Act 1974 (when the relevant sections are brought into force) makes it an offence to keep or use on a stream a vessel provided with a sanitary appliance (a "sea-toilet") and requires provision to be made for the collection and disposal of waste stored on the vessel.

Ground bait used in coarse fishing has a substantial B.O.D., but this should be related to the B.O.D. of all the other decaying organic material falling into the body of water.

Nevertheless, recreational activity can have an effect on water quality and the water undertaker must make an assessment of the acceptability of the activity from this point of view. Factors to be taken into account will include the source of the water and its quality at the point of intervention of the activity, the effect of the activity on the water, the subsequent use of the water, and the availability and cost of treatment necessary to make it suitable for that use. These particular points are dealt with more fully in other Chapters.

A further consideration is the physical effect of recreational activity on the water and thus on the whole environment. For example, the propellers of boats stir up water plants and mud in shallow waters. The resulting turbidity can stop light from reaching plants, and this can lead to the almost complete disappearance of water vegetation with consequential damage to fisheries by way of loss of spawning grounds and food. The disturbance of the water and loss of vegetation, and indeed the very presence of people on the water and surrounding land may drive away wild life of many kinds. The frequent use of locks may cause shoaling in a river to the possible detriment of land drainage and to the boating recreation itself. Indiscriminate use of water level regulating devices for recreational purposes may affect land drainage, irrigation, water quality, fisheries and general environmental amenity.

Noise generated by recreational activity, whilst having no direct affect on water quality, is generally regarded as a pollutant especially in the rural surroundings usually associated with water. Excessive recreational activity must then be regarded as an enemy of nature conservation and the maintenance of a quiet rural environment. In any situation the would-be provider must carefully weigh the importance of all these factors. On the other hand, the local authority provider in an urban situation may well wish to create a "honeypot" where recreational activity has priority possibly at the expense of conservation of the original environment. It is sometimes possible to establish a somewhat pseudo-environment with tame birds, captive fishes and the like to complement some of the more intrusive recreational activities and to satisfy the particular public enjoying the whole range of facilities offered at the site.

LAND ADJACENT TO WATER—AS A PHYSICAL SUPPORT TO RECREATIONAL ACTIVITY

Is the Element Suited to the Activity?

Many of the requirements of the water element which have been considered in connection with a recreational activity are relevant to the land element also. Size, shape, orientation, slope, and existing use must all be given consideration. Many of the needs of different activities will be readily apparent, but some are referred to here. For example, sailing ventures need sufficient land at the water's edge for a clubhouse and for boat storage. It must also be determined whether the land is suitable for correct siting of the fixed equipment in relation to the prevailing wind, and whether advantage can be taken of a sheltered creek or whether an artificial harbour must be considered. A grass ski slope obviously needs land at an acceptable slope and of at least a minimum length. Hang gliding cannot be considered unless some kind of suitable launching area is available. Air currents must also be suitable, and the proximity of an area of water could create undue safety risks.

The structure of the soil is also important. It must be suitable for the proposed activity. For example, a heavy clay soil liable to poaching is unlikely to be suitable for intensive horse riding in the winter, unless the track can be varied frequently. Also, land liable to summer flooding is unsuitable for car parking and picnicking areas.

The structure of river banks and reservoir margins must also be considered—they can be vulnerable both from boat wash and anglers' feet. Consideration must also be given to the fact that where there are likely to be concentrations of large numbers of people, then toilet and other facilities must be readily available.

Is the Activity Suited to the Element?

As with water the effect on the element is all important. As already indicated recreation activities can literally wear away the land by erosion, and the anticipated level of use and any necessary protective treatment of the land surface are matters for consideration for each activity.

In addition, there are recreational activities which can foul the land and thus endanger the quality of the water. However, it is now considered that at a reasonable level of use many recreational activities can be permitted without causing unacceptable risk of pollution of the land and the water.

2. WATER-BASED ACTIVITIES

ANGLING

Coarse Fish Angling

Coarse fish angling is normally practicable where the chemical and biological quality of the water is capable of supporting a reasonable benthic fauna and flora and where the velocity of the flow is not so great as to inhibit use by coarse fish of the water as their habitat. Coarse fish have adapted to a fairly wide range of conditions within which these two criteria are met. The "raw materials" for coarse fish angling are thus usually provided naturally and they are protected and fostered by the water authorities under the Salmon and Freshwater Fisheries Act 1975.

Sometimes recreation providers, in order to create a wider range of angling, introduce additional species to waters which, whilst able to support the growth of the fish, may not necessarily be capable of providing the condition suitable for natural breeding of the species. This later situation applies more particularly to game fisheries.

It is pertinent to sound a note of warning here about the dangers of introducing exotic species for whatever reason—there have been cases where the balance of nature has been disturbed, with unforeseen results. In other cases, efforts to improve angling have not justified the expense involved.

Physical conditions relating to the water should be taken into account when planning the use of the water for angling.

The area of the water is unlikely to cause any particular problems, although on large areas it may be necessary to use punts or boats if all the fish are to be brought within reach of the angler. The depth of water is, however, an important factor. It is generally accepted that a depth of at least 1 m of water in summer is necessary for successful angling. Waters with "deeps" of, say, over 14 m (such as may occur in reservoirs) do not usually provide very good winter sport because as the water temperature drops the fish tend to go down out of the shallower parts and out of the reach of the angler. Coarse fish are not normally affected by fluctuations in level of water caused by operational use, but a severe drought can introduce distress, particularly in rivers and relatively small shallow reservoirs, due to deoxygenation, temporary restriction of habitat, and loss of feeding areas. Operational use of a water may, however, cause mud to be exposed on the banks and this may add to difficulties of access for the angler. The fish may become more vulnerable to anglers as the water level drops. De-watering of river reaches and fenland drains for land drainage and other works obviously cause local crises for the fish, which have to be rescued, but are unlikely to affect the planned long-term angling use of a fishery.

The most favoured conditions for coarse fish angling will include a limited but varied bankside growth, shady trees on southern banks, and some aquatic weed. Too much weed, however, can make the water unfishable! Water temperature has a marked affect on fish behaviour and their inclination to take the anglers' bait and, of course, icy conditions on still waters makes angling impossible.

Coarse fish anglers require reasonable access to the fishery and because of the weight and encumbrance of their gear it is desirable to avoid a long walk to the stances. Car parking off the highway, especially at match fishing venues, is highly desirable. The provision of reasonably level stances is also important but this may be difficult to arrange at reservoirs with sloping concrete sides, which can be dangerously slippery; punt fishing may be appropriate in such locations. It is desirable to have fairly deep water accessible from the bank to permit the use of a keep net.

Coarse fish anglers do not generally make large demands for lodges or even shelters but particularly at reservoir sites and intensively used match fishing venues it will be necessary to provide toilets.

The degree of stocking both as to numbers and species is largely a question of fisheries management and is of course directly related to the demands of the anglers. Under normal breeding conditions and reasonable angling use the "native" fish are likely to be able to maintain their stock naturally, and re-stocking will usually be confined to re-establishing the water after a disaster or in the creation of a new enclosed fishery. Variety in angling can sometimes be obtained by introducing selected species into waters where the conditions are on the fringe of the particular species' natural habitat.

It is worthwhile to draw the distinction between the duties of the water authorities under the Salmon and Freshwater Fisheries Act 1975 to "develop maintain and improve" all fisheries in whosoever ownership they may be, and their right as owners of fisheries on some stretches of river and on enclosed waters owned by them to manage for recreational purposes the angling of those fisheries.

Coarse fish angling can, and does on occasion, cause difficulties, for example aggravation to adjoining owners caused by trespass to gain access; erosion of banks at stances; the danger to wild life from discarded fishing lines and leads and, perhaps more emotive than real, the B.O.D. of ground bait.

The effect of other recreational activities involving the use of mechanically driven boats on coarse fish angling can be substantial, particularly if the use is intense. The frequent passage of boats destroys for the angler his tranquillity and is a nuisance to his casting—it is also claimed that it disturbs the fish. The propellors can stir up the water and reduce light penetration resulting in the loss or change of flora and thus the loss of fish habitat and spawning grounds.

Coarse fish angling is essentially an individual pastime, although anglers frequently come together in match competition or fishing club groups. It can therefore be managed by the owner on an individual day or period ticket basis. The management and collection of the ticket fee can be expensive in the case of an extensive but lightly-used fishery. The owner could let the fishery and its management to a club at a substantial rent, in which case his only expense is likely to be collection of the rent.

There is a need for tuition in coarse fishing and owners managing their own fishing may consider granting facilities to the local education authority to run or organize courses. Clubs may make arrangements for tuition either collectively or individually. The National Anglers Council have a training scheme and maintain a register of coaches.

Game Fish Angling on Rivers

Angling for trout in rivers and lakes has been practised for centuries and it is now more than 70 years since game fishing was first introduced on water supply reservoirs. The stocking is normally with rainbow trout as well as with the brown trout indigenous to rivers in Great Britain.

The pursuit with rod and line of salmon, sea-trout, and brown trout is primarily for sport, with the provision of food as a secondary objective for many game fish anglers. The well-being of game fish in particular is dependent upon clean well-aerated water. Such conditions are abundant in most of the upland areas of the U.K., but are scarcer in the lowlands, where the rich chalk-streams are highly prized.

The general duty of water authorities to maintain and improve the quality of river waters is thus of particular value to game fish anglers. The duty also includes the maintenance, improvement, and protection of fisheries and to this end there is particular concern for the enforcement of byelaws, which are designed to prevent over-exploitation of the fish stocks from the estuaries up to their spawning head-waters. Other requirements include the provision and maintenance of fish passes; monitoring the quality and temperature of water release from river-regulating reservoirs; having regard to the effects of land drainage and river management works; investigating the influence of sexual attractants (pheromones) upon the runs of migratory fish in search of spawning beds; research into the nature and quantity of fish-food supported by varying riverside vegetation, including trees; and the production of angling guides which often reveal many more locations than is commonly assumed where permits for game fishing are available at low cost.

Game Fish Angling on Still Waters

It has long been known that game fish will live and thrive in waters where they are unable to procreate because of the lack of suitable spawning grounds. This phenomenon is normally associated with still water lakes and reservoirs. There is at one end of the range of waters atrophic waters which are barely capable of supporting fish in a thriving condition and at the other waters in which trout will thrive and grow rapidly although they cannot reproduce.

The demand for game fish angling has lead to the development of "put and take" fisheries, where native and exotic species of trout are artificially introduced in variety into the water with the express intention that, before they die, they should be caught by the angler. These fisheries vary widely in character and satisfy differing angling demands. They comprise the reservoirs and lakes of mountainous areas, where the acidic water and available food are capable of supporting only the native brown trout and where stocking is at a fairly low level and occasional only to satisfy the light angling use by those anglers seeking an attractive environment in which to catch wild fish. There are also the fisheries, near heavily populated areas, which although not particularly rich in food are subjected to intense angling pressure and where it is necessary to introduce stock fish at frequent intervals in order to ensure as far as possible a consistent catch. Additionally, endeavours are made to control the supply of fish in the reservoirs by imposing bag limits on the number of fish taken.

In addition there are the reservoirs of the lowland areas which are rich in food and where stocking is reasonably heavy—a policy of maintaining 30 to 60 fish per hectare might be typical. In these waters the growth of the fish is rapid, and anglers expect large well-grown fish to feature consistently in their catches. The usual size of "stock" fish is about 250 to 300 mm in length, since a specimen of this size is regarded as acceptable to an angler as a catch. Larger fish are sometimes introduced as "loss leaders", in order to persuade the angler that he has a chance of catching the "big one".

The size of stock fish, the varieties and/or species, the numbers introduced, and the frequency of introduction are an intricate problem of management and will depend on a mass of considerations including the size of water, its quality, the climate and the type and intensity of the angling demanded, and the financial return required. The recording of catches is an important aid to management, especially of newly established fisheries, to assist in the maintenance of fish density per hectare.

Private owners of reasonably small put and take game fisheries seem generally to let the fishing rights to small clubs or syndicates with a fixed number of rods and with fairly strict bag limits. On the other hand, many municipal authorities, including the water authorities, have recognized the increasing demands of the modern angling public and issue day and season tickets on their game fisheries.

A fishing club or syndicate will probably ask for very little more than a satisfactory stocking programme at their fishery—indeed, they may even undertake this task themselves. An owner of, say, a large reservoir where day permits are issued will have to ensure that the waters are consistently well stocked so that anglers have a fair chance of catching fish every day of the season. It has become usual at most intensively used fairly large permit fisheries to provide a fishing lodge to varying degrees of pretension: such items as a rest room, changing room and weighing and fish preparation room are commonly provided; restaurants and bars are occasionally included. On the larger fisheries it is now common practice to provide fishing boats, either hand-propelled or power-driven. These boats are usually about 5 m long, with a fairly wide beam, and they can accommodate two or three anglers. A launching site or jetty will be required. All fisheries will need some car parking facilities and it is important to provide at permit fisheries for the maximum anticipated number of cars. The combination of the angling car park with other visitors' car parks can be helpful in this respect, since peak uses do not necessarily coincide.

Sea Angling

Sea angling is an extremely popular activity around the whole of the coastline of the British Isles. Shore fishing takes place from all suitable casting areas, including piers, breakwaters, sea walls, rocks and beaches. The main requirements here are for right of access to such areas, together with nearby parking facilities.

SAILING

Dinghies are by far the commonest sailing craft used on inland waters, but on large waters where conditions are suitable substantial keel boat fleets can develop. At the other end of the scale the recent growth of interest in board-sailing (or windsurfing) is leading to increasing pressure to accommodate this branch of the activity. All three branches of the sport have generally similar requirements, but any special needs of particular branches are mentioned below.

The actual area of water is by no means the only criterion to be taken into account when deciding upon the type of sailing and the sailing capacity on a specific stretch of water: the general success of a sailing club can depend as much on its atmosphere and the qualities of its officers as on the nature of the water area it uses. The figures quoted below should therefore be taken as a rough guide only for use in planning for sailing on inland waters. Sailing, other than in keel boats which require a greater depth, can take place on almost any stretch of water provided that there is a depth of a little over 1 m, but the minimum area of enclosed water needs to be at least 4 hectares. For a club to be successful and have a well-developed racing programme a water area of 20 hectares or more is needed, with space to accommodate a racing course with at least three legs.

The size of club that a given area of water can accommodate is a vexed question, but a rough guide is that a density of 2½ boats per hectare on the water is about the maximum acceptable. The maximum number of boats likely to be out on a normal busy day is about one-third of this total, and the average number of people in the club per boat is about 1.5 to 2. The following formula can be regarded as giving a rough guide:—

        40 hectares of water area = 100 boats on the water
        100 boats on the water   = 300 boats in the club
        300 boats in the club   = 450-600 people in the club

The quality of the sailing that can be expected on any particular stretch of water will be governed to some extent by the general orientation of the water and its relationship to the geographical features of the neighbourhood. Rapid and hazardous weather changes can occur on some reservoirs and the safety precautions must be determined in relation to the competence of the sailors involved in such situations.

The main facilities required on the water are buoys to mark any racing courses and any areas where sailing boats or other users are not allowed to go. The small boats will be trolleyed to and from the water but the larger keel boats will require moorings and these need to be sited where they will cause least inconvenience to the general traffic on the water. It is not unusual to separate large waters into different areas for different activities, but this can lead to large areas being unused for long periods and may not be so necessary as it would appear at first sight. It has been shown that a large water can be operated successfully with very little segregation, provided that the different users co-operate together in arranging programmes of use. At times this will mean that one activity may have priority over another.

Facilities for the launching and recovery of boats will need particularly careful planning if congestion at peak times is to be avoided. Slipways should have a relatively flat and even gradient—preferably not more than 1 in 12 and never more than 1 in 9. They should never be less than sufficient width to allow two boats on trailers to pass each other. Where several slipways are contemplated to serve a large boat parking area, there is probably more to be gained from having fewer, wider slipways than more, narrower ones.

It is equally important to provide a facility where boats, having been launched on to the water, can be rigged, loaded, and moored when not sailing without obstructing the slipways. This need may be met by providing pontoons, landing stages or steep banks for mooring alongside, or natural or artificial beaches at which boats can be drawn up.

Boat parking areas should be as close as possible to the slipways and the gradients between the two should be as gentle as possible. Design density of parking and standards of construction for both boat and car parks will vary according to the size of the site, its configuration, and physical condition, but an easily recognizable and simple traffic flow system should be the aim. The crossing of flows of pedestrians, trailed boats and cars should be avoided wherever possible.

The better the surface conditions and the design of the circulation system, the greater the density of parking that can be accommodated within a given space. As a rough guide, on an all-weather surface, a maximum of about 500 boat or car spaces can be accommodated per hectare. Stacking or racking may of course enable a greater density of storage for sailboards or other such small light craft. Clubs like to have boat parking areas that are as secure from trespass as possible, in order to reduce the risk of vandalism and theft. On some sites it may be possible to achieve this by careful siting; on others fencing may be needed, and on some it may not be possible at all. Many clubs, particularly those on seafront locations, use parking and launching facilities that are entirely open to the general public.

Toilet and changing facilities will need to be provided, as will showers, particularly if the sailing continues through the winter. Some social accommodation will also be required as the club develops, although not perhaps initially. The size and quality of the accommodation will vary according to the aspirations of the club and the objectives of the water undertaker, as also will the method of provision. A common arrangement is for the water undertaker to lease a site to the club and for the club to be responsible for providing its own premises, with or without help from the undertaker. Where there are a number of users, some of whom might also require club facilities, it is important to avoid duplication. In such circumstances it may be possible to provide a single facility which can be used by all parties.

The only other facility likely to be required on land by a sailing club would be a race control box and signal mast which may be an integral part of the clubhouse building or may, for siting reasons, be an independent structure. Large clubs often provide a chandler's shop and bosun's hut, where there is sufficient demand.

Sailing club headquarters and moorings should preferably be located on a lee shore in order to give relatively sheltered water. Alternatively, it may be practicable to build a mole or similar structure to achieve this objective. Control buildings must, of course, have good visibility of the sailing area.

In the past, craft visiting a reservoir which is used for water supply purposes and fishing have been required to be disinfected before the craft are put on the water, but some scientists now question the need for this. This practice is referred to in Chapter 2.

If sailing on a ticket basis (either with owned or hired boats) is permitted by the owner of a water it will be necessary for him to provide facilities such as changing accommodation and safety boats comparable to those provided by a club catering for a number of boats similar to that which the owner anticipates will sail on day permits.

Sailors on public navigations such as rivers and estuaries often get together to form a club and provide normal sailing club facilities at a bank side site acquired by the club. Others, not club-minded, sail with only personal safety gear and expect no other facilities to be provided for them.

ROWING

Traditionally, two main types of rowing have become established—coastal rowing on the sea and inland rowing which takes place mainly on rivers. The sport reached its peak on rivers such as the Thames and Wye, but with the development of intensive international competition there is an increasing demand for training and regatta facilities on inland still-waters, which can provide the uniform conditions now required for meeting the exacting standards for competitions. As a result, purpose-built courses have been created, but these are so expensive and scarce that existing reservoirs which can provide a straight stretch of water of sufficient length and width are being increasingly utilized. It is necessary to ensure that these courses can still be accurately aligned even when draw-down of the reservoir water occurs. The users of large exposed waters sometimes find conditions very rough, and areas where large waves are likely to build up on open stretches of water will not be ideal. Long pulls to and from start and finish points should be avoided in competition rowing. Navigation and land drainage authorities can sometimes assist the sport by removing obstructions and excessive weed growth, and by improving bank side paths in the course of normal land drainage works.

Inland rowing on many rivers is suffering increasingly from competition with other recreational activities. Also, it is rarely possible on rivers to accommodate the long straight courses that are needed for national and international competitions. Modified forms of competition rowing have been devised to meet local river conditions, such as the "Bumps" on the Cam and the Isis.

The demand for rowing facilities on rivers and still waters can vary from a single club or school wanting somewhere to learn and train, to the properly marked out 1000 and 1500 m straight courses which may be used by several clubs, and the full 2000 m course with six lanes required for international competition. Rowing is essentially a competitive sport, and wherever it is accommodated other than for the most rudimentary training purposes, there will be a requirement for exclusive use at times of whatever course is available. In the case of a river this may mean some arrangement whereby other traffic is confined close to one bank, routed along an alternative arm, or stopped entirely for a specified number of hours. The navigation authority will need to have specific powers if they wish to enforce this requirement, although it is not infrequently achieved by general consent and good will. On a reservoir, time-zoning may be appropriate.

The design of facilities for launching and entering boats into the water needs careful thought. Ideally, a bank side step or a pontoon of sufficient length and with a freeboard lower than that normally provided for sailing dinghies should be made available. On land the facilities required for the participants will be the same as those for a small sailing organization. However, special provision will need to be made, in the form of a long shed, for storing the boats on site. Special parking arrangements may be required for the trailers used to transport the boats. Rowers are usually accompanied by coaches or instructors during training sessions and by officials when racing is taking place. A power safety craft will also be needed.

CANOEING

The organized use of canoes for recreation in Great Britain dates from the middle of the nineteenth century. The Canoe Club was formed in 1866. The Prince of Wales became Commodore in 1867, and in 1873 the club became the Royal Canoe Club by command of Queen Victoria. It will be seen, therefore, that canoeing is not a recent phenomenon but can take its place alongside angling as a long-established recreational use of water. It is now one of the most rapidly growing pursuits, judged by the number of canoes sold each year.

As with many other recreations, canoeing has developed into a wide range of competitive and informal activities: some requiring fast-moving river for white ("wild") water racing and slalom events, and others uniform still waters for sprint racing and sailing.

The increase in the number of canoeists has occurred in the last 30 years with the advent, first, of the folding canoe and then the easily constructed plywood and fibreglass canoes. This growth has created problems for angling interests and riparian owners, for even on the limited number of waters with public rights of navigation care is needed to avoid conflict, and uncontrolled access to the water's edge may be harmful to crops and livestock. There is widespread agreement that in the pursuit of recreational interest minimal trouble is created for other interests by those who belong to clubs or are otherwise aware of the codes of practice such as that published by the British Canoe Union. The problem is exacerbated by many who canoe either in ignorance or disregard of any recognized code of practice, often by trespass. These people are often the most difficult to detect and control. Unless there is a public right of navigation, access to the water is a matter for agreement between the riparian owner and organized canoeing groups, and the casual canoeist needs individual permission, in the same way as does the angler.

Some agreements are being arranged between fishery interests and the British Canoe Union and other organized groups. Such agreements usually specify the time of year and/or height of water when canoeing is permitted. Information about agreements and other matters is obtainable from the "river advisers" appointed by the British Canoe Union. In addition, some water authorities have provided information for canoeists by the publication of guides.

Many water authorities use electronic equipment to monitor water levels in rivers, and it is possible for recreational users of such waters to be able, through the public telephone system, to get information about the state of the river.

Where rivers are regulated by reservoirs for water supply purposes it is sometimes possible to arrange for releases of white-water for organized training and special events, and the cost of this "natural" facility is only a fraction of that of creating and operating artificial white-water courses. In such cases water authorities must have ample notice in advance of events.

It may be practicable on some rivers, even quite slow flowing low land rivers, to adapt overflow weirs to provide modest slalom training courses for canoeists who do not have the advantage of natural white-water near their homes. A "slalom course" may involve little more than an adaptation of the outfall channel. It is unlikely to be functional in times of low flow or, for this reason, very suitable for competition events but it will give many valuable training days during the course of the year.

From the safety point of view canoeing on reservoirs is best carried out under the auspices of a club; indeed, on large reservoirs in remote areas, the "loner" seeking a Rockies style canoe/camping holiday can be a potential worry to the reservoir manager.

MOTOR CRUISING

This recreational pastime of navigating mechanically propelled pleasure craft along the waterways systems including rivers, canals, lakes, broads and a few of the very large reservoirs, requires land-based facilities such as moorings, shops, inns, and boatyards. Inland cruising is a growth activity with an estimated annual increase of 10 per cent until 1977. However, in recent years the level has fallen. The majority of boat owners are members of clubs or associations who represent their interests on a national or regional basis.

Motor cruisers may be considered under several headings. There is a whole range of craft from those offering sleeping and complete domestic facilities through to those which have the minimum needs for day cruising, with the occupants either staying the night in inns or else camping. Some boats remain afloat permanently whilst others are trailed back home after each cruise. In addition, there are the hire craft which are used by the public for holidays or for the occasional outings.

The frequency of use of the motor cruiser varies considerably. For example, during the summer season in the Broads and Thames about 40 per cent of the registered craft might be in use at any one time, whereas on other navigations the figure may drop to under 20 per cent. The use of hire craft varies between 70 and 90 per cent from April through until September, and it is, of course, the latter craft which make the most consistent use of the navigation facilities. The private owner must restrict the use of his boat to weekends and perhaps for summer holidays.

The design of the inland waterways cruiser is limited to the dimensions of lock pens, depth of water, and to the height over the water of fixed obstructions such as bridges, guillotine gates, etc. The limits on size are about length 46 ft, beam 7 ft, draught 2 ft and height above water level 5 ft 11 in. There are specific navigations that can accept boats of greater dimensions.

For economy reasons cruisers constructed for inland usage have comparatively low-powered engines and usually have flat shallow-draught hulls. These craft are unsuitable, and indeed dangerous, for use in tidal waters. Where a navigation opens into the open sea many owners prefer to have boats designed for coastal cruising and to use them with caution on the inland navigation. Often in these cases, cabin tops are designed to collapse to meet height restrictions.

Navigations vary considerably in physical characteristics. In many cases the rivers have been utilized by the construction of locks and sluices to hold a sufficient depth of water to permit navigation, and canals have been constructed for the purpose of providing for water-borne transport. There are also navigable land drainage dykes and drains, broads and lakes. These varied navigations support craft ranging from sea-going merchant ships to the smallest cruisers or day boats.

Waterways in the low flat countryside require few, if any, locks and thus allow relatively unobstructed navigation. In other districts the navigation "climbs" over hills by the use of locks, which may have the conventional straight forward "V" doors or which may incorporate land drainage guillotine gates. More sophisticated boat lifts are sometimes used to transfer craft from one level to another. Some of the navigations have lock keepers to operate the system whilst others provide the boat owners themselves with facilities to operate the locks.

It is important that navigation authorities should make every effort to ensure that the navigation is clear of obstruction. Shallows areas, etc., should be well signed with notices. With the increasing trend to extended cruising it is essential that planned closures to navigations for repairs, etc., should be widely circulated well ahead of the closure date. This may apply particularly to Continental craft visiting for the holiday periods.

Motor cruiser operators, whether they are from the private sector or the hire fleet, require certain facilities on the banks of a navigation. First and foremost there must be permanent moorings for the craft. The navigation authorities for the most part would prefer that these should be provided in off channel marinas, boatyards, or mooring areas. In the case of river navigations these are often provided in old wet mineral pits that have a "cut" into the main channel, or else in a disused arm of a canal system.

Other facilities which are also required include fuel and water points, boatyard facilities for lifting the craft out of the water for repairs, slipways for launching trailer boats, sanitary and refuse disposal sites, and overnight moorings[1].

Boat users have varied individual preferences for casual moorings. Many are socially gregarious and travel from one waterside inn to another, welcoming the activities of other users, whereas there are those who wish to cruise on undisturbed water and to moor away from the madding crowds.

POWER BOATING

This is an international sport using high-powered craft raced in similar style to motor and motorcycle events and often sponsored by commercial interests. Because of the possible danger to other water users, ideally power boats require the exclusive use of waters, but these may be shared in suitable locations by time-tabling and zoning. It is highly questionable whether power boating would be acceptable on water supply reservoirs even if the risk of accidents and pollution from fuel spillage could be overcome. However, as many power boats are small and the waves on coastal waters make racing conditions unpredictable, there is undoubtedly a demand for organized power boating to use some sheltered inland waters. Suitable sites might be found in estuaries, docks and harbours, non-potable water reservoirs, and pits.

WATER SKI-ING

Water ski-ing may be practised as an informal recreation or as a highly skilled and competitive sport of international importance. The demand for recreational ski-ing water is strong, and this has been encouraged by the development of relatively cheap, small-powered boats and the increased ownership of cars with which to transport them. Whether the demand will continue to rise in the face of higher fuel costs is uncertain.

There is at present enough water-space along the coast and in tidal estuaries to meet much of the foreseeable demand for recreational water ski-ing. These resources could be supplemented in future by the large water surfaces which would be created by estuarial barrage schemes constructed for the purposes of water conservation or electricity generation.

If recreational water ski-ing on inland waters is to be considered, care should be taken in selecting a site so as to avoid, as far as possible, damage to amenity interests. The activity should be managed and controlled by a responsible club.

Water ski-ing as a competitive sport needs special consideration and for training and competition requires uniform still waters which enable exacting international standards to be met. The main events are slalom, jumping, and figure (trick) ski-ing; for these a water area of about 12 hectares will suffice, containing a slalom course of 800 by 100 m. Because of the growing eminence of the U.K. in this sport there is an increasing demand for suitable inland water areas, which can sometimes be met at reservoirs. However the following considerations need to be taken into account:—

Effect on Water Quality

Research in the United States of America and elsewhere[2,3,4] has indicated that the effect of conventional outboard petrol engines on the chemical quality of water and on aquatic plants and animals is insignificant, but the particular study did not measure the lead content emitted by petrol additives. However, any concern on this account, and from the accidental spillage of fuel, can now be overcome by the use of propane gas fuelled engines, which have been developed by the British Water Ski-ing Federation for use on water supply reservoirs.

Body contact effects can be minimized where desirable by the use of "dry suits", which seal the body completely except for the mouth and nose, and which also protect the user from low water temperature more effectively than "wet suits".

Any decision to allow water ski-ing must take into account factors which include the original quality of the water, the size of the reservoir in terms of the time during which the water is retained before passing into supply (itself a purifying process), and the standard of treatment subsequently applied to the water.

Noise

This form of nuisance is probably the one most feared by the general public and by local residents. However recent trials have demonstrated that the recorded mean noise levels created by boats used for training and competition purposes are substantially below the maximum recommended by the Noise Advisory Council, and are also no greater than recorded mean local highway noise or the noise of waves.

Wave Action

It has been said that waves created by water ski-ing can accelerate the erosion of banks and cause annoyance and danger to anglers, canoeists, and other users. Measurements of wave frequency and height have been carried out in conjunction with noise tests, and these show that properly managed water ski-ing creates waves which are acceptable at a range of 25 m and negligible at 60 m. The key factor is management and control of those extrovert skiers who delight in showing-off by spectacular behaviour at high speed and close range. It must be admitted that the spectacle is enjoyable to many waterside visitors, but provision for these is better made by occasional organized events.

Facilities

Apart from the use of the water surface itself, the only essential requirements are course marker-buoys, a floating take-off platform for jumps, and a floating pontoon jetty or slipway running-down to average draw down level. Toilets and changing facilities are desirable.

SUB AQUA DIVING

This activity is more likely to take place in still waters (reservoirs, lakes, mineral workings, etc) than in rivers, other than in their estuarial reaches. It requires good visibility and the presence of interesting underwater features. Sites with an appreciable depth of water (more than 25 m) are likely to be of particular interest. Deep inland water can provide ideal safe conditions for developing the basic diving skills learned in swimming pools and shallower waters to the stage where divers can confidently cope with the more variable conditions to be found at sea. Inland waters with depths around 30 m are particularly valuable in this respect.

The availability of a good diving site will encourage the formation of a local club, and a better-than-average site is likely to attract other clubs in the locality or even region, who will seek to use the site on a visiting basis by arrangement with the local club. Facilities and management procedures should therefore be designed with this possibility in mind. The main problem areas likely to be encountered are:—

(1) The need to ensure that divers are competent or under competent supervision and are following the correct procedures: this is best achieved under club discipline. Individual diving is to be discouraged.

(2) The provision of adequate means of access to diving locations on large water areas— divers may be able to work from the shore on some waters, but often they will need to be transported to their diving locations by boat, and the boat with a competent crew will need to be stationed at the dive location throughout the duration of the dive.

(3) The avoidance of situations of conflict where other uses, particularly those involving powered craft, are taking place. Diving need cause little or no inconvenience to other recreational activities, but the dive location should be clearly marked, the divers should be instructed to surface only in the marked area or other agreed locations, and the other users should be made aware that diving is in progress and encouraged to keep away from the dive zone.

(4) The need to ensure a rapid and effective response in the event of emergency situations. Immediate access to first aid and resuscitation facilities is essential and where deep diving is in progress it is advisable to have a standby procedure for moving casualties without delay to a hospital which has decompression facilities.

Other than the normal parking, boat launching, changing and toilet facilities the only special provisions that may be called for are a secure storage space for personal diving equipment. At heavily used sites, a compressor for charging air bottles may be necessary, but these machines can be noisy and generally at a typical reservoir site recharging can probably be done elsewhere.

Finally, it should be borne in mind that if a competent body of divers is established at a particular site they can be of considerable help to a water undertaker and to other recreational users in searching for or laying down objects under water.

SWIMMING AND BATHING

Casual swimming and bathing already take place in many rivers and lakes. Health and safety hazards are the main consideration, together with the effect on fisheries and the need for participants to obtain the permission of owners. The modern trend is, however, for health authorities to discourage river and lake swimming and bathing on the grounds of water quality, and sites where public bathing was formerly encouraged have in many cases fallen largely into disuse for that purpose. Nevertheless, some of these bank sites are easily accessible playground areas for ball games, picnicking, etc., and local authorities may provide car parks and picnic areas if the land can be acquired. Swimming may be tolerated by the riparian owner, but local authorities would be prudent not directly to encourage swimming by the provision of facilities directly related to it, unless they have satisfied themselves that the health and safety requirements relating to the use of the water for swimming are met.

From the water quality point of view bathing in river-regulating and impounding reservoirs could often be permitted if subsequent treatment standards are sufficiently high. Because many reservoirs are deep and cold, and may have precipitous margins of soft muddy shores, safety precautions are essential; if a reservoir already has staff on site which could supervise bathers, and selected shallow shores are available and marked, the risks would seem to be acceptable. Conditions might be enhanced by the provision of sand and gravel beaches or (following another European practice) the construction of moored floating swimming baths, which abstract and purify their own water and effluent as self-contained units.

Long distance competitive swimmers seek open water suitable for racing over distances of 8 to 12 km. Coastal waters are sometimes rough on the pre-arranged date for events, and large lakes and reservoirs might be considered, in consultation with the local amateur swimming association representatives, although they too can be quite rough in some wind conditions. Undertakers should ensure that health and safety requirements can be met before making provision for swimming.

MODEL BOATS

Model boats are small-scale replicas of almost any type of boat or ship, or they can be designed in their own right to perform many of the functions of racing craft, short of carrying people. They can be very sophisticated with radio control and powered by specially designed engines. Model sailing boats are unlikely to cause problems and merely require water areas with a good hard shore line for the convenience of the operator.

Model power craft, often with radio control, have caused considerable complaints about noise and undertakers should give careful consideration to this problem before introducing this form of recreation on a water area.

3. LAND-BASED ACTIVITIES

CAR PARKING

The majority of water recreation is provided in a rural situation and many participants can be expected to travel to and from the sites by car. If the visitor is then to take part in a sporting activity he will wish to park his car, and from his point of view the aesthetic positioning of the car park is probably of no great importance provided that it is convenient for his ultimate destination. Other visitors by car may wish only quietly to view the water, the activities on the water, and the other scenic attractions of the area. Some of these visitors may not even get out of the cars or they may simply wish to walk the shortest possible distance to sample other attractions provided such as a visitors' centre, museum, refreshment centre and toilets. For these visitors it is important that the siting of the car park is such that it permits them to view the water and partake of the facilities with the minimum physical effort.

Car parks must be convenient to the highways to avoid congestion on entry and exit roads. By common consent all car parks should be screened from views across the water and should be unobtrusive in the countryside. The landscape architect is thus set quite a task. Views of the water must be available from the car parks but the converse must be avoided. The parks must also be functional for the sailors, fishermen, and other sportsmen but they must not intrude into the views from other parks, picnic areas, and walks. It is a curious fact that a fleet of dinghies sailing on the water presents a highly desirable view—indeed, they are even acceptable when parked on the shore—but a fleet of cars (no matter how neatly parked) is never attractive and is, at best, tolerable. Perhaps familiarity breeds contempt!

Ideally, car parks should be located inconspicuously in clearings created in existing established woodland; newly planted saplings may take 20 years or more to provide effective screening. As for picnic areas, any planted vegetation should be typical of the locality and should not comprise exotic shrubs and flowers more suited to urban and suburban situations.

In some cases separate "functional" car parks for each of the major activities on the water are often provided near their fixed equipment on the shore, and separate "viewing" parks are arranged for visitors not intending to be active on the water, but it is desirable to consider whether a car park can perform the dual function. This will help to reduce the number of sites needed, and to ensure that environmental considerations are given full weight. It is important, as far as the user is concerned, that the park he is using should not intrude on his view. Fishermen can probably use car parks in conjunction with viewers rather more readily than can boaters who, in any case, may require a reasonably secure boat park as well. Boaters and fishermen can sometimes share facilities amicably.

When setting up a new facility the experience of others with similar enterprises should be drawn upon. Advice can often be obtained from such bodies as the local Tourist Board in assessing the numbers of parking spaces to be provided and their likely frequency of use. It is probably wise to provide for maximum anticipated numbers—nothing causes more annoyance than cars cruising around unable to find parking spots and being left as a consequence in all sorts of unauthorized places. Obviously, it is easier to assess the requirements of the active sportsman than it is to forecast the likely demand from the occasional or "viewing" visitors. It is sensible therefore to provide a proportion of the parking spaces by way of reinforced grass or gravel rather than tarmac. These meet the occasional need adequately, are "kinder" to the environment, and are, of course, less expensive to install.

Whether to charge for car parking has always been a vexed question. There seems to be two main arguments in favour of charging. Firstly, an income may be derived and, secondly, better control may be exercised. Both arguments can be countered—if the site is extensive and the use is not intensive then collection and policing costs can eat seriously into the income. On the question of control on such sites, it is argued that charging encourages cars to be left in unauthorized places thus adding to wardening costs and police costs of traffic control on the highway. A further argument against charging the "viewing" public is the annoyance caused to the individual at having to pay merely to look at an asset already paid for by way of water or other charges. Apparently, no distinction is made in the public mind about the provision and use of picnic areas, toilets, information centres, etc., and these facilities are traditionally "free" when provided by the local authority. The view is advanced that it is reasonable to ask the active sportsman to contribute towards the cost of providing car parks for his own use—this can most easily be done by adjusting the rent to his club or the price of the period ticket which he buys for his sport. For pragmatic reasons it is suggested that it might be reasonable to charge the "viewing" public at sites with easily controlled accesses on days of most intensive use, such as at weekends. At other sites and at other times the cost of collection and control may represent too high a proportion of the fee to make the exercise worthwhile when set against the irritation which is caused by charging.

"Honesty-boxes" have proved to be moderately successful on some sites, but they are at risk from thieves unless they are robustly constructed with perhaps a secret chamber, into which coins can flow by gravity, concealed at some distance from the box itself. "Park and display" machines also show a good cash return, but may require fairly frequent checking by staff. However, their use may, if feasible, need byelaw permission. Where electricity is available, coin-operated barriers are useful on intensively used sites.

PICNICKING

Picnic areas will normally be associated with sites to which the public are attracted by the water scenery generally. However, such sites need not necessarily have water vistas and there are attractive woodland sites around many reservoirs from which the water is not visible at all. Some picnic areas have even been established, along with attractive walks, on land which is part of sewage treatment works. Such a site can form a useful recreation area catering for the needs of those for whom the works was built in the first place. Because picnic sites are generally used in the summer months it is practicable for them to be located on flood plains, washes and the like albeit that they would be unusable at times of flood.

Car-parking facilities will obviously be needed at picnic areas. However, the general requirements are traditionally green grass with a overall impression of rural tranquility, although intensive use of a site can sometimes temporarily dispel this atmosphere. For some picnic areas rustic tables and benches are a great asset, particularly when the ground underfoot is wet. Charcoal-burning cooking stoves are gaining in popularity, and they can be provided under cover. However, these lead to a departure from the traditional "English" picnic. The area will require a convenient water point and near-by lavatories should be provided, probably at the car parking area. The planning and general layout of picnic areas and their associated parking facilities is discussed in more detail in Chapter 4.

The question of rubbish disposal at picnic sites is one of endless debate. The protagonists of "carry your rubbish home" provide no receptacles at all and rely on education and a sense of responsibility amongst the users to keep the site tidy by putting the rubbish in the boot of the car. A supply of empty bags on site has sometimes been helpful in this respect, but the degree of success is varied. Furthermore, all picnickers do not come by car and there is some predisposition against touting the empty drink can around for the rest of the day in the plastic carrier in which it was purchased possibly from the shop at the main reception site. Others provide receptacles and endeavour to make them attractive by covering them with rustic bark or even forming them into the shape of wide-mouthed nursery animals some of which, in the United States of America, acknowledge contributions of rubbish with a word of thanks! If receptacles are provided in whatever form they may be presented it is important that they should be large enough to cope with maximum demand, should be easy to empty, and should be regularly emptied. They should also protect the contents from the weather and vermin. The all too familiar sight of bins overflowing with wet rubbish and surrounded by vermin is an indication of the extreme difficulty of meeting such a specification. The totally enclosed large steel drum with a flap opening is one practical answer, although it may be difficult to transfer the contents to a refuse vehicle and expensive to cart the container to the disposal site.

Children in the picnic party appreciate a few "static" toys to divert their interest. Traditional park toys include swings, roundabouts, rocking horses, and the like; adventure playgrounds with old steam engines, logs of wood, hill and dales are a modern variant. It becomes a sensitive decision as to how far manufactured entertainment should be provided and how far enjoyment of the unspoilt rural situation should be preserved at any particular site. One view is that the average family is usually looking for something to "do", even though it wants the rural atmosphere ostensibly preserved. Those who merely want to enjoy exclusively a genuinely unspoilt rural setting are probably in a minority. The two objectives are probably incompatible—if the majority seek an active day out "in the country" the tranquillity essential to the need of the minority will inevitably be lost.

CAMPING, CARAVANNING AND OVERNIGHT ACCOMMODATION

The potential for water space recreation in remote areas is unlikely to be realized until provision for overnight stays is increased in quantity, and in variety, to suit all ages and pockets. The rising cost of fuel and transport is also likely to increase the demand for facilities which will reduce daily travelling.

When considering the developments for recreation at a particular location it is desirable to avoid those areas which are so beautiful, tranquil, and environmentally fragile that they would be utterly spoilt by obtrusive visitor pressure. But at some locations provision for weekly and longer term stays can reduce the need for frequent day visits, and hence the traffic congestion on local roads.

Accommodation may take the form of tents, caravans, cabins, cottages and converted surplus buildings. These may all be in addition to existing guest houses and hotels, which have a long tradition of enduring success where they are associated with angling and other recreations linked to lakes, reservoirs, and rivers. Temporary camps built for reservoir construction workers can sometimes be suitably designed and located for subsequent conversion to visitor accommodation, thus reducing the heavy capital costs which discouraged new public investment solely for recreation. In the past many such opportunities have been missed.

Factors to be considered in selecting locations include:—

(a) Market research to assess potential demand and economic viability. For this, the Tourist Boards and local planning authorities can usually advise, as can the increasing number of recreational consultants.

(b) The existence of well grown opened-out woodland to screen the development in rural areas, because new tree planting may take at least 20 years to provide effective cover.

(c) Road access; except for horse riders, cyclists, and back-packers or other walkers.

(d) Southerly aspect; especially in deep narrow valleys, where it is important to avoid the cold shadow which lies for much of the day and year.

(e) Well-drained soil, especially for tents and caravans.

(f) Conflict with the policies of local planning authorities, especially in national parks, which may be against increasing self-serviced accommodation. It may be argued that although there is ample serviced accommodation it is not of a kind or at a price which is sought by more and more visitors, especially the young. It should also be borne in mind that the object is to give priority to areas which are deficient in existing accommodation, and that the season of use could be extended outside the overcrowded summer holiday period by anglers, walkers, climbers, naturalists, and even for winter sports activities.

(g) Water, sewerage, rubbish disposal, electricity, and telephone services—because experience has shown that initial private arrangements are often followed by demands for main public services at a high cost which largely devolves upon the general consumers or ratepayers.

(h) Effluent disposal, for even though sewage treatment plant may meet health requirements, there are some reservoirs where any increase in nutrients, e.g. phosphate from household detergents, might increase the growth of algae beyond the capacity of existing water treatment works.

(i) Availability of staff to manage and supervise all aspects of the accommodation sites.

In the case of reservoirs, the water undertaker will no doubt wish to consider whether the need for overnight accommodation largely generated by recreation on the reservoir can best be met by the undertaker providing the facility on land within the reservoir land boundary or whether, with the co-operation of the local planning authority, encouragement should be given to nearby private owners to do so. If reservoir land is the preferred location, then the undertaker may have the further choice of leasing concessions to private individuals or local authorities, or of providing and managing the sites directly.

VISITOR CENTRES

The pleasure enjoyed by people visiting a water resource mainly to look is enhanced if an opportunity is afforded for them to learn something about the area they have come to see. The casual day visitor will probably not wish to delve more deeply than this, but the sites are capable of providing the facility for more formal study and this is dealt with in more detail on p. 85.

A typical provision for the casual visitor might comprise an attractive building at the main "viewing" car park, offering toilet accommodation, including one for use by the disabled. Some provision for refreshments should also be provided; this could vary from a "tea-wagon" operated by a concessionaire to a restaurant and/or snack bar, with or without a souvenir shop built as an integral part of the building and run by a concessionaire or by the owner. The information area might consist of a reasonably large room with a counter manned by information staff whenever the volume of visitors justified it. The area could be stocked with literature covering such things as a guide to the water with a map and notes of facilities provided, a code of visitors' behaviour, a safety code, and information on local places of interest, local geology, local history, the nature conservation areas, and the fishery, sailing, boating and other major recreational activities. Some information could also be provided about the water area and the reason for its construction. The literature could be supplemented by static displays, and in this connection archaeological finds and natural history displays are always studied with great interest. Co-operation could be sought with other providers of tourist attractions in the locality and with the Tourist Board in the display of material and literature. Such co-operation is likely to be readily forthcoming. Souvenirs could be sold over the information counter, but if the number of visitors is substantial it might be better to provide a separate adjacent shop for this purpose. The area could usefully include space for showing information films on a back projector.

There may be opportunities for other interpretative centres at, say, a large reservoir. The public are often admitted to certain parts of nature conservation areas and this provides an opportunity for a more specialist centre dealing with matters affecting the reserve. Here, also, it will be desirable to provide toilet accommodation and possibly catering and souvenir facilities. If there is a fish production unit where the public can be admitted to selected parts an "interpretative room" is a possibility and a modest aquarium would almost certainly be a "winner" from the interest point of view, particularly if the public could buy food and feed the fish.

EDUCATION AND INTERPRETATION

Public understanding of the water industry could certainly be improved and the same could be said about the state of knowledge of the environment generally. The Countryside Commission, the Nature Conservancy Council, and numerous other bodies are making efforts towards this end and where water areas or facilities connected with them can help it is desirable for them to be so used. Three main objectives can be identified:—

(1) To add to the recreational experience of people resorting to sites in the countryside.
(2) To improve their understanding of and respect for what they see.
(3) To make a positive contribution to education by providing practical experience and instruction to supplement classroom learning.

By imaginative use of the facilities at any particular site it will be possible to:—

(a) Inform the public about the water industry; improve their understanding of the water cycle; describe significant new developments; etc.
(b) Explain associated matters such as fish husbandry, angling, and the various water sports activities.
(c) Describe particular features of the site and its surrounding environment and explain how and why the reservoir was built and how it works.
(d) Improve knowledge of the countryside generally.

The services and facilities provided can vary enormously and will depend on objectives, resources available, accessibility of the site, demand, etc. They can range from display boards, waymarked trails with explanatory leaflets, guided trails, through to purpose-built visitor centres either manned or unmanned with sophisticated displays and audio visual presentations, and also study and lecturing accommodation for school parties, etc. People in general are always seeking information about what they see and as a general rule it will always be preferable to provide some information rather than none at all and to make it simple, clear, and attractive.

The provision of tape-recordings from "listening posts" at points of interest has proved to be successful, and can be a great saving in staff time required to cope with organized parties or casual visitors.

Formalized Education in Recreation Pursuits

At a number of reservoirs, on river banks, and at wet mineral workings the local education committee has taken the opportunity by licence-to-use, lease, or purchase of the site to establish a centre for instruction in recreational pursuits appropriate to the location of the site. Local schools may be encouraged, by a fairly simple slipway on a small safe reservoir or wet pit to teach quite small children to sail under supervision and safety cover.

The education authority may purchase a wet mineral working, lease a site on a reservoir bank or a river bank and provide facilities for the teaching of sailing, canoeing, fishing, nature study, horse riding and in fact the great majority of the sports dealt with in this Chapter. Where the education authority owns a site or has a long lease (e.g. from the water authority) they may build very substantial centres, sometimes with residential accommodation, workshops for equipment repair, etc. In such cases it is then not uncommon to find the centre being used in the winter months for courses not directly associated with water recreation, such as the arts, drama, and craft courses. These arrangements generally work well and are to be encouraged; the young people can learn and enjoy their sport at a price within the range of their pockets, and adults can pursue their chosen further education in attractive surroundings. The criticism has been voiced that after learning a sport with the education authority the young person, on leaving school, cannot afford to partake in the sport at adult level and prices. Perhaps the solution is for clubs and providers to keep the facilities offered unpretentious and inexpensive, at least for the younger people.

NATURE CONSERVATION

In considering the natural history features of any particular site two main objectives must be borne in mind:—

(1) To conserve those features that are of particular importance.
(2) To enable people to see and understand what is being conserved without harming it.

It is often said quite strongly that these two objectives are incompatible, but whilst this may be true in some circumstances it is more often than not possible to achieve both and this should be the normal aim. The interest of a site may derive from its general flora and fauna which can be of local, national, or even international importance, or from the presence of a specific plant or creature which again may be of various levels of significance and which may be present either all of the time or at only certain times of the year.

These considerations will determine how an individual site or a particular part of it will need to be protected—whether no access at all should be allowed, whether restricted numbers either of specialists only or of the general public could be permitted at certain times; or whether access can be freely available subject to visitors being encouraged to keep to certain defined routes.

In most cases the facilities required will be fairly modest—small and rudimentary car parks at strategic points, perhaps with information boards and boxes for explanatory leaflets and in some cases specially constructed viewing hides may be appropriate. Sophisticated interpretation centres are only necessary at particularly important sites where large numbers of people can be accommodated without detriment to conservation. These tend to be associated with some other facility, e.g. the headquarters or local centre of a conservation body or an interpretation centre, with a wider role than nature conservation alone. It is often possible for the information and literature about a conservation site to be provided in a general purpose visitor centre, which may be located some distance away.

Land management in nature conservation areas can give rise to a number of problems. The conservationists will normally wish to see as little interference with nature as possible, whether by grazing or by chemical or mechanical means, but adjoining farmers may become very concerned about such areas developing into breeding grounds for weeds and pests which might then invade their land. It is usually possible to work out some compromise acceptable to both sides, and in several instances water undertakers have found it advantageous to enter into agreements with local naturalist organizations or groups of such bodies under which the naturalists are responsible for implementing an agreed management plan.

FACILITIES FOR THE DISABLED

Statistics show that there are over 3 million persons in the U.K. suffering from some degree of disability, and Government has stated that in planning for recreation the special needs of the disabled should be recognized and that they should be given the opportunity to participate not only by using the facilities specifically designed for them, but also by sharing as many facilities and activities as are practicable with their families and the community at large. Some water authorities have made special provision for the disabled, for example the Welsh Water Authority[5].

The particular needs of the disabled include:—

Facilities within easy reach of populated areas, because many disabled people cannot travel long distances.

Safe access to the waterside and viewpoints, with paths and toilets suitable for wheelchairs.

Reserved parking space and permission to use service roads otherwise closed to the general public.

Equipment adapted or purpose-built for active recreation. For example ramped angling stations at points where the fishing is best and with ample space for casting; boats and hoists to accommodate wheel-chairs; pontoons with wheelchair anchorages; handrails where needed, and bridges of sufficient width; sailing boats with unobstructed decking.

Organized competitions and other special events, for which voluntary helpers are normally available.

The help of local angling and sailing clubs for tuition and of voluntary societies and individuals to assist the wheelchair-bound, the frail, and the blind.

Self-guided trails for the blind and partially sighted; these can be provided with handrails or kerbs to assist movement, and with braille plates or listening posts which describe the sounds, feel, and the smell of the stopping point.

In designing any facilities to meet the needs of the disabled the advice of many public and voluntary agencies is readily obtainable, including local authority Social Service Departments and the British Sports Association for the Disabled or its regional branches.

It may be considered that the provision of special facilities is of greater value to the disabled than the granting of relatively small financial concessions for licences and permits. The new regional water authorities do not have statutory financial duties or responsibilities for the disabled nor for pensioners and juveniles, but most have continued to grant concessions inherited from their predecessors, who, if they were local authorities, regarded such assistance as part of their general welfare responsibilities. Concessions do not form part of other public industries' policies, for example gas, electricity, and coal, and it has been suggested that financial assistance which may be needed should be provided through the social services and income tax systems rather than through attempts to shape income from general consumers as instruments of social policy[6]. In addition, water authorities have a duty to take steps (as from not later than 1st April 1981) to ensure that their charges do not show undue preference to any class of persons (Water Act 1973, Section 30 (5)).

Finally, there is the problem of deciding which of the many classes of the disabled, together with pensioners and juveniles, really qualify for financial concessions. The testing of disability and means is not a task which any water authority would wish to undertake when there are local authority and other public agencies better qualified to decide. A simple way of providing financial assistance to deserving cases who are disabled would be for the social services to grant an allowance to applicants on production of a full price licence or permit. Meantime, it is desirable that water authorities should concentrate their efforts upon practical measures, as outlined above, to help the disabled to enjoy the recreational resources provided by water and associated land, while leaving the question of concessionary licences and permits to be decided by each authority—perhaps as a demonstration of its social conscience. The cost of doing so is likely to be very small, but a record of concessions granted, and their value, should be kept as a guide to future policy decisions.

If it is decided to grant concessionary licences and permits to the disabled, the criterion for eligibility may be judged by the capacity of the individual to earn a living in full-time employment, i.e. a diminished ability to earn because of disability or immobility. The starting point for this judgement is that beneficiaries should be unemployed disabled persons in receipt only of state benefits, and it follows that applications for concessionary licences and permits should be supported by any one of the following documents:—

Either
(a) A current unemployment benefit card on which the holder is registered as disabled, or which is supported by:
   —A green card (registration as disabled);
   or—A war-disabled pension book;
   or—A doctor's certificate of permanent disability;
or (b) Invalidity pension book;
or (c) Non-contributory invalidity pension book;
or (d) Attendance allowance book;
or (e) A letter from the Regional Sports Association for the Disabled, certifying membership and unemployment.

ORGANIZED TRANSPORT

The use of passenger cruisers for recreation has long been established in the English Lake District and in the alpine lakelands of Europe. In Scotland the steamer *Sir Walter Scott*, which has operated on Loch Katrine (which supplies water to the city of Glasgow) for many years, is a well known feature in the area. The greatest potential for such facilities on reservoirs would appear to be in places where there is already excessive pressure from motor-vehicles and from people on the waterside, resulting in traffic congestion along perimeter roads and erosion of the water margins. Some reservoir shores are also dangerously steep and inaccessible to visitors, or cannot be opened to public access because of water quality constraints. In these circumstances the provision of well designed cruisers by commercial operators on an experimental basis would seem to be worthwhile, and the service would be of value to anglers wishing to reach, or return from, distant points on large reservoirs.

The cruisers could contain their own refreshment and sanitary arrangements, while scripts for the helmsman, or tape-recordings, could describe the scenic and other natural features of the area. If powered by steam and of elegant design the cruisers would be quieter, and more attractive both to the public and water quality officers than vessels propelled by internal combustion engines, but the labour costs of running and maintaining such boats may be high.

Organized transport on land associated with water can have the same advantages as cruisers in regard to relieving congestion, the control of sanitation, and for informing visitors. Experience with "park and ride" schemes has been gained, for example, by the Goyt Valley experiment conducted in the Peak National Park. In such cases it is important to provide a frequent, regular, and reliable service time-tabled to suit the time of year and public holidays.

Tourist railways also offer opportunities to reduce excessive road traffic and pedestrian pressures on the waterside, as exemplified by those "Little trains of Wales" in proximity to reservoirs, lakes, rivers, waterfalls, and the sea. All appear to achieve financial viability through their passenger income and the efforts of enthusiastic volunteers. The track-beds of railways which are sometimes used for the construction of dams are always worth considering for leasing to a private railway developer, especially if they offer the possibility of reducing excessive road traffic. While redevelopment as steam railways is more popular, consideration could also be given to using tractors towing trains of passenger wagons.

RAMBLING

Walking by dedicated ramblers is a long-established recreation. Participants are normally self-contained experienced map-readers who do not seek waymarked routes, nature trails, and the like which mainly benefit the relatively inexperienced visitor to the countryside. In less vigorous lowland areas the provision of gravel tracks and generally level paths is not an uncommon feature of heavily used venues.

The Ramblers Association seeks more routes which are not only interesting in themselves, but which could linkup with existing public footpaths to form networks of walking routes. As with other routes which water owners may agree for public use, it is advisable to grant permission in preference to dedicating as a public right of way, against the possibility of needing to close or divert the route for operational or other purposes. The Ramblers Association is endeavouring to have these "permitted" paths indicated on Ordnance Survey maps, and this could help all concerned to distinguish those routes which are normally open for public use by permission from public footpaths.

Another organization which can advise and assist in the selection and management of walking (and cycling) routes is the Youth Hostels Association, while close liaison with local planning and national park authorities is always useful.

ORIENTEERING AND WAYFARING

Orienteering is a test of skill involving both mental and physical prowess, during which a series of control points have to be found by map and compass navigation for a coded record to be punched on the competitor's map. Courses are laid out to suit all ages and skills, and because of the Scandinavian origin are usually preferred over the undulating forest land commonly found in reservoir catchment areas. There are parent bodies for the sport in England, Scotland and Wales.

Wayfaring is a development by the Forestry Commission from orienteering, which is intended for the family or individuals who do not wish to compete in events. As with orienteering proper, the pursuit provides a challenging way of exploring the countryside, using a map to find a number of control points. Further information may be obtained from a local Forestry Commission officer.

No problems arise from orienteering or wayfaring provided that arrangements are made in advance by a responsible organization. Charges may be made for permission to hold orienteering events, and for the provision of maps for wayfaring.

HORSE RIDING

The most popular form of riding, associated with reservoirs, lakes and rivers, is pony-trekking. Many upland reservoirs and their catchment land can provide trails with superb scenery, some of which may link up with existing public bridleways to form extensive networks. In other cases, where the construction of a reservoir has severed traditional bridleways, it may be practicable and desirable to permit horse riding along tracks joining the severed ends and thus preserving a reasonable "ride" even though the catchment area may not be extensive. As with any agreement to permit public use by horse, on foot, or with vehicles, it may not be desirable to dedicate routes as public rights of way, and a suitable precaution against acquisition of a public right is annual recorded closure for 24 hrs at a time when use is minimal.

Occasional closure or diversion may also be necessary to reduce the erosion and churning-up and perhaps fouling of over-used routes, which can otherwise be made unusable for walkers and cyclists.

If it becomes necessary through pressure of numbers to control access, a simple form of permit is desirable, with charges linked to the number of horses, length of route, and to commercial or private use. The advice of the British Horse Society and/or a local Forestry Commission officer will be helpful in these respects. In many rural areas without heavy "tourist" traffic the granting of permits with or without an associated charge may be inappropriate, and the main reason for keeping the use "permitted" rather than "public" will be to prevent poaching of the soil by arranging diversions and to facilitate temporary closure if repairs to the water installation of the reservoir so necessitates.

It is, of course, essential that the horses are well cared for, and the registration and annual inspection of riding establishments through membership of the British Horse Society or local Pony Trekking Society is designed to ensure this. Such organizations have also been instrumental in bringing about a significant improvement in management standards, and can assist with the reduction of problems such as dangerous congestion of narrow roads and disturbance of livestock.

GUN AND FIELD SPORTS

Wildfowling and other forms of sporting shooting, fox and hare hunting, and deer control are, like angling, traditional and legitimate sporting activities. They can, incidentally, generate significant income for the owners of water and associated land.

This is not the place to debate the issues surrounding "blood sports", and owners of sporting resources will wish to form their own policies as they think best, having regard not only to the recreational aspects of the sport but also to the desirability of protecting their own and neighbours' crops and livestock from pests, of selective culling to reduce overcrowding, starvation, and disease and to the conservation and well-being of wild life generally in the area. Bodies such as the Nature Conservancy Council, the Wildfowling Association of Great Britain and Ireland, and the British Field Sports Society may be able to offer advice on these aspects to the owner who is formulating policy.

If game shooting is to be an important element of recreation at a reservoir, consideration may be given to laying out the plantations and planting them with appropriate species to form suitable pheasant coverts and associated drives. The provision of a gamekeeper's house may be necessary, and sufficient land should be made available for rearing meadows, release pens, etc. Grouse and partridge shooting may require the construction of butts, but these would normally be the responsibility of the gamekeeper. Habitat and crop management will be necessary to provide a good shoot. The most common method of exercising the shooting is by letting to a shooting tenant, who provides his own keeper.

Traditionally, wildfowling involves the construction of suitable creeks with hides but wildfowling is of all shooting probably the most sensitive issue when conservation interests are being considered. The owner of a water area providing nature conservation areas would be well advised to assess carefully the compatibility of shooting with wildfowl conservation before incurring expenditure on special provision for the wildfowling interest.

Fox and hare hunting are unlikely to demand much special provision, except perhaps hunting gates and the avoidance of the use of barbed wire to enclose grazing animals. The catchment areas of upland reservoirs are likely to provide suitable habitats for the quarry. Deer would seem to demand no more than a suitable natural habitat; where they are present their management may justify the employment of a game warden, either by the owner or the sporting tenant.

The last most important requirement is to ensure that adequate safety precautions are taken at all times, and particularly if shooting is allowed in areas to which visitors are usually permitted. It may well be necessary to exclude visitors from the area when shooting is taking place, and certainly all users of guns and rifles and those under whose control they are must be well versed in field sporting lore and etiquette. There is no room for the "cowboy" in the quasi-public environment of many water areas and reservoirs.

ARCHERY

This is an acceptable recreation on land surrounding water, provided that a suitable shooting area can be laid out, away from the public and from farm animals. Club organization is probably the preferable method of management, and the club might well be required to permit shooting on a daily basis, if conditions are suitable.

CAVING

The majority of caves used for recreation and scientific study have been formed by the solvent action of acidic streams passing through limestone fissures. The water from caves may pass into a large reservoir which is used for supply purposes, and if the water receives suitable treatment there should be no more danger arising out of caving activities than from other activities taking place on gathering grounds. But if water from caves goes into direct supply, precautions must be taken to counteract pollution, which may arise from the tracker-dyes used to trace cave systems, from faeces, and through excessive turbidity created by trampling and excavations.

ɔ-operation in these matters is obtainable through parent bodies such as the
ional Caving Association and local affiliated groups.

ᴋᴏ CK CLIMBING

If a water ownership contains land with rock-climbing potential it is desirable,
before agreeing to requests for facilities, to consult nature conservation bodies about
the natural history status of the climbs, and local planning and highway authorities
about such matters as road access and car parking. Indiscriminate car parking and
behaviour incompatible with the Country Code can annoy tenant farmers in the
area, and it is advisable to have a form of licensing to clubs operating under the aegis
of the British Mountaineering Council.

HANG GLIDING

The only specific connection of this sport with water and surrounding land is that
such land in highland areas may provide suitable launching sites. It will be advisable
for the water undertaker to licence the facility for club use only and the club must
take full responsibility for the safety of its members: this might include the provision
of a rescue boat if there is danger of landings in water. The sport can be of
annoyance to local farmers when sportsmen have to be recovered from unscheduled
landing sites. Provision for car parks and spectators is necessary, as with other
similar sports.

MOTOR SPORT

On some reservoir catchment lands motor sports have long been established in the
form of car rallying, hill-climbing, and motor cycle trials. For these, the organizers
seek private roads or tracks because of statutory prohibitions on public highways
(including footpaths and bridleways), and the fact that many private roads provide
interesting testing conditions. A race or trial of speed between motor vehicles on any
public highway is a punishable offence under law, but other trials may be permitted
if previous authority has been given by the highway authority and the consent of the
landowner obtained in writing. However, even if the highway authority and landowner grant permission for the use of the public footpaths or bridleways, a driver
must exercise a very high standard of care to avoid charges of reckless and dangerous
driving.

The co-ordinating bodies for car rallying are seeking more facilities to enable them
to host the special stages of international, national, and club events. These stages are
trials of speed over rough tracks, preferably on forest land of a kind found in many
reservoir catchments. Although special stages are of short duration and cars are
subject to noise level tests, they can have considerable impact on the environment.

Hill-climbing takes place over short steep gradients, preferably with a sequence of
sharp bends. Use of service or construction roads of this type below reservoir dams
may therefore be requested and in order to help in reaching a decision to grant
permission it is recommended that the organizers be allowed to hold a demonstration
for the owners and managers concerned.

Motor cycle trials are long established tests of skill over rough tracks and
participants include the police, armed and civil services, and often older riders of
good reputation.

Other motoring recreations include four-wheel drive competitions, safaries, motor
cycle scrambling, and autocross.

In considering applications to hold any of these events it is necessary to bear in
mind the possible effect on water quality arising from accidents (e.g. oil spillage), as

well as the impact of noise, traffic congestion and crowds upon local communities, the disturbance of livestock and wildlife, and the damage to roads. Nevertheless, there are some possibilities of meeting requests for motor sports on selected land associated with water, provided that guarantees are obtained from the organizers that the arrangements have the approval of appropriate governing bodies such as the Royal Automobile Club, and that adequate insurance cover has been arranged.

TRADE FAIRS, EXHIBITIONS, DEMONSTRATIONS, AND GAME FAIRS

There are two aspects of these events to be considered (1) the suitability of the site for the event and (2) participation in the event by the water undertaker.

The environs of a reservoir or lake may well offer an attractive venue for a trade fair, exhibition, or demonstration, connected with water particularly if the water itself is to be used for demonstration purposes. There is a recent tendency however for large functions to be accommodated on permanent sites which are adequately provided with roads, services, grandstands, etc., and it is perhaps appropriate to note that reservoir sites are particularly vulnerable to damage arising from the lack of provision of services such as sewers, roads, and water. Existing services built for operational and recreational use are unlikely to be able to cope with a great influx of people and traffic associated with a large national or regional event, and may have to be supplemented on a temporary basis—this can be expensive. There would not seem to be any particular suitability of a reservoir lake or river site for events not connected with water use, except as a means of raising revenue.

Where an event, e.g. a trade fair for sailing and fishing boats, is considered appropriate to a water environment the site owner will have a good opportunity of "joining in" the show by a temporary extension of say the information centres on a stand at the fair, by safety demonstrations, and by selling the permanent recreation at the site generally. Live demonstrations of all the sports may be appropriate and amateur groups are often willing to participate without charge, although car parking facilities and subsistence are appreciated. These efforts will probably be welcomed by the organizers as additional interest; in any case the right to run them can be reserved when the site is let for any particular function.

Water undertakers on the recreation front may wish to organize the fair or demonstration themselves and to sell trade stands to interested parties; this can be a somewhat demanding commitment and will probably depend on the degree of voluntary help from the interested sports.

PUBLIC ASSEMBLIES

The remote and beautiful atmosphere of some reservoir catchments has occasionally been invaded by large congregations of "Hippie" people, who have set up primitive camps without asking permission. Sanitary arrangements are usually absent and conditions can become very bad. Eviction can be difficult and may require legal action.

The same remoteness and wide spaces may also attract the interest of pop festival promoters, who do ask and pay for the permission and make some arrangements for sanitation and medical first-aid. The distance from large populations, elevation, exposure, and level of rainfall of many upland reservoir sites is likely to deter the commercial promotor, and there seems little reason to agree to requests elsewhere if there exist other locations better capable of dealing with large crowds; for example, agricultural showgrounds.

Exhibitions and equipment demonstrations related to the water industry, water-based recreation, wildlife conservation, and pest control are suitable for reservoir areas, provided that adequate arrangements exist, or are made, for car parking, sanitation, refreshments, shelter, medical aid, and of course insurance.

SECONDARY ACTIVITIES

Depending on the nature of the site and the main activities contemplated, a whole range of supporting activities can be considered. These include adventure playgrounds, golf courses, ski-ing facilities, etc. The typical reservoir environment may well be particularly suitable, for example, for a golf course on the grassed areas not used extensively for agriculture or for a ski slope (grass or nylon) on the back slope of an earth dam.

They can contribute to the enjoyment of the primary water sports activities, e.g. adventure playground for the children of sailing club members and to the general objectives of the water undertaker to provide a wide range of recreation opportunities.

The facilities required will vary greatly, and will range from a small area of land and modest expenditure such as would be required for a children's playground to the large area and significant capital outlay that would be needed for a golf course. The decision as to what provision may be made depends entirely on local circumstances— Authority objectives, supply and demand situations, planning authority attitudes, etc.—but certainly where the addition of any of these facilities would make a positive contribution to the basic recreational use of the site there is every reason for at least giving them sympathetic consideration.

If a water undertaker runs farms on land associated with water, or can make arrangements with his tenant farmer, farm "walks" attract a good deal of interest from the visiting public or organized parties. Some degree of supervision may be necessary to ensure that, mainly through ignorance, visitors do not harm livestock and crops or indeed themselves. Information facilities such as those provided for general rambling will also greatly increase the interest.

LEASING OF CONCESSIONS

It is perhaps labouring the obvious to say that the visitor to a recreation site at which he expects to spend a substantial part of a day will wish to be fed and watered. He may choose to satisfy his needs by bringing his own provisions, but there is bound to be a proportion of people who will wish to obtain food and drink on site. The sportsman will seek to be able to purchase tools and accessories of his trade. Many visitors will wish to carry away mementos of their visit—there is almost a feeling of deprivation amongst some day-visitors and holiday makers if there is no opportunity for them to spend their money!

If a substantial recreational facility is let to a club with some sort of headquarters building at the site, the club can reasonably be expected to meet the above needs of their members, but for all others—casual visitors, day ticket sportsmen and members of small clubs with no on-shore facilities of their own—the owner of the water complex may wish to consider making provision. The important decisions, usually clearly related to finance, which have to be taken are the level of service to be provided, the housing of the service, and the method of management. Once again the "market" is one of the major considerations. How many people will come? From what social groups will they be from? Why will they come?

A site with good recreation facilities within reach of large areas of prosperous sections of the population might well justify a full-scale restaurant with licensed bar and possibly evening entertainment, whereas a fairly small remote site with only unpretentious recreation facilities might justify only a mobile van dispensing tea and ice-cream at weekends. Likewise, a large enterprise with hundreds of day-ticket sporting customers might justify a tackle and accessories shop.

The owner of the site must decide whether he is to provide the buildings to house these services or whether it can be left to another to do so. If the building is provided by the owner he may decide to let it on lease with the right to trade; he may grant a concession to a trader to trade in it on terms to be agreed; or he may run the enterprise himself. If no provision to house the service is made by the owner he is more or less restricted to granting a concession to a trader able to provide the service in his own accommodation, either fixed or mobile.

As a general rule it can be said that granting leases and concessions removes from the owner the risk of a "trading" loss but by the same token passes the profit-making chances to the trader. At some remoter reservoirs the keeper's family may welcome the opportunity to lease or manage refreshment facilities, which will bring them social contacts as well as extra income where there is probably a shortage of employment within easy reach.

PUBLIC LIABILITY AND INSURANCE PROVISIONS

One of the more open-ended questions needing to be faced in the management of recreational facilities is that relating to accidents which, despite the most stringent precautions, may nevertheless involve either the public or employees whilst they are present on recreational facilities provided by a water authority. Physical circumstances and individual risks will vary from situation to situation and, particularly where a large public body is concerned, the response will need to be conditioned to that body's established general attitude towards public liability insurance. Regard will need to be paid to contemporary trends in the incidence of claims and to the considered capacity of the body concerned to cover such claims itself. One of the assessments which will need to be made will therefore relate to the commercial wisdom and necessity of effecting differing types of insurance cover, as well as identifying the kinds of individual cover most likely to apply to the recreational activities being carried out at any particular site.

Cover against such eventualities as public liability for injury to third parties and damage to their property; injury to employees (under employer's liability provisions); and damage to the property of the promoting authority, may appear to be virtually essential and can be readily secured commercially. The recreation manager, however, will then need to consider whether any individual commercial package fully covers all the risks likely to arise, and whether the incidence of claims, or their magnitude, warrants seeking an extension of the basic policy to cover additional eventualities.

The subject is a specialized one and the manager responsible for a recreational facility owned by a water authority is advantageously placed in that he can call upon internal specialist advice as well as being able to look to the precedents governing his employer's attitude generally to insurance provisions. The situation is referred to here less by way of providing a definitive answer than of alerting the reader to a situation where local priorities will have an important influence on the type of insurance to be provided.

4. REFERENCES

1. Eastern Council for Sport and Recreation, "Minimum standards for moorings, boat basins, and marinas".
2. Briedenback, A. W., 1973, US Environmental Protection Agency, "Analysis of pollution from marine engines and effects on environment".

3. Atkins, P., 1973, International Council of Marine Industry Associations, Zurich, "Effects of outboard engine exhaust on the aquatic environment".
4. International Council of Marine Industry Associations, Marine Environment Committee, "Recreation in a marine environment". (An illustrated summary of reference No. 3, containing extended bibliography.)
5. Davies, J. A. 1978, Public Works Congress, I.W.E.S. Session, "Development of the Lliedi reservoirs for recreation".
6. National Water Council, 1976, "Paying for water".

ove left. Rutland Water (Anglian Water Authority). Rescue craft and crew engaged in simulated cue.

ove right. Bewl Bridge reservoir (Southern Water Authority). Sub-aqua enthusiasts during a training ssion. One of the interesting features of this reservoir is a submerged mill, which provides a novel m of "wreck" exploration.

Above left. "White water" canoeing on one of the fast flowing rivers in Wales (Welsh Water Authority).
Above. Canoe training session at Draycote Water, Severn-Trent Water Authority *(T. Schofield)*.
Left. Family outing on the river Avon (Wessex Water Authority).

Top. Car parking and picnic area at Derwent Water, Sunderland and South Shields Water Compar
Above. Sailing on the river Trent, near the confluence with the river Stour (Severn-Trent Wat
Authority). The cooling towers of Ratcliffe Power Station are shown in the background *(H. McKnight).*

Chapter 4

PLANNING AND CONSTRUCTION
OF RECREATIONAL FACILITIES

1. INTRODUCTION

THE planning and construction of the various facilities concerned have an important bearing upon the success of any recreational development. If the standard is high, visitors are more likely to be attracted to the site and to obtain maximum enjoyment from it. Conversely, if it is low, they may find the site unattractive and its potential may then be grossly under-utilized. A low standard can also have a detrimental effect upon the amenity of the surrounding area. It is, therefore, in everyone's interest that these aspects should receive careful attention.

STRATEGY

The facilities required at any recreational site depend, principally, upon the activities involved, and can vary considerably in size, scope, and sophistication according to the circumstances prevailing at each particular location. Ideally, the specific activities to be catered for at each site should be determined on the basis of a comprehensive regional recreational strategy, rather than in isolation. In this way, the optimum benefit to the community as a whole is more likely to be realized.

In the formulation of such a strategy, a multiplicity of factors has, of necessity, to be taken into account and consultation with the appropriate Regional Sports Councils and other interested parties is usually essential and can prove to be of great value. Factors to be considered may include the primary responsibilities of the waterworks owner in respect of water supply and pollution prevention; the demand for the various types of activity in the area—which is often difficult to determine because of the lack of reliable information; the extent to which that demand is already, or is likely in future to be, satisfied at other locations in the region; the recreational capacity of each site; the ownership of sporting rights; the position of the sites concerned and of similar ones in the area, relative to each other and to centres of population; the compatibility of certain activities with the environmental conditions found on many sites, with other types of activity, and with the interests of nature conservation; the ability of individual sites to meet the requirements of a number of pursuits in regard to such characteristics as the size and shape of the water area, water quality, and the degree of variation in water level and such matters as the extent of the water undertaker's land ownership; and climatic and other conditions prevailing on site which might adversely affect the safety of visitors.

INFLUENCE OF SITE CHARACTERISTICS

Each site possesses a unique combination of natural and artificial features which can influence its development for recreational purposes. Its physical and ecological characteristics may impose constraints upon the intensity of use which can be tolerated on certain sections of the area without causing unacceptable degradation and also upon the site as a whole, if all its character is not to be lost. Sites for which water undertakers are responsible differ markedly in this respect between exposed and hilly upland areas and relatively flat and well wooded lowland sites. It is of great importance that none of them should be over exploited, so as to avoid the destruction by the sheer weight of visitors, of the very thing which they have come to enjoy. An awareness of the fragility of the areas which are involved, accompanied by a corresponding sensitivity of approach to the problems posed by each particular site, is required if the best results are to be achieved, and if the recreational potential of each is to be fully realized without detriment to other important or transcendent interests.

Site characteristics may also influence the position and size of individual facilities. In some circumstances, it might be preferable to concentrate major facilities into a small section of the site so as to discourage large numbers of visitors from using the more vulnerable areas such as nature reserves, or those which present dangers to the unwary or less fit members of the public. This arrangement may also be preferable in some upland settings where a proliferation of smaller, scattered facilities could well introduce a more intrusive and objectionable alien element into an otherwise uncluttered landscape of large expanses of bare moorland or rough grazing, than would a single large scale development. In other situations, especially on sites abounding in small wooded areas, it may well be better for the facilities to be dispersed to give a more informal atmosphere and to take maximum advantage of the natural landscaping which such cover provides. In yet other cases, a concentration of major facilities in one area combined with a series of smaller ones strategically located around the remainder of the site may be the most appropriate arrangement.

NEW RESERVOIRS

The construction of a new reservoir presents a rare, though welcome, opportunity for planning any associated recreational development, free from many of the complications often found with an established site, where the position of existing features such as access or site roads, public utility services, etc., may be far from ideal from the recreational viewpoint. Because of the greater freedom available, a more satisfactory and effective layout is usually possible on a new site, notwithstanding the fact that the essential requirements of the principal project inevitably take precedence over those of the recreational interest. With good forward planning from the inception of the scheme, appreciable savings can often be made in the overall costs. It may, for instance, be found possible, by aligning the dam's permanent access road along a different route to that which would otherwise normally be chosen, to reduce substantially the length of recreational site roads required. The resulting economies in expenditure can often be considerable, even in cases where the length of the access road is thereby increased. Savings may also be possible by incorporating the contractor's site roads into the final network, particularly if, with his co-operation, they can be judiciously routed along suitable lines from the outset of the contract. Similarly, the contractor's site services such as water supplies, sewers, and sewage treatment works can often be advantageously incorporated into the permanent site infrastructure. The small additional expenditure involved in constructing them initially to the standards and capacity and in locations suitable for this purpose is generally far less than the cost of building separate facilities for both temporary and permanent use.

DEVELOPING FACTORS

A number of factors affecting the design and construction of recreational facilities have recently assumed greater significance than formerly, as a result of developing social trends and legislative action. This is particularly the case in the fields of safety, both of staff and visitors, protection against the activities of vandals, and the provision of special facilities for the disabled. It is important that their implications should be taken into account along with the many other considerations affecting these aspects of the development of a recreational project.

The management of the facilities referred to this Chapter is dealt with in Chapter 5.

2. ACCESS ARRANGEMENTS

PUBLIC HIGHWAYS

Impact of Increased Traffic

Additional recreational facilities inevitably generate an increase in traffic on the local public highways. The extent of the increase depends generally upon the scale of the activities involved and on the sizes of the population in the areas which are within reasonable travelling distance of the site. In this context travelling time may be more significant than actual distance. Other factors, such as the existence of competing facilities, variations in the demographic structure of the local population, i.e. in ages, incomes, occupations, etc., and in their response to additional recreational opportunity can also influence the extent of the increase.

It has widely been found in this country that the majority of visitors to a recreational area live within a radius of 50 km of the site. A recent survey carried out at Rutland Water[1] (in the East Midlands) showed that virtually 70 per cent of visitors to the picnic areas had travelled less than that distance. There is some evidence also, that participants in certain activities may be prepared to travel greater distances, and this is illustrated by the results of a similar survey carried out in 1978 at the same reservoir[1] into the length of journeys made by anglers.

There is no absolutely reliable means of forecasting the increase in vehicular traffic likely to occur as a result of a specific recreational development. An assessment of its magnitude may be obtained from consideration of the type and scale of the development and of the contributory population within a 50 km radius, or other such distance as may be indicated from available statistics in respect of similar sites or activities already existing in the area, taking into account the effect of the differing circumstances obtaining in individual cases. In general, the maximum increase occurs on Sundays and Bank Holidays in summer. The average numbers using the car parks and picnic areas at Rutland Water on Sundays in the summer of 1978 was some 36 per cent of the weekly total. This proportion is similar to that experienced at a more remote upland site, Scar House reservoir in North Yorkshire, where Sundays account for about 40 per cent of the weekly attendance. These percentages could, however, vary from site to site and may not apply to all activities.

The impact of the additional traffic on the public highways is, of course, greatest on the roads in the immediate vicinity of the recreational site, since it is there that all the extra traffic converges. The degree of impact can vary considerably, depending, inter alia upon the magnitude and incidence of the increased flow in relation to the pattern previously established, the carrying capacity of the roads concerned, and the number of alternative routes leading to the site. Where large increases are involved, it may be possible to reduce the effect by providing alternative entrances to the site from different roads, or by the institution of a one-way system with the entrance on one road and the exit on another. The appropriate highway authority should always be consulted where significant changes in traffic flows are anticipated, and the local Police Force can often give useful advice.

ACCESS AND SITE ROADS

Layout

The layout of access roads from the public highway to the site of water-based recreational facilities and, in the case of enclosed waters such as reservoirs, of those to different parts of the associated land can appreciably affect the enjoyment of visitors to the site. An imaginative layout taking maximum advantage of opportunities for opening up scenically attractive vistas to the car-borne visitor will enhance his pleasure. It may sometimes be worthwhile to choose a route which will conceal a particularly picturesque view until the last minute to achieve the most dramatic visual impact. These and other landscaping possibilities for roads are discussed by Gibberd[2].

Within the site itself the layout of roads can be so designed as to attract the bulk of visitors to specific large scale facilities such as major picnic areas, or to disperse them more widely in accordance with the managerial policy adopted for the particular site. The enjoyment of areas set aside as nature reserves, or for the use of those visitors who prefer tranquil surroundings, can be increased by choosing routes which avoid them altogether or which, at least, do not approach them too closely. Where this is not feasible, and it is desirable to discourage cars from lingering in the area, the construction of ditches or small earth banks or the placing of wooden posts or large stones along the roadside can prove very effective.

The roads themselves must be capable of carrying the anticipated traffic flows without difficulty and must be safe to use. Design criteria for the layout of roads in rural areas are set out in a Ministry of Transport manual[3], which provides advice on aesthetics, alignment, carriageway widths, gradients and cambers, the radii of curves, sight lines, visibility at junctions and bends, frequency and location of passing places on single track roads, drainage, etc., much of which is relevant to roads giving access to recreational facilities, particularly on the larger sites. On new roads where these criteria cannot be met because of adverse site characteristics, or on existing roads where improvements to achieve these standards are not feasible, it is usual to restrict vehicle speeds accordingly.

On many of the smaller recreational sites single track roads with passing places have been found in practice to be adequate. They may also be suitable for a large proportion of site roads on larger scale developments, especially where it is desired to restrict the amount of traffic in a particular area. This type of road is normally subject to appropriate speed restrictions, in the interests of safety. Roads leading to major sailing, parking, and picnicking facilities will generally need to be of two-lane construction to cope with the concentration of traffic attracted to these points. An exception could be where a one-way system of traffic circulation was in operation. The minimum widths suggested in the manual[3] for single and two-lane carriageways are 3.5 and 5.5 m respectively, but it may be that in many cases the smaller widths set out in the Department of the Environment's bulletin on residential roads[4] will be more appropriate to the traffic volume anticipated.

The location and design of the junction of an access road with the public highway are of great importance, since it is at this point that the maximum number of hazardous traffic movements is likely to occur. The junction should preferably be sited away from features on the highway which restrict vision, such as bends and vertical curves, or which add to the number of potentially conflicting traffic movements, for example other junctions. Suitable visibility splays and possibly, on major roads, accelerating and decelerating lanes should be incorporated. Where vehicles may have to wait at the entrance to the site to obtain tickets, etc., the issuing point should be set back a sufficient distance from the junction to prevent obstruction of the main highway. The position of the junction and its detailed design are matters calling for close consultation with the appropriate highway and planning authorities, whose requirements, as set out in the planning consent issued under the terms of the relevant Planning Acts, will have to be met.

Design and Construction

The type of road construction employed varies from site to site and sometimes even from place to place within the same site. Where traffic is light, unsurfaced roads of quarry waste or of similar material such as hardcore are frequently used, blinded with a layer of quarry fines, preferably of local origin for aesthetic and economic reasons. More heavily used roads are generally surfaced and can be of either flexible or rigid construction, the former type predominating. The principal factors governing the structural requirements of the road itself are the traffic loading and the bearing capacity of the subgrade, but the effect of frost action has also, *inter alia*, to be taken into consideration.

Private cars normally constitute the majority of vehicles using access and site roads, but account has to be taken of the number of commercial vehicles which may also need to use them. These can include service and maintenance vehicles and large coaches, and it is on their numbers and axle loadings that modern pavement design is based. Guidance on the structural design of pavements is given in Road Note 29, produced by the Road Research Laboratory[5], which sets out both the basis and the method of design. It deals with the estimation of traffic loading, where axle loads are both known and unknown; the bearing strength of subgrades, giving tabulated values for typical British soils; the design of the various elements of flexible and rigid pavements in a wide variety of materials; and the frost susceptibility of soils and road materials. Specifications for the various constructional materials involved are to be found in a separate publication issued by the Department of the Environment[6].

Special consideration of the arrangements for the drainage of surfaced roads within the catchments of direct-supply reservoirs is necessary in order to minimize the danger of taste problems occurring in the supply through pollution of the raw water by hydrocarbon derivatives which may be contained in the run-off. These substances can originate from oil accidentally spilled on the road surface from vehicles, or, in the case of flexible pavements, from the surfacing material itself. On the type of roads concerned, drains are normally unnecessary: their absence is an advantage in that it leads to maximum dispersion of the run-off, thus allowing the utmost use to be made of the filtering effect of the soil. It is only in rare circumstances that this arrangement is insufficient to prevent contamination of the water. Where drains are found to be necessary and it is not feasible to arrange their discharge outside the catchment boundaries or to suitable soakaways, the materials used in the construction of the contributing length of road should be selected with great care. In its 1972 report on Recreation on Reservoirs and Rivers[7], the then Institution of Water Engineers recommended that "Any roads, hard standings, parking areas, etc., the drainage from which gains access to reservoirs, should be constructed of and maintained with materials which do not contain phenolic or other tainting materials".

Great care needs to be taken in the location of traffic signs and of those giving essential information for visitors, such as the sign indicating the position of the site entrance, or giving directions to the various facilities. They should be displayed in prominent positions where they will not be obscured from the driver's view by trees, bushes, buildings, etc. and they should be so placed as to give sufficient advance warning to permit unhurried manoeuvring. At the same time they should not present an obstruction to vehicles overrunning the verge or to visibility at junctions and bends. The Ministry of Transport recommends a minimum distance from the edge of the carriageway of about 1.25 m for a traffic sign and 1.5 m for the signpost, on rural roads[3]. The number of signs should in general be kept to a minimum and they should preferably be as simple and unobtrusive as possible consistent with fulfilling their purpose, so as not to detract from the visual amenity of the site. Traffic signs should be of the standard regulation pattern for instant recognition in the interests of road safety, and should be replaced immediately if removed or damaged.

FOOTPATHS

In addition to constituting a recreational facility in themselves, footpaths can provide a suitable means of access to those areas of a recreational site where the presence of vehicles is undesirable, or where the construction of roads is not feasible. Many reservoir catchment areas possess an established network of public footpaths which may, at least, form the basis of a more extensive system or may even already be adequate, in general, to accommodate the needs of the increased numbers of visitors generated by the development of any new facilities. Similarly, existing footpaths are frequently to be found along river banks.

Layout

The layout of new footpaths merits careful consideration. Firstly, if they do not have some objective or do not follow natural "desire lines" they may well not be used. The objective can be some attractive feature, for example the water itself, a viewpoint from which a pleasant scene or a mobile activity such as sailing can be observed; or simply the observation of indigenous flora and fauna, as is the case with nature trails. Desire lines, i.e. the routes which the great majority of people would naturally take, are difficult to predict. A number of factors influence them, such as the natural human inclination to take the shortest distance between two points, the slope and nature of the ground, and the presence of obstacles or of an intermediate focus of interest. These points are discussed at length in a booklet issued by the Countryside Commission for Scotland[8].

Secondly, footpath layouts must be carefully chosen so as to promote the achievement of management objectives for the particular site. These may include steering the majority of visitors away from sensitive areas such as nature reserves, dispersing them as widely as possible so as to minimize overcrowding or general site degradation, and keeping people out of range of fly-fishermen's backcasts and away from other potentially dangerous situations. Further considerations are the desirability or otherwise of linking the site paths to the general footpath system in the area, and of either maintaining them as permissive footpaths or dedicating them for public use under the National Parks and Access to the Countryside Act 1949.

In planning the alignment of footpaths in detail, it should be borne in mind that informal routes are generally the most appealing in the type of setting usually found on catchment areas. Indeed, the Gosling Committee in its 1968 report[9], commented that much of the value and charm of a footpath lay in its waywardness. Where possible, routes with gentle gradients should be chosen also, in the interests of older or less fit visitors and, in the case of unpaved paths, to minimize erosion from rapid run-off.

Types of Construction

The surfaces of footpaths normally consist of either grass, gravel, or paving material such as tarmacadam, concrete or flags and are suitable, in that order, for progressively greater intensities of use. Of these, grass usually predominates and is the one most in harmony with the surroundings generally associated with water-based recreational sites. This type of path can be created quite readily and inexpensively, for example simply by cutting the grass along the chosen route to provide adequate delineation. Unless the pressure of use exceeds the ability of the surface to withstand the accompanying wear and tear, it requires little maintenance. If wear does take place, the surface can often be restored, provided that the grass is not worn completely away, by reinforcing it with jute or plastic coated wire mesh held in place by long steel pins. Once the grass has grown through it, the mesh is completely hidden and provides, within limits, an effective means of protection against subsequent deterioration.

Gravel pathways are generally reserved for those routes subjected to moderately heavy use, or to sections of a grass footpath where inferior ground conditions demand a more resistant surface. The usual type of construction is a layer of gravel, of about 25 mm nominal size, surfaced with pea gravel or blinded with crushed fines and compacted with a vibrating hand roller. The gravel may be laid on top of the ground or on an excavated base. In the former case, the grass may grow through it to give the appearance of a grass path but, in the latter, the gravel will remain in evidence and should preferably be of local origin for aesthetic reasons. The thickness of gravel required will depend upon the bearing capacity of the ground and, in practice, usually varies between 100 and 150 mm. Typical examples of this type of construction are given in the Scottish Countryside Commission's footpath booklet[8]. Maintenance requirements vary, in general, with the amount of use received and are likely to entail filling in depressions and channels, accompanied in extreme cases by scarification of the surface, followed by hand rolling.

The use of paved surfaces is normally confined to the busiest footpaths such as those leading from large car parks to picnic sites or toilet blocks, to areas around information centres, clubhouses, or other buildings, or to relatively formal landscaped areas, partly because their artificial appearance clashes with more natural surroundings. For similar reasons tarmacadam or flagged surfaces are usually preferred to concrete, which has a generally harsher appearance and can be rather difficult to maintain. A tarmacadam footpath typically consists of a 15 mm wearing course of fine cold asphalt over a 30 mm basecourse of dense bitumen macadam laid on a crushed stone base of 100 mm consolidated thickness. Flags are usually laid on a 25 mm dry sand/cement bed, on a similar base. Both types are generally constructed with a 3 per cent camber or crossfall, and may be bounded by concrete or tanalized timber edgings.

In very boggy areas where footpaths of normal construction are unsuitable, gravel or paved pathways can sometimes be successfully built on a supporting membrane of synthetic fabric, of which a number of types, manufactured largely of poly-propylene, are now available. In these locations also, timber construction often proves to be successful. This is particularly the case where the decking is supported on piles and cross-members, rather than laid directly on the ground where it may sink into the surface and become uneven. The timber can be of rustic appearance so as to blend in as far as possible with the environment.

Before undertaking construction of the more expensive types of footpaths, it may sometimes be prudent to delineate a proposed route by simple markings or by cutting the grass, and allowing people to use it. In this way any difference between the proposals and actual desire lines can be positively established before significant cost is incurred, thus avoiding possible abortive expenditure should the two not coincide.

Other Details

The width of footpath needed will vary in each individual case with the amount of pedestrian movement involved. For paved pathways an indication of the dimensions necessary, including the width required for wheelchairs, can be found in the Department of the Environment's design bulletin 32[4].

The provision of effective drainage is essential on sections of a footpath where the natural system is inadequate. On unpaved paths, unless it is provided, such lengths can turn into quagmires in wet weather, with the result that people will tend to walk round them, causing progressive and unsightly widening. On paved paths the foundation could well be softened leading to distortion, or, in extreme cases, disruption of the surface, with consequential heavy maintenance or repair costs.

A certain amount of signposting is often necessary to indicate to visitors the particular objective of a footpath, but it is generally accepted that it should be kept to a minimum for aesthetic reasons. The wording should be concise, for example 'viewpoint' or 'nature trail', and the materials used should harmonize as far as possible with their surroundings. In this respect, signs with unpainted pressure creosoted posts are generally more appropriate in informal settings than other types. Signposts should be complemented by waymarks at points where difficulty may be encountered in following the route of the path. Recommendations for types of markings suitable in different situations are contained in the Countryside Commission's 1974 report on the waymarking of footpaths and bridleways[10], together with guidance on their frequency and location. People can also be directed along the route subconsciously by simple expedients such as keeping the path in good repair whilst deliberately neglecting deviations and preserving or even reinforcing existing obstacles like walls, fences, marshy patches, gorse or other bushes in areas bordering the path.

BRIDLEWAYS

Bridleways, like footpaths, are to be found along river banks and on many reservoir catchments and it is becoming the practice in this country, when new reservoirs are constructed, to provide replacements for existing bridleways which will be submerged by the water. Recent examples of this development are to be found at the Queen Mother reservoir at Datchet, at Bewl Bridge reservoir near Tunbridge Wells, and at Rutland Water, operated respectively by the Thames, Southern, and Anglian Water Authorities. Brief details of the facilities available for riders at these reservoirs are given in the Journal of the Water Space Amenity Commission[11,12].

Although the practice is by no means universal, bridleways are generally segregated from footpaths because of the potential conflict between riders and walkers and of the damage which can be caused to footpaths by horses' hooves. Similar considerations to those in respect of footpaths, apply to their layout, status, surfaces, drainage, signposting, and waymarking, etc.

3. SITE FACILITIES AND ACCOMMODATION

CAR PARKING

Car Parks

The mode of transport of the overwhelming majority of visitors to recreational sites today is the private car and, as a result, car parks have become an essential feature of almost all water-based recreational developments, either as general purpose parking or as adjuncts to specific facilities such as sailing centres, clubhouses, outdoor or educational activity centres, etc.

Location

Car parks can appear extremely unsightly in rural surroundings, particularly on sites possessing open aspects. Because of this, the exercise of considerable skill is required in their location if an undesirable degree of intrusion into the landscape is to be avoided. Suitable concealment may be available from natural features such as woodlands, depressions or folds in the ground, hillocks, etc., or from man-made features such as cuttings or quarries. Car parks bordering open areas of water are particularly difficult to conceal, and they have the additional disadvantage of being potential sources of hydrocarbon pollution. For these reasons this type of situation is usually avoided.

Parking areas associated with specific recreational facilities are almost invariably situated adjacent to them for obvious reasons and, in these cases, it is frequently the factors governing the location of the facility which determine their general position. A further consideration to be taken into account in selecting the site for a car park is the possibility of its future extension. A location offering scope for ready enlargement has the economic and practical advantages of enabling development to be carried out in stages to meet growing demand.

Capacity and Layout

The optimum overall capacity of general purpose car parks on any site where new development is planned, is difficult to quantify, depending broadly as it does upon the same factors which influence the extent of traffic generation by the development as a whole (already referred to on p. 91). In some cases, the determining factor may be the limited recreational capacity of the site itself but, where this consideration is not paramount, the number of parking places provided will essentially be dependent upon an assessment of the maximum number of vehicles likely to be present on the site at any one time during a peak day, i.e. the difference between the numbers having entered and those having already left, as distinct from the total daily attendance. The pattern at similar developments in the locality may provide some guidance in this respect. Within the overall total, the capacity of individual car parks can vary enormously in accordance with the physical characteristics of the site and the managerial policy adopted on such matters as the concentration or dispersal of visitors. On major developments they can be quite large[1,13].

The capacity of car parks associated with specific facilities will be governed by the type of facility involved and the likely maximum simultaneous attendance by people connected with the particular activity concerned. A common provision at sailing clubs, for example, is one parking space per boat, plus 50 per cent extra for visitors and spectators. This figure may have to be increased for a club with a large social membership.

The most economical pattern of parking is that with bays arranged at right angles to the aisles. With this layout and a normal bay size of 5 × 2.5 m, with a 6 m minimum aisle width, an area of one hectare will accommodate a total of 500 cars. This density should be reduced on car parks serving picnic areas, to allow somewhat larger parking bays to be provided so as to facilitate the unloading of picnic baskets and other equipment. Angle parking also requires a larger area, for example with bays at a 60° angle to the aisle, a minimum of 15 per cent more land is required than with right-angle bays, even taking into account the narrower aisle width of 5 m required, but this disadvantage may be worthwhile where it is desirable to encourage one way traffic circulation through the parking area.

Types of Construction

The most suitable type of surface for any particular car park will vary in accordance with the intensity of use it receives, the ground conditions, and the general character of the site. For very light use on level, firm and well-drained ground, a grass surface may be sufficient, reinforced with gravel or some type of paving at those places such as entrances, exits, and aisles between parking spaces which are subjected to heavier local traffic. For slightly heavier traffic or less favourable ground conditions, specially designed hollow concrete blocks through which the grass can grow, often provide a satisfactory finish of pleasing appearance. More heavily trafficked areas require surfacing with gravel or quarry fines laid, where necessary, on a base of consolidated hardcore, quarry waste or similar material, or bound with cold bituminous emulsion. In these cases the surfacing material should preferably be of local origin so as to harmonize, as far as possible, with its surroundings. The most intensively used car parks are normally paved with tarmacadam and their design and construction are generally similar to those of the corresponding type of access road. If they lie within the catchment of a direct-supply reservoir their drainage also requires similar consideration to that of surface roads (p 93), because of the danger of taste problems arising from possible pollution of the water by hydrocarbons.

Careful consideration should be given to the necessity for surfacing the whole of a large car parking area, in view of the fact that it will usually only be fully utilized during peak periods, i.e. at weekends and Bank Holidays. It may be possible to make considerable economies by confining the more expensive types of surfacing to the smaller area required to accommodate the numbers of vehicles using the site during normal weekdays. Visitors can be encouraged to fill up these areas first, so as to minimize maintenance of the sections with less resistant surfaces, by ensuring that cars can only reach the rest of the car park after passing through them.

On paved parking areas, it is usually desirable to mark the parking bays, either collectively or individually by such means as white lines. In addition, on all car parks, positions for coaches or the cars of disabled drivers should be clearly indicated by surface lettering or by suitably placed signs.

Landscaping

On exposed sites, where adequate natural concealment is unavailable, it is becoming common practice to employ landscaping techniques to reduce or obviate the otherwise intrusive effect of a car park on its surroundings. Large areas of hard surfacing can be broken up by the creation of artificial ridges or the planting of strips or clumps of suitable trees, etc. These means can also sometimes be used successfully to hide the entire parking area from view. In other instances it may be sufficient merely to plant hedges or to construct walls around the periphery. Whatever method is used, the final appearance should, where possible, harmonize with the surrounding countryside. For example, any trees introduced should be of the same species as those occurring naturally in the locality; artificial ridges or mounds should be avoided in extensive flat areas; and hedges should not be planted in upland areas where they are normally conspicuous by their absence.

Equipment

General purpose car parks are almost invariably equipped with litter bins or, alternatively, depending upon managerial policy, notices requesting visitors to take their litter home and with notice boards or signposts indicating the recreational facilities available on the site. The larger ones are also generally provided with toilet facilities and often, where appropriate, with information or interpretation centres, maps of the whole recreational site they serve, refreshment kiosks, etc.

BOAT PARKING

Dinghies and small keel boats are normally brought ashore after each day's sailing, but larger keelboats and cruisers are generally taken out of the water only at infrequent intervals. Parking areas are required for the onshore accommodation of both categories.

Location

The majority of the smaller boats are usually manhandled, during launching and recovery, and because of this and the frequency with which these operations take place the boat park is normally located adjacent to the slipway or other launching facility, for ease and convenience. A position close to the sailing clubhouse is often an added advantage from a security point of view. The site should be reasonably level, preferably firm and well drained and with space for a trailer park, about one-third of its size, adjoining. It should also be capable of ready extension, where appropriate, to cater for possible further development of the sailing facilities. The factors affecting the choice of parking areas for the larger boats are similar, except that their proximity to launching facilities is not quite so important because they enter and leave the water so rarely. Such boats rest on their trailers when ashore and do not therefore require a separate trailer park.

Capacity and Size

The size of a boat park is basically dependent upon the number of boats involved and their dimensions. Sufficient spaces should be provided for all the boats normally expected to be kept on site. For those only using the water on a daily permit basis, it is probably preferable to set aside a separate area, which could consist of a convenient section of the car park, as a combined car and trailer park. A boat park for craft which are normally kept in the water, houses only trailers for the majority of the time. Because they generally occupy a smaller space than boats, the parking area is under-utilized except for the relatively short periods when the boats are ashore. In view of this, it may be worthwhile to consider the provision of a smaller area than would otherwise be necessary and to make up the difference by allowing part of the car park to be used for this purpose in winter when the minimum car parking requirement coincides with that for maximum boat parking.

The dimensions of boats vary considerably and, as a result, so do the sizes of the parking spaces necessary and the width of the aisles between them. A space 6 or 7 m long by 3 m wide will normally be adequate to accommodate the majority of dinghies and small keel boats and their trailers, but a greater area will be required for larger craft. The aisle width is usually made slightly greater than the length of the parking bay.

Construction

The surface of the boat park should be reasonably level and firm so as to facilitate the movement of boats, and it should be maintained in this condition. The most common materials used are gravel or quarry waste blinded with fines, which blend in best with their surroundings if of local origin. The thickness of the surfacing will depend upon the bearing strength of the subsoil and the loading to be carried. The latter will be light except in the case of the larger vessels so that, in general, a relatively shallow depth of construction will be adequate.

In areas where the danger of vandalism is remote, boat parks are often left either partially or completely unenclosed. Where the reverse is the case, an adequate security fence around the perimeter can provide a measure of protection.

Like car parks, boat and trailer parks can mar an otherwise attractive scene, particularly as they are often visible, sometimes over considerable distances, because of their essential proximity to the edges of unobstructed expanses of water. Frequently, in spite of this, little attempt has been made to screen them from view, although an effort in this direction would often be a worthwhile contribution to the amenity of the locality. Much can be achieved by similar means to those available for this purpose in respect of car parks.

PICNIC AREAS AND VIEWPOINTS

Picnic areas and viewpoints are usually established in positions which are attractive in themselves, or which possess particularly picturesque views. On water catchments they often overlook the water surface, which provides a focus of interest that may be appreciably enhanced on those stretches where sailing takes place, by the presence of boats. Picnic sites may consist simply of an open grassy area without special facilities, or may be more sophisticated with equipment such as picnic tables, barbecues, toilets, etc. Car parking facilities are sometimes incorporated within the picnic site itself and are sometimes separate from it.

Location

Many factors affect the suitability of a particular site for development as a picnic area, and careful judgement needs to be exercised to ensure that the most satisfactory locations are chosen. In addition to the possession of features of interest, such as those referred to in the previous paragraph, they include the intrinsic attractiveness of the site itself, its ability to absorb visitors (and their cars) without detracting from the visual amenity of the locality, and its topography and subsoil characteristics. The possibilities for future extension may also influence the choice.

The features which help make a site attractive to picnickers are many and varied; some of them effectively indefinable. Others are peculiar to an individual area, but a number are of general applicability and these include suitable orientation and protection from prevailing winds; an adequate degree of variety and contrast, such as that between sunshine and shadow, open and closed views, sheltered and open space; and readily recognizable boundaries, such as woodlands, hedges, walls, rock outcrops, river banks, reservoir margins or fences, which create an impression of enclosure. The basis of their attraction lies in natural human preferences or psychology. For example sheltered south facing sites are sunnier and warmer than exposed north facing ones, and are therefore preferred because of the greater sense of well-being which the more comfortable conditions engender. Similarly, sites with identifiable territorial boundaries will generally be more popular because of the tendency of people to congregate around the edges of an open area, rather than in the middle.

The ability of the individual area to absorb picnickers without adverse effects on the local environment, particularly where cars are admitted within the picnic site, depends upon the degree of concealment available from surrounding woodlands or topographical features such as hills and valleys. A site devoid of such characteristics can be unacceptably conspicuous and therefore unsuitable unless landscaped and screened in a sympathetic manner.

Layout

The layout of a picnic area must also take into account natural human behaviour patterns, if the site is to be developed on the most successful lines. Generally, the participants in this form of recreation dislike becoming too detached from their cars and, indeed, many of them prefer to picnic in the vehicle's immediate vicinity, perhaps because they do not then have to carry picnic things far. The layout which most effectively caters for these preferences is one where cars can park within the confines of the picnic area itself. Parking arrangements on this type of area will vary in accordance with the characteristics of the site and the degree of use it receives. On a sufficiently large, lightly used site, with a firm, reasonably level surface, cars can be parked in an informal manner over the whole area, but, where ground conditions are unsuitable or the site is too intensively used, it may be necessary to provide driveways and hardstandings. On smaller, exposed, or very intensively used sites, a more formal arrangement may be required, with the cars parked on each side of driveways or even on a separate parking area. Where the car park is separate, it is important that it should be situated immediately adjacent to the picnic area, to which visitors should be attracted if possible, by means of such inducements as the prospect of a more picturesque view or the sight of inviting picnic tables, etc. Picnickers also tend, as previously noted, to settle near the edges of an open space. The definition of edge in this context includes, in addition to the periphery of the site, the margins of any clumps of trees, bushes, hedges, ponds, streams, etc., within its boundaries. A layout incorporating the maximum amount of "edge" will in general be the most satisfactory and, in this connection, much can be achieved by creating an irregular boundary and by planting trees, etc., in the middle of the site. A good illustration of the effects of taking such steps is given in a book by Elizabeth Beazley[14], which also contains much practical information on other recreational facilities. Any "on site" parking provision, picnic furniture, litter bins, etc., should be located near the edges of the site to take account of this particular natural tendency.

Capacity

The total number of people to be accommodated on picnic areas within any one recreational site will depend broadly upon the same factors which govern the aggregate number of general car parking spaces required. As in that case, numbers are difficult to predict with any degree of accuracy and the best guide may be the corresponding figures for similar sites in the surrounding district.

The overall area of picnic sites needed to provide for the numbers involved is equally problematical, depending, as it does, upon the density of use acceptable from the points of view both of the people concerned and of their effect upon the site. The capacity of each individual picnic area needs to be determined separately, because of the differing circumstances inevitably pertaining in each particular case. It is impossible to arrive at an absolute assessment of capacity because of the many imponderables involved. As a result, a considerable degree of judgement inevitably has to be brought to bear. One of the uncertainties to be taken into account, for example, is the difference between people's concepts of acceptable density. Some avoid crowded places whilst others prefer them, so that what constitutes an overcrowded site to one group will not appear so to another. Consideration of this point is further complicated by the fact that some areas, receiving only the same intensity of use as others, may seem more crowded. Open spaces, for instance, look more populated than those with some type of cover, since everyone is in view simultaneously, whereas in woodland many are hidden. In practice, the capacity of individual picnic areas varies from a few to a large number of people. There are corresponding variations in size, although this may sometimes be attributable to the management policy for the development as a whole rather than to the innate capacity of the picnic sites themselves. In view of the inherent uncertainties attending the assessment of demand and capacity, it may be an advantage, economically, to phase the construction of picnic areas to avoid costly over-provision.

Surfaces

For those sites where driveways and hardstandings are found to be necessary, careful thought should be given to which type of surfacing would be most suitable. Consideration of this point should, in addition to the usual factors of intensity of use, ground conditions, etc., take into account the particular purpose for which the area has been set aside. In general, the more natural the appearance the better, so that hollow concrete blocks with grass growing through them would normally be preferable to gravel or paved surfaces. The alternative types of surface usually adopted are the same as for car parks, and their suitability from the point of view of traffic intensities and ground conditions is also the same.

Equipment

The level of equipment and facilities provided on picnic sites varies in accordance with their size, the intensity of use they receive, and the managerial policy laid down for them. Small sites may be equipped simply with picnic tables and litter bins, whereas the larger and more intensively used ones will generally be provided additionally with toilet blocks, and notice boards, signposts, or maps showing the recreational facilities available locally. On the largest sites the inclusion of information or interpretation centres, refreshment facilities, a warden service, etc., may also be warranted. Facilities at viewpoints are usually confined to litter bins, seats and, possibly, information boards.

Much valuable advice and information on the planning and management of picnic sites in general is given in a Countryside Commission booklet[15] and in a book by Elizabeth Beazley[14].

SLIPWAYS

Slipways are by far the most general means of launching trailer-borne dinghies or small centreboard boats, wherever sailing activities take place on an organized basis. These types of craft constitute the overwhelming majority of those using enclosed waters in this country and a considerable percentage of those normally found on rivers. As a result, the provision of slipways is virtually universal on reservoirs which cater for recreational sailing and is common on the navigable stretches of rivers where suitable conditions for sailing, i.e. adequate width and depth and limited velocities of flow, exist.

Location

The location of slipways is influenced by a number of factors which place limitations on the choice of site. A sheltered position is desirable in order to avoid, or at least reduce, the possible danger of accidents occurring during the launching or landing of boats in strong or blustery winds. On rivers or estuaries particularly, locations subject to strong currents are best avoided for the same reason. Potential hazards, to which attention is drawn in the 1972 Report of the then Institution of Water Engineers[7], also exist on those areas of a reservoir adjacent to the draw-off tower, the overflow spillway and, in the case of a gravity structure, the dam itself. On this type of water, therefore, slipways, in common with other recreational facilities, should obviously be sited outside these danger zones.

In cases where a long slipway is necessary because of variations in water level, an additional factor influencing choice is the slope of the bank or shore between maximum and minimum water lines. If the inclination is too steep, relatively expensive construction may be needed in order to provide a gradient on the slipway suitable for handling the boats or, alternatively, powered winches or similar equipment may have to be provided for this purpose. The problem of too steep a gradient can sometimes be overcome by aligning the slipway at an angle to the direction of greatest slope, but there are practical and economic limitations to the degree of improvement which can be effected in this way.

Areas subject to the deposition of material through siltation, stream action, or littoral drift are best avoided because of the interference caused to the handling of boats and the consequent necessity of continuous removal and disposal of the deposits.

It is clearly an advantage to have boat and car parking facilities near the slipway for the sake of convenience and also to avoid the possibility of traffic between the two having to use the general site access roads, where it could cause congestion, especially at peak sailing periods. Almost invariably, the clubhouse is also situated nearby for similar reasons, and to enable close supervision to be maintained from the building of the launching and landing activities. At the very least a generous area must be available near the slipway for turning round and for manoeuvring trailers. These points should be borne in mind when selecting a site.

On rivers and estuaries the position of the slipway must be chosen so as to leave the launching area clear of navigation channels.

Dimensions

The requisite dimensions of a slipway depend upon the amount of use it will receive and on the characteristics of the site. Its width should be adequate to accommodate, comfortably, the maximum demand placed upon it, taking into account the pattern of that demand, and should preferably not be significantly less than 5 m. Widths greatly in excess of this are sometimes provided to cater for specific circumstances[16]. The length and gradient are largely dictated by site conditions, i.e. by the range of water levels and the slope of the bank or shore. The slipway is usually made of sufficient length to reach below the lowest water level at which sailing is practicable. For obvious reasons, on new reservoirs it is best to construct the slipway before impounding begins. Gradients should preferably be no steeper than 10 per cent where boats are launched or hauled ashore by hand.

Types of Construction

Of the two basic types of slipway, the solid one is the more common because it is normally easier and more economical to construct and maintain, is inherently safer to use, and frequently presents less of an obstruction to the waterway. It usually consists of a paved surface laid directly on a suitably prepared foundation or upon an intervening course of hardcore or similar material and, except on rivers, it generally follows the slope of the bank.

Foundations are not normally a problem because loads are small and it is only when soils of exceptionally low bearing capacity are encountered, such as unconsolidated silts, that special measures may have to be taken to ensure the stability of the structure. These may take the form of removing the unsatisfactory material below the structure and replacing it with a more suitable one, placing a mattress over the area, or supporting the slipway on piers resting on sound foundations below the base of the unsuitable material.

It is sometimes desirable to carry the slipway on small embankments to maintain an even gradient over depressions in the bank profile. Such embankments may be formed of a wide variety of materials which, for the sake of economy, are often selected from local sources. They must be satisfactorily compacted and in this respect cohesive materials present a more difficult problem than non-cohesive ones in that they have to be placed in layers, each one of which requires adequate compaction. In some cases, time for settlement must also be allowed before the succeeding layer is placed. The sides of the embankment may be vertical, retained by walls of sheet piling, brick, masonry, concrete, etc., or they may be sloping. In the latter case protection is usually given to the inclined surface by covering it with a layer of rubble, pitching, concrete, or gabions.

The paving itself normally consists of in situ concrete, with a minimum thickness of 150 mm, but other general paving materials are sometimes used. The surface must have sufficient roughness to provide adequate grip to facilitate boat handling. A horizontally screeded finish should prove to be adequate for this purpose where the gradient is shallow, but on steeper slopes it may be necessary to provide suitable grooves.

In some instances the action of waves or eddy currents can necessitate special measures being taken to protect the end and edges of the paving or the toes of any embankments. These usually take the form of aprons or vertical barriers of sheet piling or concrete carried down to a depth sufficient to prevent undermining of the structure by the scouring action of the water.

Where variations in water level are rapid, as in the case of slipways in the tidal reaches of rivers or estuaries, adequate drainage of the base and foundations may be necessary to prevent disruption of the paving through excessive residual uplift pressures.

The other basic category of slipway is the open framework which, though much rarer than the solid type, can have advantages over it which, in certain circumstances, outweigh its drawbacks. This may, for example, be the case where poor ground conditions necessitate the use of a piled structure, or where the slip can be subjected to particularly severe wave action or to exceptionally strong currents. The framework is usually constructed of concrete or steel and the deck of solid concrete slabbing or open steel grid. Occasionally, timber or even aluminium alloy may be used.

Whichever type of slip is provided, it is essential that it should be designed to withstand the most adverse wave, weather, and current conditions to which it is likely to be exposed. In addition, slipways on rivers should be designed and constructed so as not significantly to obstruct or interfere with the flow of water. In England and Wales, the consent of the appropriate Regional Water Authority is required to the construction of the works, under the provisions of the Land Drainage

Act 1976 and their specific requirements must be complied with. It is also important that the materials from which the slipway is constructed should be suited to the type of water on which the structure is located. This is particularly apposite in the case of reservoirs, where timber should be avoided because of the danger from waterlogged wood which has been known to cause partial blockages in outlet pipes and to foul or damage valves and other fittings. In addition, a number of upland reservoirs contain highly acidic water which can have a deleterious effect on concrete. An investigation by Halstead[17] showed that concrete immersed in this type of water lost strength and that the loss increased with time, reaching about 45 per cent after four years in the case of ordinary Portland cement concrete. High strength Portland cement concrete and high alumina cement concrete were more resistant, but the loss was still significant, at about 30 per cent, after the same period.

Equipment

Slipways should be equipped with suitable life saving apparatus and, in the case of those too steep for the boats to be comfortably manhandled, with a winch sufficiently powerful to cater for the largest craft using the facility. Undercover storage for sails and outboard motors, near at hand, is desirable and an appropriate means of refuelling may be required where the slipway is used by motor cruisers or by vessels with outboard engines. Toilet facilities should also be available nearby.

MOORINGS

Unlike dinghies and centreboard craft, the larger keelboats and motor cruisers are only removed from the water at infrequent intervals, and suitable moorings are needed for them to tie up to during the intervening periods.

Only extensive areas of water or long stretches of navigable river can afford adequate mobility to such craft. Few reservoirs in this country are large enough to accommodate them; those which can are of the direct-supply type, on which it is normally considered unacceptable to sail motor-driven craft because of the risk of contamination of the water from spillage or leakage of fuel oil[7]. As a result, the provision of moorings is rare on British reservoirs, the majority of such facilities being found along the navigable stretches of rivers.

Reservoirs on which moorings have been provided include two recently completed ones, Grafham Water (1964) and Rutland Water (1975). Similar facilities have also been proposed for Kielder reservoir, which is currently (1980) under construction. All three are large reservoirs with surface areas of 636, 1261 and 1087 hectares respectively and, although the first two are of the direct-supply type, the danger of pollution from motor-driven craft has been considered acceptable in view of the particular circumstances prevailing in each case, namely, that the stored water is derived from rivers and subsequently receives a correspondingly sophisticated form of treatment.

Mooring facilities can vary in size from those accommodating single vessels to those such as large marinas, catering for hundreds of boats. The capacity of a new development may be influenced by many factors, including the position and characteristics of the particular site, the size of the unsatisfied demand for moorings on the water concerned, and the capacity of the water to accommodate additional craft without becoming overcrowded.

As with slipways, mooring structures situated on rivers should be designed and constructed so as not significantly to obstruct or interfere with the flow of water. Their construction is also subject to the same consent requirements under the Land Drainage Act 1976.

All mooring structures should be constructed of materials which are suited to the type and characteristics of the particular water on which they are situated, in the same way as slipways, and similar considerations apply as in that case. It is also important, from a safety point of view, that walkway surfaces should have a non-slip finish, for example steel surfaces should preferably be of the open grillage type and concrete should have a tamped or wood float rather than a smooth steel-floated finish. For the same reason every effort should be made to reduce to a minimum the number of obstacles over which people using the walkway might trip. For instance, it might be possible to use mooring rings set flush with the surface, rather than bollards, for tying up the boats, or stringer-mounted fittings, instead of surface-mounted ones, so as to leave the deck clear and uncluttered.

Location and Layout

The location of moorings is affected generally by similar considerations to those which influence the position of slipways. In particular, shelter from strong winds, freedom from powerful currents, and the availability of an adequate area of adjoining land to accommodate car parks, boat parks, other ancillary facilities and, where appropriate, a clubhouse, are of considerable importance. On reservoirs, locations in potentially hazardous areas near draw-off towers, overflows, and gravity dams should be avoided and on rivers, moorings should be sited so as to ensure that boats secured to them do not interfere with navigation. Moorings situated on waters with fluctuating levels, which are intended for round-the-clock use, should be located where adequate depth is available below the lowest water level to accommodate the maximum draft of the largest boats likely to use them.

The layout of the moorings will vary with the type of water concerned. On narrow rivers they usually follow the line of the bank but, on wider stretches of water, jetties or stagings are sometimes constructed out from the bank in a variety of configurations. Whichever layout is adopted, ample space must be allowed for safe manoeuvring into and out of the berths. In this connection a minimum clear waterway 1.5 times the boat width will generally be required between parallel rows of moored boats to enable a single vessel to pass between the two. Similarly, a channel into which cruisers have to turn through 90° from their berths will need to have a width of at least 1.5 times the length of the boat. In a book on the development and design of marinas, Adie[18] illustrates a number of alternative layouts and also gives a wealth of information relevant to the planning, construction, and management of mooring facilities. Similar information can also be found in a book on the planning and administration of recreational buildings edited by Mills[19].

Different layouts possess different characteristics. Some are more economical than others in the length of jetty required to accommodate a given number of boats; some provide greater convenience for embarking and disembarking; some provide greater flexibility for accommodating boats of different length; and some achieve a greater mooring density than others, partly because of the variations in manoeuvring space required. The balance of advantage and disadvantage must be judged in each particular case in accordance with the circumstances obtaining at the individual site.

The number of craft which can be accommodated on a specific length of any type of structure will depend upon the size of boat involved and the method of mooring. Boat sizes can vary considerably, but the majority normally lie within the range 4 to 20 m long by 1.5 to 6 m wide. The usual methods of mooring are in a single row alongside the jetty or with the stern of the craft up to it. The first of these is more convenient for embarking or disembarking, but the second provides a greater number of berths per unit length of jetty. Vessels are sometimes moored alongside a jetty three or four abreast but, whilst this method also provides a greater mooring density, it suffers from the disadvantages that the crews of the outer boats have to clamber over the inner ones and that the boats are more difficult to manoeuvre in and out of position.

Types of Construction

Mooring structures are generally of three basic types:—

(1) Fixed jetties, quays, or landing stages;
(2) Floating jetties or piers connected to the bank by hinged walkways; or
(3) Posts, or anchored buoys or pontoons.

Fixed Moorings

The first type, i.e. fixed mooring structures, can be of either solid or framed construction, the former being more generally known as quays. They are most suited to locations with only small variations in water level, such as natural lakes or the lower, non-tidal reaches of navigable rivers. Where greater variations in level occur, steps, step irons, or ladders would be necessary to enable people to board and disembark from the boats and these could prove hazardous, particularly for the less athletic.

Quays, which form the boundary between water and land, must adequately support the ground on the landward side and consequently their walls must be properly designed for this purpose. A code of practice issued by the Institution of Structural Engineers on behalf of the Civil Engineering Codes of Practice Joint Committee[20], gives valuable practical guidance on the design and construction of the three basic types of earth retaining wall. The first is the sheet pile wall, which consists of close-fitting sheeting driven into the river or lake bed to a sufficient depth to ensure that it will not move forward or overturn under the pressures exerted by the bank. The piles may either act purely as cantilevers or may be tied back near the top to anchor piles or blocks set back an adequate distance into the bank. Steel or reinforced concrete piles are the ones in most general use although, for low walls, timber sheeting may occasionally be suitable. Their heads are usually encased in a concrete capping beam. The second type of retaining wall is the reinforced concrete cantilever, which consists of a vertical wall with an integral base projecting to one or both sides. A wall with a backward projecting base relies for its stability against overturning on the counterbalancing effect of the weight of the bank, whereas one with a forward projection relies solely upon its own weight. The third type, which also relies upon its self weight for stability, is the gravity retaining wall. This may be constructed of masonry, brick, or concrete, although gabions are sometimes used where there is a ready local supply of suitable stone for filling the baskets. A roadway or footwalk usually runs alongside the quay to provide access to the boats and this may be paved, surfaced with gravel, or decked with timber. Quay walls which jut out from the bank into the body of the water are almost invariably of similar construction to the gravity type of retaining wall.

Each type of quay wall can be constructed in many different forms. In both the Code of Practice[20] and the book by Adie[18], illustrations are given of the principle alternatives. Whatever type of construction is employed it is of prime importance that the base and ends of the wall should be adequately protected against the scouring effects of the water. This can be done by carrying the base of the wall down to a sufficient depth below bed level to prevent it being undermined, or by providing a suitable apron covering those areas of the adjoining bed which could otherwise be eroded, and by carrying back the ends of the wall an adequate distance into the bank.

Floating Moorings

Fixed jetties or landing stages of framed construction consist of a decking supported on a framework of piles and beams, the usual materials of construction being timber, reinforced concrete, or steel. This kind of structure may have advantages over the solid type in a number of situations, for example where poor ground conditions dictate the use of piled foundations or where it is important to minimize the degree of obstruction offered to the flow of water. It may be necessary in some cases to provide suitable protection to the bed and banks of the water in the vicinity of the structure, to prevent excessive local scouring caused by the turbulence created by water movement around the submerged frame members.

Floating mooring structures connected by walkway to the bank can, in general, satisfactorily accommodate greater changes in water level than fixed ones. They are, therefore, of more universal applicability and can normally be used in all but a small minority of circumstances. The considerations determining their layout and size are similar to those referred to ab"ve in respect of the fixed-type of mooring structure. The basic form of construction consists of floats hinged together in a variety of configurations to form a continuous walkway between land and boat. They are usually held in position laterally by piles or other anchoring devices placed at suitable intervals along their length. In some instances, where the material is satisfactory for the purpose, the surface of the float itself may form the decking, but in other cases, a separate deck, often supported on trimmers above the float, is necessary. The piles and decking are usually of timber, steel, or concrete but the floats are generally made of a wider range of materials including expanded polyurethane and glass reinforced plastics. In exceptional circumstances, it may be necessary, in order to prevent the landward end of the walkway becoming too steep at periods of low water, to support it at a level above the natural bed of the water area. This can be done in a number of ways, for example by providing stops on the anchor piles, separate ancillary piles, concrete strip footings, or small embankments at appropriate levels underneath the floats for them to rest upon.

Mooring Posts

The third category of mooring structure, i.e. the mooring post, buoy, or pontoon, differs from the other two in that access to the boats is by water rather than walkway, which brings with it a concomitant requirement for mooring or launching and, perhaps, parking, the tender craft necessary for this purpose. It is generally the cheapest type of structure to provide but, against this, in many situations must be considered the much lower mooring density normally possible with this kind of arrangement.

Mooring posts can satisfactorily cater for a similar range of water levels to those for which floating piers are suitable. They may consist of single posts, with boats on swinging moorings, or of a series of posts or piles to which the vessels can be secured fore and aft by slip moorings. In the former case the length of cable must be sufficient to allow for the variation in water levels, three or four times the difference in depth being usually adequate.

Buoys and pontoons to which boats are moored are normally held in position by cables or chains attached to suitable anchoring devices. They are usually capable of accommodating a greater range of water levels than other types of mooring system, and may, therefore, prove to be the most satisfactory ones for use on reservoirs subject to frequent, large fluctuations in depth. The length of anchor cable generally needs to be between four and six times the maximum depth of the anchorage point.

An alternative mooring arrangement used on non-tidal stretches of river is the buoy anchored to the bank by means of a simple hinged or pivoted frame.

ASSOCIATED FACILITIES

The extent of facilities, equipment, and services associated with a particular set of moorings will depend, largely, upon its type and size and can vary from a negligible level of provision in the case of simple mooring posts to an extremely comprehensive one in the case of a large marina development. It can include, *inter alia*, any or all of the following:—

Administrative, clubhouse and overnight accommodation
Restaurant, refreshment, and toilet facilities
Car, boat, and trailer parks
General stores, chandleries, and boat salerooms
Workshops for the repair and maintenance of boats
Storage facilities for maintenance equipment, sails and spars, outboard motors, spares and small equipment, etc.
Hoists, cranes, winches, gantries, and other equipment for the launching, recovery and general handling of boats
Fire-fighting and life-saving equipment
Water supply, and sewage and refuse collection and disposal facilities
Electricity supply and telephones
Sales and storage facilities for fuels, lubricating oils, and bottled gas.

CLUBHOUSE ACCOMMODATION

The great majority of clubhouses on water-based recreational sites are connected with some form of boating such as sailing, cruising, or rowing, although they may, occasionally, be shared with angling clubs. The building is normally located close to the water, the mooring or landing facilities, and the boat park. Its situation should preferably be one from which a clear and unobstructed view, free from the sun's glare, can be obtained over the whole field of activity. The site should also possess sufficient space for a suitable car park adjoining.

The type of building provided depends, *inter alia*, upon the size and financial resources of the club and can vary, in practice, from a small, simple, demountable timber structure, through prefabricated buildings to a large clubhouse of conventional construction. Whatever its type, however, the materials used and the design should be such that the appearance of the clubhouse is aesthetically pleasing and in harmony with its surroundings. This objective can often be achieved by employing the traditional, local style of construction, although this is by no means essential, particularly with good, imaginative design.

Standard and Layout of Accommodation

The accommodation necessary will depend not only upon the size of the club's active membership, but also upon the number of social members and the extent of their activities. Basic facilities generally include a clubroom, a kitchen or kitchenette, male and female toilets, showers, lockers, changing and drying rooms, and one or more storerooms, but many clubhouses are also equipped with a "wet bar", where members can obtain refreshments without having to change to go into the main part of the clubhouse. The larger establishments may additionally be provided with an entrance hall or reception area, committee rooms, office, lecture rooms, first-aid and recovery rooms, snack bar, lounge bar, dining room or restaurant, viewing or sunbathing terrace, control tower, caretaker's flat and, occasionally, overnight accommodation. At clubs where the social activities extend to dances, parties and film shows, etc., a dance floor is usually incorporated in the clubroom, lounge bar or restaurant, as most appropriate, and projection equipment is provided. The latter can serve a dual purpose where instruction involving the use of training films is given on the premises.

The size of the clubhouse will depend basically upon the number of members and also upon the level of accommodation provided, which can vary considerably. As a consequence no general standards for the overall floor area required which would be of universal applicability are available, even in per capita terms. However, general guidance on the space requirements for individual rooms is available in a number of publications, including the book edited by Mills[19] on the planning of certain categories of public buildings, section 10 of which contains recommendations in respect of rooms of the same type as many of those normally found in sailing clubhouses and also discusses a number of factors affecting the choice of the most suitable dimensions.

In planning the internal layout of a clubhouse, careful consideration should always be given to the position of individual rooms in relation both to the building generally and to one another. This aspect of the design is of prime importance to the creation of conditions conducive to the optimum utilization of each room and to ease and economy of circulation throughout the building, which enable the clubhouse to fulfil its role in the most successful and effective manner. In large establishments the rational grouping together of rooms with connected functions into specific areas of the building can assist considerably in the achievement of this goal. Suitable groupings might well be of committee room(s), lecture room(s) and office(s) into a business area; clubroom, lounge, bar, restaurant, kitchen and viewing terrace into a social area; and changing rooms, toilets, showers, etc., into a changing area. An entrance hall can frequently be used with advantage to link the various areas together. Other relevant considerations include the necessity for direct external access to the changing area from the moorings and slipways, for ready access from the clubroom or lounge to the observation terrace, for these rooms to overlook the water and to be equipped with large observation windows to enable members not taking part at the time to watch the activities in progress.

Provision for Disabled

Today, increasing numbers of disabled people are taking part in sporting activities, including sailing, and this factor should also be taken into account, preferably in the initial stages of clubhouse design when the facilities to enable handicapped people to make full use of the building can often be incorporated at negligible additional cost. This is particularly the case with single-storey structures. The type of provision needed is the substitution of ramps with shallow gradients for steps, of doors about 1 m wide for those of standard width, the provision of suitable sanitary accommodation, incorporating the specially designed sanitary ware which is now available, of handrails, coat hooks, wash basins, mirrors and benches at convenient heights for wheelchair users, and of folding seats and non-slip floors in shower cubicles. General recommendations in respect of the facilities involved are set out in British Standard Code of Practice CP96[21], which contains diagrams illustrating various of the provisions which can be made.

Precautions Against Vandalism

The majority of clubhouses are sited in fairly isolated locations and, except for the few large ones which support resident staff, are left unoccupied and unattended for appreciable periods of time. These circumstances can present ideal opportunities to vandals although, fortunately and somewhat paradoxically, the very isolation of the buildings may, in itself, provide some degree of protection against their attentions, because it puts the clubhouse outside their normal sphere of activities and makes it less obvious as a target for them. Because of the apparently ever-increasing risk of damage from this cause it is, however, only prudent to ensure that the exterior of the building, at least, is made as vandal proof as is feasible, by the use of appropriate materials in its construction, some of which have been specially developed for the purpose. A number of possibilities in this direction are referred to in the Section on Ancillary Facilities (p. 119), together with other precautionary measures which can be taken to protect the various facilities against this type of activity.

STAFF ACCOMMODATION

Standard of Accommodation

The level of accommodation provided on site for the use of staff engaged upon the supervision and operation of recreational facilities varies greatly. On many small sites, manned only on an intermittent, part-time basis, no provision at all is made. On many others, accommodation is minimal and is seldom available exclusively for recreational purposes. Probably the most widespread example of this is the small reservoir site with limited facilities, where the reservoir keeper commonly combines recreational duties with his normal operational ones and uses the same premises for both functions. The accommodation available in these cases usually consists of a house in the reservoir grounds, normally incorporating a small office, stores for materials, plant, and equipment and, possibly, a small workshop area and a garage for any transport required.

On the larger sites, where staff is employed full-time on recreational duties, appropriate accommodation is normally provided specifically for their use. This is particularly the case at some of the more recent major reservoir and marina developments where the need for suitable premises has been appreciated from the outset of the scheme, enabling their planning to be integrated readily and advantageously with that of the project as a whole. The extent of the accommodation required varies with the numbers and types of staff employed, which, in turn, is primarily dependent upon the size and nature of the facilities provided and upon their overall layout. On a major reservoir development catering for the general range of facilities, it may include:—

Manager's office
Offices for senior personnel such as a recreation officer, chief warden, or engineer
Warden's or bailiff's office
General office
Reception area
Information and enquiry office
Ticket offices for the issue of tickets and permits for admission to the site, car parks, and
   nature reserves and for daily sailing or angling, etc.,
Meeting/lecture room
Kitchen
Messroom or canteen
Male and female toilets
Locker rooms
Rest room
First-aid room
Car parking space, and
Staff houses.

More specialized facilities such as outdoor pursuits centres, may have additional requirements.

The type of staff accommodation needed at a large marina is basically similar, in general, to that necessary at a major reservoir site, although there are a number of minor differences reflecting the narrower range of activities for which a marina normally caters. An example is the typical requirement for a berth reservation office rather than the ticket issuing offices found on reservoir sites. Fuel and chandlery sales points may also be provided at marinas, whereas this type of accommodation is exceptional on British reservoirs where the presence of motor-driven boats in sufficient numbers to justify their existence is extremely rare. Such points are, however, more common on the larger reservoirs in the United States of America, as reported by Johnstone and Brown as a result of a study tour on the amenity use of reservoirs in that country[22].

As in the case of clubhouses and other buildings, particularly on sites with a high amenity value, the appearance of the premises accommodating staff should be aesthetically pleasing and in harmony with their surroundings, both in style and scale. Construction materials are usually carefully chosen with this consideration in mind, and also with a view to providing the maximum degree of resistance to damage by vandals.

Location and Size of Premises

The location of the principal administrative accommodation will depend to some extent upon the characteristics and layout of each particular site, but a position from which the major facilities can be overlooked will generally be an advantage from the point of view of the supervision of the recreational activities involved. Where separate offices or kiosks are needed for the issuing of admission tickets, etc., they are usually, but not invariably, located at the entrance to the facilities for the use of which the ticket is required.

The size of individual premises varies considerably in accordance with the numbers and types of staff to be accommodated. At any particular location this is determined by the overall numbers involved and their necessary geographical distribution throughout the site. Within the buildings themselves, the size and other essential features of certain of the rooms are governed by a number of statutory public health, building, and local authority regulations, in the interests of public health and safety. These regulations are mandatory in many instances and their provisions must be adhered to with this type of accommodation as with any other. Examples are the Building Regulations and the Offices, Shops and Railway Premises Act 1963, which stipulates minimum sizes for offices although, in practice, these are usually exceeded.

Off-site Accommodation

Certain activities connected with the supervision and operation of recreational facilities inevitably take place off site, especially in the case of river-based recreation. These include the issue of rod and fishing licences, sailing permits, navigation licences, the registration of boats, and the provision of information and advice on many aspects of recreational activities. The work involved normally forms an integral part of the overall administrative and information functions of a water authority, although it is supplemented, generally, by the issue of rod and fishing licences from fishing tackle shops and, occasionally, from other local shops and post offices, where these are more conveniently situated. As a result, most of a water authority's share of the work is almost invariably carried out from office accommodation already provided at such places as head offices, divisional or district offices, depots, etc., and there is rarely more than a limited need for separate accommodation at other locations. Where such a need exists it is normally sufficient to provide a small office, complete with essential, domestic and sanitary facilities, for the use of the appropriate staff.

Off-site accommodation is sometimes also required for employees who may be engaged on intermittent, part-time supervision of a number of small unmanned sites. Such staff is usually based at a local operational depot and uses existing accommodation which may or may not be separate from that used for other purposes. Possible requirements are a small office, a garage, stores for materials, plant and equipment, a small workshop, and access to a messroom, locker room, drying room, sanitary facilities, etc.

4. SITE SERVICES

Electricity and water supplies are normally provided to all recreational facilities habitually frequented by large numbers of people. Both services are usually considered to be essential in the case of buildings such as clubhouses, large toilet blocks, information or interpretation centres, outdoor centres, etc., as well as at maintenance depots and other staff accommodation.

ELECTRICITY SUPPLIES

The great majority of recreational sites in this country are within reasonable distance of the nearest public electricity supply. As a consequence, and because a mains supply is also the most convenient one from an operational point of view, it is the kind almost invariably installed in practice. In the case of reservoirs, such a supply is often already available in the vicinity of the dam.

Electricity demand for recreational purposes is generally small, and mains capacity in the area will usually be adequate to cope with any increase in consumption from this type of use. However, consultation with the appropriate Electricity Board is advisable at an early stage in the development of additional facilities, as reinforcement of the local supply network may sometimes be necessary. This is particularly the case where large scale facilities or extensions are to be provided in sparsely populated areas. In estimating the loading requirement of any proposed project, account must be taken of the diversity factor, i.e. the ratio of actual loading to installed capacity, and of any likely future developments.

Where a number of scattered installations within a site are to be supplied, an internal distribution network is necessary and this may take the form of either an overhead or an underground system. The overhead type is generally the less expensive but can, in certain locations, appear unsightly. Where there is a danger of this type of construction detracting from the visual amenity of an area, it may well be worthwhile, for aesthetic reasons, to lay the cables underground.

Alternative sources of supply to mains electricity are available which may, in certain circumstances, be more economical. One of these, which has universal applicability, is diesel generation, and suitable plant covering a wide range of outputs is readily available. Control of the generators can be by hand, usually be means of push buttons, or automatic, with the set starting up when an electric lamp (other than a fluorescent tube) or other appliance is switched on and shutting down when the last item in use is switched off. Major disadvantages of this type of generator are that it is noisy and requires frequent attention. To avoid disturbance to visitors or nearby residents, it must be housed in a building with adequate acoustic insulation.

Another alternative is turbine generation, but the application of this type of plant is limited to reservoir sites where the continuous discharge of large quantities of water occurs. Many turbines have been installed at British reservoirs for local power generation, one example being at the Ladybower reservoir of the Severn-Trent Water Authority.

WATER SUPPLIES

At any recreational site, the use of water is almost entirely for domestic purposes and, in the interests of public health, it is important that a reliable supply, adequate in quantity and satisfactory in quality should be available. It is essential that the sources from which the water is obtained should be capable of meeting the peak daily demand, which normally occurs on Sundays and Bank Holidays during the summer or, in the absence of balancing storage, the maximum instantaneous demand resulting from the simultaneous use of a number of the fittings and appliances installed. The water must also receive suitable and effective treatment.

The mains and service pipes distributing the water to the points at which it is required must be designed to carry the maximum instantaneous flow likely to occur, with a reasonable allowance, where appropriate, for potential future increases. A method of assessing the probable demand from a group of fittings is set out in British Standard Code of Practice CP310[23] which, *inter alia*, also gives general guidance on what is considered to be good, standard practice on the design and maintenance of water supply systems and on the laying, jointing, inspection, and testing of mains and services to buildings.

Sources of Supply

Mains

A supply from the public distribution system provides the most satisfactory and trouble free source of water and, for this reason, is used wherever possible. In many instances, however, no treated water mains pass within a reasonable distance of the site and, on economic grounds, alternatives may have to be found. Where such sources are employed, care needs to be taken to protect them from pollution. A water supply hygiene booklet issued by the National Water Council[24], which brings up to date the Ministry of Housing and Local Government's 1967 Memorandum 221 entitled "Safeguards to be adopted in the Operation and Management of Waterworks", contains recommendations on the measures to be taken for their protection.

The principal alternatives sources in practice are:—

(a) springs;
(b) boreholes; and
(c) reservoirs themselves.

Rivers are not normally a feasible proposition because of the complexity of the treatment required.

Springs

Springs can be subject to considerable fluctuation in output and in water quality, so that great care is required in their selection to ensure suitability for supply purposes. Their minimum output usually occurs during periods of maximum recreational activity and it is important to establish that, at such times, their flows exceed the anticipated demand placed upon them, taking into account the effect of any storage capacity available in the supply system. This can best be done by gauging the flow over a series of prolonged dry periods. Similarly, the water quality should be determined by carrying out sufficient chemical and bacteriological tests on representative water samples to give a reliable indication of the overall standard. Where time does not permit adequate investigations to be made, expert advice should be sought on the springs' likely output and it's quality. Springs in upland areas frequently have the advantage that their elevation enables a supply to be given under gravity.

Boreholes

Boreholes, properly planned and constructed, normally provide a reliable supply of good and consistent quality. Their location is often crucial in that respect, and for this reason should be chosen only on the advice of a skilled and experienced specialist.

For the vast majority of recreational developments, there should be no difficulty (subject to licensing procedures) in obtaining adequate quantities of water from a borehole in any of the recognized aquifers, but pumping tests must be carried out to establish the output/water level relationship in every case. At the same time analyses of the water are necessary to ascertain that it is of suitable quality.

The construction of boreholes is usually carried out by specialist contractors, although at least one water authority has begun to develop its own expertise in this direction. Great care has to be taken to ensure the verticality of the hole to avoid subsequent operational difficulties during insertion and withdrawal of the pumping equipment.

Reservoirs

Where recreational developments take place at reservoirs, the reservoir itself may be utilized as a source of supply. The suitability of any such source is readily ascertainable for the majority of existing reservoirs from available water quality data going back over many years.

A supply from this type of source is completely secure so long as the water level is higher than the point of draw-off. Maximum reliability is, therefore, assured by taking the supply from the outlet pipework where practicable, and this is usually also the most convenient arrangement. A suitable pumping installation is essential since, with very few exceptions, the facilities supplied are situated above reservoir level.

Treatment

Treatment given to the water obtained from local sources varies with its individual characteristics and, generally, with the type of source involved. In all cases the advice of an experienced waterworks chemist should be sought. With spring and borehole sources it is normally only necessary to disinfect the water, but reservoir supplies generally require filtration, sometimes preceded by sedimentation. At some reservoirs, however, disinfection alone may be acceptable.

Package treatment plants manufactured by a number of equipment suppliers are available in a large range of capacities, as an alternative to plants of conventional construction where more extensive treatment than disinfection is required. For individual installations with only small demands, filters of diatomaceous earth may provide suitable treatment, if properly maintained.

SEWERAGE AND SEWAGE DISPOSAL

A foul sewerage system and a satisfactory means of sewage disposal are essential for all recreational facilities provided with a water supply for domestic or similar purposes. The quantities of sewage to be dealt with from all but the largest developments are small and, for this reason, it is rarely feasible to install an extensive sewerage system at a recreational site. As a result, relatively short lengths of drain or sewer leading to local disposal facilities are the rule rather than the exception.

A separate sewerage system may be installed for carrying surface water drainage from paved areas such as car parks and from the roofs of the larger buildings. The discharge is usually to soakaways or, if not subject to undesirable contamination, to the nearest watercourse.

Drains and Sewers

Wherever possible, drains and sewers are designed to operate as a gravity system and must be capable of conveying peak discharges under those conditions. For foul sewers serving a group of facilities, the peaks coincide with and approximate to maximum instantaneous water demands. For smaller individual facilities, they can exceed this figure because the rate of discharge from certain fittings can be considerably higher than the filling rate. This is notably the case with W.C. cisterns, and, where these are installed, the minimum peak flow in the sewer is likely to be about 1.5 l/sec.

Part N of the Building Regulations[25] sets out certain requirements which must be observed in relation to the drainage system from buildings, and the British Standard Code of Practice CP 2005[26] indicates what is considered to be good practice in the design and construction of sewers, manholes, storm overflows, and other associated works.

Within the catchment areas of direct-supply reservoirs, particular care should be taken to prevent pollution of the water by sewage. For this reason, at vulnerable points such as crossings over feeder streams, pipes of ductile rather than brittle material should be used, and nearby manholes should have sealed covers.

SEWAGE TREATMENT AND DISPOSAL

The most satisfactory means of disposal of the sewage from recreational facilities is to the public sewers but, because many sites are in isolated positions this is not always possible or feasible. The basic alternative disposal systems available are:—

(i) Small conventional treatment plants
(ii) Septic tanks, and
(iii) Cesspools or storage tanks.

All of them can be obtained in prefabricated form, and these have the advantage over plants of traditional construction that they are usually less conspicuous and more odour free. In addition, where they are employed intermittently, for example in connection with recreational facilities which are used on a seasonal basis only, they also have the important advantage that they can be brought back into full operation after a period out of use, quicker than traditional types. They may, however, be more expensive to install and their operating costs can be substantially higher.

All three types of installation should be located a reasonable distance away from the facilities which they serve and at a level which, preferably, will permit the sewage from those premises and from possible future developments on the site, to gravitate to the plant. At the same time they should not be located in a position where they could be subject to flooding or where there would be difficulties in providing suitable road access for the removal of sludge or the contents of cesspools.

Conventional Works

Conventional sewage treatment plants are of two main types, those based on biological filters and those based upon the activated sludge principle. Neither of them is normally used in connection with small scale developments because, amongst other things, their operation and maintenance requirements are more demanding than those of the alternative installations. Within the two types of plant there are a number of different systems, the choice of which will depend upon the specific circumstances of each individual site. The principal ones are described in British Standard Code of Practice CP 302[27], which sets out guidelines as to what is accepted as being good practice in the design, construction, and maintenance of such installations. A Water Research Centre report, TR 107[28], gives details of the equivalent package treatment plants and discusses their selection to suit particular conditions.

Septic Tanks

Septic tanks are probably the type of treatment plant most commonly found on the majority of recreational sites. They consist of a tank or, preferably, two tanks in series, in which the sewage solids are settled out and retained under anaerobic conditions whilst the effluent is discharged. They are not, in themselves, sufficient to produce an effluent of Royal Commission standard. If this quality is to be achieved, secondary treatment is necessary and this usually takes the form of biological filtration, followed by further settlement in humus tanks. Exceptionally, some form of tertiary treatment such as sand filtration, land irrigation, or settlement in lagoons may also be provided. Disposal of the final effluent can be to stream, to underground strata via soakaways or subsurface irrigation located above the highest level of the water table, or, less commonly, to the land surface. Both CP 302[27] and TR 107[28] deal at some length with the design, construction, and maintenance of this type of installation, and regulation N 17 of the Building Regulations[25] contains requirements relating to their siting and construction.

The location of conventional and septic tank installations and the position of their final effluent discharges is doubly important where recreational sites within the catchments of direct-supply reservoirs or immediately upstream of river intakes are concerned. In these circumstances the treatment plant and the discharge arrangements should be situated outside the catchment or downstream of the intake, respectively. The sludge should similarly be disposed of outside those sensitive areas.

Cesspools or storage tanks are generally suitable for only the smallest scale developments or for single scattered elements of a larger development. The impervious type, which is essentially a watertight storage tank, is the preferred one in all circumstances and, where there is the slightest risk of contamination of water destined for drinking purposes, no other type should be considered. The capacity of the cesspool should be sufficient to contain all the foul sewage likely to be discharged to it at peak periods of activity on the site, between consecutive emptyings. This type of installation is the simplest one from an operational point of view, since it requires the minimum of supervision and attention, but care must be taken to ensure that the tank is always emptied before it starts to overflow. The contents should always be disposed of outside water supply catchment areas and are usually conveyed by the emptying vehicle to the nearest sewage treatment works. Requirements as to the construction and siting of cesspools are contained in regulation N 17 of the Building Regulations[25], and a guide to good practice in their design and construction is set out in British Standard Code of Practice CP 302.200[29].

Chemical Closets

On recreational sites where the level of activity is generally low, for example those catering largely for angling, it is quite common to provide toilet facilities in the shape of chemical closets spaced out at suitable intervals along the water's edge and set back a reasonable distance from it. The closets are usually housed in small wooden buildings of the "sentry box" type and require frequent, regular emptying. The contents should be disposed of to holding tanks, sewers, or sewage treatment works. On navigable rivers, disposal points for the reception of the contents of the chemical closets installed on cruising craft are provided at marinas and, often, at strategic points along the river banks. They usually take the form of sluices housed in small buildings and discharging to holding tanks or direct to sewer. Holding tanks merely provide storage for the toilet contents, and must themselves be emptied at suitable intervals. Provision may need to be made for diluting the contents of the tanks, or of the closets themselves where direct disposal is practised, by several volumes of water or sewage, before discharge to the sewer or the sewage works, to prevent the chemicals interfering with the treatment process.

WASTE AND RUBBISH DISPOSAL

Waste and rubbish on recreational sites consists almost solely of litter left by visitors or of refuse from facilities such as clubhouses, refreshment kiosks, or administrative accommodation catering for their various needs.

Litter

There is considerable divergence of opinion as to the most effective way of dealing with the problem of litter. One point of view is that adequate litter bins should always be provided, but holders of the opposite viewpoint maintain that the presence of these receptacles in itself encourages the haphazard deposition of rubbish around the site and so discourages what is, in their eyes, the much more desirable practice of taking it home. There is, however, general agreement that a clean and tidy site is likely to deter people from scattering litter indiscriminately and, regardless of whichever policy is adopted, care should be taken to ensure that the site is constantly maintained in a tidy condition. This may involve frequent inspection and collection of a variety of discarded items left on the ground, as well as the emptying of litter bins before they overspill.

Litter bins, where provided, are usually sited at points such as picnic areas, car parks, toilets, and refreshment facilities, where the greatest concentration of visitors occurs. They need to be readily visible to be effective and should be as attractive as possible. A large selection of proprietary makes in a variety of materials is available, and the final choice for each location will depend upon a number of factors. The design and material chosen should be appropriate to the surroundings, for example bins with a rustic timber finish may be more pleasing aesthetically at a woodland picnic site than concrete, wire-work, or fibreglass ones.

The overall capacity of the bins required will be governed both by the number of visitors using the particular facility, and the frequency of collection. In general, on a large site, it is preferable to have a greater number of smaller bins strategically situated throughout the area rather than a smaller number of larger receptacles, owing to the natural reluctance of visitors to carry their rubbish any great distance. In exposed locations where litter may be scattered by the wind from open bins, or in places where birds or animals could cause the same disturbance, litter bins with lids should be provided. Recommendations on their siting, selection, installation, servicing, and maintenance are given in British Standard Specification BS 4324[30].

These matters are also discussed in some detail both in the Countryside Commission's booklet on picnic sites[15] and in Elizabeth Beazley's book[14]. The two types of bin most generally suited to the majority of recreational sites, because of the ease and convenience with which they can be emptied with minimum risk of the litter being blown away, are those in which the rubbish is contained in a disposable plastic bag or paper sack, or in a removable wire mesh, plastic, or sheet metal container. The former type tends to be somewhat unsightly in appearance and may not be suitable on that account in a number of locations.

Refuse

Refuse produced from all but the largest recreational premises, where bigger receptacles may be necessary, is usually stored in conventional dustbins adjacent to the buildings themselves and, preferably, concealed from the general view of visitors.

5. ANCILLARY FACILITIES

GENERAL

Ancillary facilities can probably best be defined as those which play an essentially supporting role to the ones used directly for recreational purposes. In general, they provide services which contribute to the wellbeing and enjoyment of visitors making use of the principal facilities, and may include toilets, information and interpretation centres, outdoor play areas for children, shops, cafes, ticket offices, shelters, and observation hides.

Their numbers, types and sizes vary considerably from one site to another, toilet facilities being, understandably, by far the ones most commonly provided. The remaining types, in contrast, are generally found only on the comparatively small number of larger sites, or on those possessing a feature of exceptional interest.

BUILDINGS

Buildings of some kind are an essential component of most types of ancillary facility. It is equally as important to the preservation of the amenity of the locality that such buildings should blend in with their surroundings, as it is with all other premises on the site.

The problem of their successful integration into the landscape is an extremely complex one, which requires a skilled and sensitive approach if the most satisfactory results are to be achieved. Of the many factors which may enter into consideration of the problem, a number are of general applicability. One of these is the aesthetic aspect of location. It would obviously, for instance, be inappropriate in almost every conceivable circumstance, to place a building on the skyline where it would be silhouetted starkly against a much lighter background. A far better solution would be to set it against a backdrop of trees or even a hillside, where it would be far less conspicuous. Another important factor is the relative scale of the structures. Small buildings scattered around a site can often detract from its amenity value, especially where there is a general lack of cover. This undesirable possibility can sometimes be avoided by combining the buildings together or incorporating them into a larger one, such as an administrative block where this is convenient. As a rule also, the style, materials, and general colouring of the buildings should be in harmony with the character of the site and that of the immediate locality. Too much variety in these particular details is usually best avoided, since it tends to promote disharmony and to distract the eye.

On many sites, existing buildings are available which already harmonize well with their surroundings. Such structures may often be adapted for the required use with considerable advantage, in preference to constructing entirely new ones.

VANDALISM

By their very nature, ancillary facilities in general are used quite intensively by visiting members of the public. As a result, the associated buildings and equipment frequently suffer abnormal amounts of damage through exceptional wear and tear, accidents, or vandalism. Of these, vandalism, i.e. deliberate destruction, is unfortunately assuming greater and greater proportions at the present time, to such an extent that, in some cases, it can account for the majority of the damage sustained. It is, therefore, becoming a factor increasingly to be taken into consideration at all stages of the development and use of both recreational and ancillary facilities.

Whilst it is never possible to eliminate damage altogether, a number of measures can be taken to limit it to the minimum practicable, in the interests of reducing both consequential maintenance costs and inconvenience to users. Care must, however, be taken not to create a "fortress" from which escape is difficult in an emergency. At the development stage, for example, wear and vandal resistant materials, equipment, and features can be incorporated to lessen potential damage from all three of the causes referred to above. In this connection, close consultation between the architect or designer and the undertaker's maintenance staff is essential to ensure that the benefits of the latter's valuable practical experience are taken full advantage of. Similarly, once construction of the facility has been completed, adequate supervisory measures and prompt attention to repairs will usually prove effective means of discouraging damage by vandals.

It is only possible here to touch briefly upon a few of the many considerations involved at the design stage which can appreciably affect the susceptibility of a building to vandalism. A Design Council book[31] deals at greater length with the problem of vandalism and covers the social background to the type of behaviour involved, as well as suggesting examples of precautionary measures which can be taken against damage to a wide range of structural elements and equipment.

Probably the most important considerations are those concerning the exterior detailing and the particularly vulnerable elements such as glazing, wall surfaces, and fittings. Careful detailing of the external features of a building can significantly reduce the likelihood of damage. Unnecessary projections and ledges which facilitate climbing, are best avoided, as are exposed drainpipes, hidden corners, large accessible glazed areas, flimsy fittings, and lightweight, partition-type walling etc. The latter is also best avoided on internal walls. In general, simple robust construction is desirable. External doors should be of solid construction, with locks to British Standard BS: 3621[32], and the opening lights of windows should preferably be lockable with their maximum opening width restricted to 125 mm by mechanical means, to make entry to the building as difficult as possible during periods when it is unsupervised or unoccupied.

Glazed areas are exceptionally vulnerable to damage. The avoidance of low level glazing and the use of small panes of glass will make maintenance cheaper and easier and, in locations where its appearance is acceptable, wired glass may also help. Increasingly, however, use is being made of toughened or laminated glass or of substitutes such as polycarbonates, acetates and polyesters, sometimes bonded with steel mesh. These substitutes are virtually unbreakable but suffer from the disadvantages that they can easily be scratched, tend to discolour in sunlight, and require special care in fitting because of their high coefficient of expansion. Also, they are at present expensive.

Surfaces, especially those of walls, are also very vulnerable, in this case to defacement by graffiti. Perhaps the most effective type of facing for areas likely to suffer from this type of attack is a durable, heavy duty, textured and glazed ceramic tile of which there are a number on the market. These are not readily marked or scratched, and they can almost invariably be easily cleaned with proprietary solvent cleaners without leaving unsightly stains. They are also attractive in appearance but will not be suitable for all the surfaces at risk. Rough surfaces such as stone, rough textured brick, and rough cast are often less tempting to vandals but are more difficult to clean if defaced. For these and other surfaces, special paints and protective sealing coatings are available, together with solvents for removing any graffiti which may appear. It is important to ensure that any solvent used is compatible with the protective coating, otherwise the surface may be damaged.

A number of fittings such as lights, door furniture, coat hooks, mirrors, and sanitary ware are also favourite targets for vandals. In general, such items should be of strong, durable and non-corrodible construction with tough, smooth surfaces and concealed fastenings. Lighting installations can best be protected by using recessed fittings with polycarbonate luminaires and siting them out of easy reach. With door furniture, knobs are less readily damaged than lever handles and are generally to be preferred for that reason. For situations in which the incidence of vandalism has been found by experience to be excessive, or, from knowledge of the area is expected to be so, sanitary fittings of stainless steel are available and are worthy of consideration. The building of plumbing and other pipework into the structure, where possible, is usually also worthwhile. Damage to sanitary fittings and pipework often results in the escape of water, and a useful further precaution which may be advisable is to construct the floors of sanitary facilities with suitable falls to gulleys or channels to minimize any consequential damage to the building through flooding.

Once a building is in use, adequate supervision will help to deter vandals. Fortunately, on recreational sites operated by water undertakers, supervision is seldom required on a continuous basis. In the rare situations where it is, for example where persistent vandalism or theft occurs, or where a valuable exhibit is on permanent display at an interpretation centre, the facility may well be manned during the day with reliance being placed upon intruder alarms, occasionally incorporating closed-circuit television surveillance systems, for protection during the night.

Intruder alarms can be either audible or silent. The former types are intended to scare off potential miscreants before they can do any damage, whilst the latter are designed to alert appropriate members of the undertakers' staff or the police to their presence so that preventative action can be taken. They do this by transmitting an alarm signal and/or message over telephone lines connected to either staff houses on site, to a continuously manned control room, or to the local police station as pre-arranged. There are many different kinds of alarm system available ranging from the "very" simple to the highly complex, activated by an equally bewildering array of triggering devices, some of which are listed in the Design Council's book[31]. They all suffer to some degree from a tendency to send out false alarms, and they require require regular servicing and maintenance.

Because of the costs involved, the installation of such a system should not be embarked upon lightly. The advice of experts will in any event be needed, because of the specialized nature of the knowledge required to select the most suitable system to fit the particular circumstances of each individual case. The crime prevention officer of the local police force is usually in a good position to give such advice, and is often called in for this purpose.

PROVISION FOR THE DISABLED

Another general point which must be considered in the design of the majority of ancillary facilities, is provision for the disabled, referred to in more detail in the section on Clubhouse Accommodation, p. 109 of this Chapter. The inclusion of such provision is particularly important with this type of facility, especially so in the case of toilets, since they tend to present greater difficulties to larger numbers of disabled people than do most other facilities on the site.

In addition to general considerations, there are others with specific applicability to individual types of ancillary facility. A number of these are briefly outlined below for certain of the more frequently encountered facilities.

TOILETS

The provision of public toilets is essential on many water-based recreational sites for the maintenance of hygienic conditions and the prevention of water pollution. This is particularly the case on sites subjected to intensive use or catering for long stay activities. Toilets should, ideally, be so situated that the visitor can always find one within easy reach. On the larger scale developments, this will inevitably necessitate the provision of a number of lavatories, strategically positioned throughout the site. Such developments often incorporate a series of separate recreational facilities, and a suitable overall distribution can sometimes be achieved by consciously providing each one with its own toilet accommodation.

On intensively used sites, toilets are most commonly located near other facilities such as car parks, picnic areas, slipways and the like, where the greatest concentration of visitors occurs. In this type of situation they usually take the form of toilet blocks because of the necessity of accommodating large numbers of people. Where use is less intensive but relatively continuous, such as by anglers on the banks of reservoirs, it is normally sufficient to provide individual chemical closets spaced out at suitable intervals.

It is difficult to generalize about the numbers of WCs, urinals, and wash basins required in toilet blocks, since these will depend upon several factors which vary in individual cases. They include the number of visitors using the recreational facility which the block is designed to serve, and the length of their stay on site. Each case, therefore, needs to be considered on its merits. A related point, often overlooked, is the desirability of establishing a satisfactory ratio of male to female toilets. In this respect, it should not be lost sight of that women usually take the responsibility of looking after children and tend to take the young ones of both sexes to the ladies lavatories. As a consequence, where families form a large proportion of visitors, the provision for females needs to be correspondingly greater than that for males.

For toilets serving picnic area, car parks and other general facilities, the following provision, calculated on the basis of the maximum simultaneous number of visitors expected to use the facility, should normally prove adequate:—

Males	Females
1 No. for the first 200	1 No. for the first 100
2 No. for 200—500	2 No. for 100—250
3 No. for 500—1000	3 No. for 250—500
plus 1 No. per 800 above 1 No. urinal for 50	plus 1 No. per 400 above

Toilet accommodation attached to camp sites, clubhouses, etc., will need to be considerably more generous, possibly as high as 1 WC per 20 females and 1 per 30 males plus urinals.

With chemical closets where the volume of use is light, the numbers required are usually determined solely by the distances which visitors have to walk to reach them. These should obviously not be so great as to discourage use being made of the facilities.

Toilet blocks should not be obtrusive but, at the same time, for obvious reasons their location should be readily apparent to potential users. Prominent positions near the entrance to the recreational facilities they serve, have the advantage that the whereabouts of the blocks are usually noted by visitors on their arrival, so rendering subsequent searching unnecessary. On the larger picnic areas, car parks, etc., signposting may, in addition, be required.

It is important to ensure that public toilets can be maintained in a fully operational and hygienic condition with the minimum of attention. They should be easily cleaned, well ventilated and light, with a high degree of resistance to damage whether deliberate or accidental.

Cleaning can be facilitated by keeping the floors as clear of obstructions as practicable and by constructing them with suitably sloping impervious surfaces, leading to drains set into the floor, for ease of washing down. For the same reason, wall finishes should also be impervious. A further aid to cleanliness is the rounding of all angles, at least between walls and floors, with an integral coving. Needless to say the floors should be non-slip as well as impervious, in the interests of safety and hygiene. A number of surfaces are suitable in both respects, including quarry tiles and granolithic concrete.

Most toilets on recreational sites are unattended and, therefore, are particularly susceptible to damage from vandalism. As a consequence, it is doubly important that the steps outlined previously should be taken to combat this possibility. Windows, wall surfaces, sanitary fittings, exposed pipework, and light fittings are exceptionally vulnerable in this type of installation.

On sites where intensive use is only seasonal, it may not be necessary to provide permanent toilet facilities. In such cases, consideration could well be given to employing purpose-built mobile trailers which could be removed in winter for repair and overhaul. There are several suitable, proprietary makes on the market and such an arrangement has the advantage of avoiding damage by vandals during the off-season as well as, generally, being appreciably cheaper to provide than an equivalent permanent on-site structure.

INFORMATION AND INTERPRETATION CENTRES

On the larger sites, or on those which contain a feature of special interest, information and/or interpretation centres are usually considered to be desirable assets.

The principal purpose of the former type of centre is to provide visitors with information, usually in the form of descriptive pamphlets, booklets, and maps, as to what the site has to offer in recreational terms. The most essential feature of such a centre is a counter or desk at which the relevant literature can be obtained and where, preferably, knowledgeable staff is available to answer queries and to give advice.

Interpretation centres, on the other hand, seek to explain various aspects of the site or of particular features of it, with a view to widening the visitors' appreciation and understanding of his surroundings and so stimulating a greater interest in them.

Suitable subjects for interpretation may include both historical and present-day human activities, buildings and other structures, archeological remains, geological features, flora, fauna, the effects of social and economic change etc., but rarely, if ever, will any of these be of equal importance on any particular site. Information might also be provided, in the case of reservoirs, on the primary function of the reservoir and works, and on the details of their construction. This is often a good public relations exercise.

The heart of an interpretation centre generally consists of an exhibition area where photographs, diagrams, sketches, models, specimens, artefacts, maps or descriptions illustrative of the chosen subjects can be displayed. At the more sophisticated centres, audio visual displays may be either incorporated into the exhibition area or, if sufficiently large, housed in a separate room set aside specially for the purpose. To be effective, the entire display should be eyecatching, not too extensive and arranged, ideally, in such a way that the visitor is automatically led from one exhibit to the next in orderly progression, without conscious effort on his part. Descriptive notices are best kept as brief as possible, consistent with providing adequate information, in order not to bore the visitor with too much detail. In this way, the formation of irritating circulatory bottlenecks, through people having to stop for relatively lengthy periods to read them, is also avoided.

Interpretation is usually confined to subjects specifically related to the site, so as to avoid the danger of turning the centre into a general countryside museum for which it may be far from suitable, both in size and location, and for which the necessary expertise may not be readily available amongst a water undertaker's regular staff. On a site possessing a multiplicity of potential subjects, it may well be worth while concentrating only on those which are of greater significance or public interest and dealing with them in a comprehensive manner, rather than attempting to cover the whole spectrum of possibilities less thoroughly.

On some of the larger sites, the information or interpretation centre may sometimes be combined with other facilities such as toilets, ticket office, and cafés to form a complex often referred to as a visitor centre.

Information and interpretation are generally required at the beginning of a visit rather than at the end and, for this reason, the associated facilities are usually situated near the entrance to either the site, or a car park or picnic area, as may be most appropriate in the prevailing circumstances. The principal exception to this rule is where the interpretation centre is, for greater effectiveness, located adjacent to the point of interest which it seeks to illuminate.

OUTDOOR PLAY AREAS

Outdoor play areas for children are sometimes provided on recreational developments, most frequently in conjunction with camping or caravan sites, but also, occasionally, near car parks, picnic areas and similar facilities where large numbers of families are likely to spend appreciable periods. They may take the form of adventure playgrounds or of the more traditional type complete with swings and slides, etc., the former generally blending in better with natural surroundings and the latter with more formal ones.

The equipment for adventure playgrounds can be of the simplest kind. Old tree trunks, climbing frames made from logs, swings from old tyres, etc., are usually quite suitable and have the advantages of cheapness and of requiring the minimum of maintenance. Sandpits and shallow ponds are also in keeping with this type of play area, although the latter can present dangers to toddlers unless adequately supervised.

Equipment for the more traditional kind of playground is, of necessity, more expensive, both to purchase and to maintain. It is also generally more dangerous because of its essentially mechanical nature and it is, therefore, important to ensure that this factor is taken fully into account when assessing the suitability of the alternatives available. Most manufacturers nowadays produce equipment which incorporates safety features such as rubber seats for swings, one piece surfaces for slides, effectively secured covers over moving parts, etc., from which a satisfactory choice can usually be made. In the same cause, constructional details such as rounded edges and non-slip surfaces for paddling pools are often adopted, and slides can sometimes be built on a suitable natural or artificial slope, only just above ground level so as to obviate the risk of injury to children falling off them.

TICKET OFFICES

On some recreational developments offices are provided for the issue of admission tickets to individual facilities or to the site as a whole; or of licences and permits in connection with a variety of activities including angling, sailing, and birdwatching. Such offices are generally to be found only on the larger sites where the value of the tickets sold justifies the employment of the necessary staff, or on those where this duty is undertaken voluntarily by members of clubs or other bodies interested in the particular activities concerned. In other cases, ticket machines are sometimes installed as an alternative, on the grounds of economy.

The size of office required will depend upon the number of staff involved, but often, in practice, need only be sufficient to provide adequate accommodation for one person. The type of building can vary from a wooden hut to a structure of more permanent materials and may stand alone or form part of a larger unit such as an information centre, clubhouse or administrative block, depending upon prevailing circumstances at the particular site. On recreational developments with only seasonal demands, it may be an advantage to install offices of prefabricated construction (of which many types are readily available on the market) so that they can be removed during the off-season for repair and to obviate damage by vandals when the site is unfrequented. Adequate heating is desirable in view of the sedentary nature of the work carried out in these offices and, frequently, because of their exposed locations.

Perhaps the single most important factor to be considered in relation to the provision of ticket offices is their location. This will be influenced to some extent by the purpose which the tickets serve and by certain site characteristics such as size, the number of individual facilities for which tickets are required and their proximity to each other, and by the number of separate access points. On a compact site with only one access, a single office near the site entrance is probably the best arrangement but, on a large site with a number of scattered facilities or with multiple entrances, separate offices, each serving one individual facility or a group of facilities will usually be preferable. For obvious reasons all ticket offices should be located in conspicuous positions near the facilities with which they are concerned, with those issuing admission tickets situated at the entrance to the facility or the site, as the case may be.

SHELTERS

Shelters strategically located around a recreational site can prove a great boon to the visitor, adding considerably to his enjoyment and comfort. They may provide protection from the elements, whether from the sudden unexpected storm or, in more favourable climates, the heat of the sun; or, a welcome resting place in which either to recuperate during or after strenuous exercise, to watch the various activities in progress, or merely to sit and admire the view. They are especially valuable at the ends and, where appropriate, at the intermediate points along footpaths and trails, at some picnic areas and viewpoints, and at bathing and outdoor play areas.

By virtue of their primary functions, many shelters, particularly those intended for the use of hikers, are isolated and therefore exceptionally exposed to the dangers of vandalism. For this reason they are usually best kept as simple as possible with the bare minimum of fixtures and fittings and are generally robustly constructed, preferably without windows. In the less isolated locations more elaborate structures may occasionally be warranted.

Shelters should, in general, be orientated so as to afford maximum protection from the prevailing wind. This is not, however, always practicable. The direction which shelters whose main purpose is to provide a viewing platform face, will, for instance, necessarily be dictated by the bearing of the scene or the activity to be observed from them, rather than by wind direction.

Shelters whose principal function is to provide protection from the elements will also need to afford an acceptable degree of protection from winds blowing from other quarters. There are many designs in existence which satisfactorily fulfil this requirement. A particularly interesting example, because of its simplicity and compactness, is the one developed by the United States of America National Park Service specifically for the use of hikers, which takes the form, in plan, of a swastika.

HIDES

Hides are an invaluable aid to the successful observation of wildlife in its natural habitat. Not only do they provide shelter for the observer in inclement weather and that modicum of comfort essential for long periods of concentrated observation, but they also enable him to watch the behaviour of birds and animals in an undisturbed state, unaffected by his presence.

The hides should be carefully sited, on the expert advice of ornithologists, zoologists, etc., preferably of those possessing detailed knowledge of the individual site or its immediate surroundings. Generally, where possible, their orientation should be such that the sun will be behind the observer during the more important viewing periods, even at the expense of the hide having to be located somewhat further away from the wildlife under observation than would otherwise be necessary.

It is also important that watchers approaching and leaving the hide should be adequately screened from the view of the creatures concerned, so that their movements will go undetected and cause no disturbance to normal wildlife activity. Natural screening of the approach with trees and bushes is generally preferable, but earth banks, walls, and fences of close-boarded timber or of hessian are also often used, especially in exposed locations where natural cover would be out of place or difficult to establish.

Hides are normally of simple but robust construction. The most common material used is probably wood, which is generally the one most in harmony with the surroundings of this type of facility. In damp situations however, stone, brick, or blockwork must be used for those parts of the structure coming into regular contact with water.

Good detailing can add greatly to the success of a hide. It is, for example, essential to ensure that, in the interests of comfort, the floor is so constructed that it does not puddle in wet weather and that the entrance is covered with a hessian or other flexible screen to prevent the movement of people into and out of the hide being observed by the wildlife, against the lighter background of bright woodland, field or sky. A book by Elizabeth Beazley[14] contains valuable guidance on many practical details of this type of structure, based upon the Slimbridge Wildfowl Trusts' long experience of their use.

6. CONSERVATION ASPECTS

As public authorities generally have become owners or managers of large acreages of land their obligations as custodians of the environment for future generations have become increasingly important. This was first underlined legislatively in Section 11 of the Countryside Act 1968 and confirmed, in the case of the water industry, in Section 22 of the Water Act 1973. These Acts impose a duty to protect features of special interest wherever possible or, when this cannot be done, at least to give responsible agencies the chance either to remove such features for preservation elsewhere, or to record them *in situ* before they are lost. This obligation embraces features of natural history or scientific interest, buildings and other objects of architectural, archaeological, or historic interest, the protection of scenic beauty, and access to open countryside.

The recreational planner needs to look at conservation in two ways:—

(1) In considering what recreational activities to accommodate at any site he should establish whether there are any features worthy of conservation and how these might be affected by recreational use.

(2) In deciding what to do with any such features he should consider, as one of the options, how they might be used for recreational purposes.

Historic and Architectural Features

The possibility may occur on some sites of finding a compatible recreational use for ecological features of conservation interest. They could, for instance, perhaps be utilized for educational purposes. It is more likely to arise, however, with features of historic, architectural, or archaeological interest where adaptation for some recreational use may be an additional argument in favour of their protection or rehabilitation. It may mean that interesting remains need not be maintained as empty relics but can take on some contemporary function which might also produce an income to contribute towards their upkeep. Such a feature might well become a museum, an exhibition or display centre, a clubhouse for a recreational activity, or accommodation incidental to recreational use (offices, stores, workshops, etc.), either standing alone or as an incidental part of the recreational development of a larger property. At worst it might be dismantled and its matererials used in some new structure on site, the use of exterior materials in particular being helpful in blending new buildings into scenically important landscapes.

It is important when considering the future recreational use of any property (as with any other form of development or maintenance work) to identify at the outset the features of conservation interest that exist, why they are important, and to what extent they are sensitive to change. Such features may be of local, national, or even international importance depending, *inter alia*, upon whether their occurrence is common, rare or indeed unique. Whilst architectural features can usually be recognized, historic or archaeological features may be hidden and may not in fact be discovered except by chance during the course of excavation work, in which case emergency action to preserve or to record and remove them may become necessary. Most buildings and archaeological sites of importance will already be included as listed buildings or scheduled ancient monuments in official or semi-official registers and will accordingly enjoy varying degrees of protection. Local Planning Authorities will normally have comprehensive records or be able to direct enquirers to the relevant statutory and voluntary organizations.

ECOLOGICAL FEATURES

Features of ecological importance may not immediately be apparent, but reference to the appropriate regional office of the Nature Conservancy Council will normally produce the required information and may lead to further investigatory work by the Council or appropriate voluntary organizations. Lists of Sites of Special Scientific Interest and statutory Nature Reserves are readily available, and are often supplemented by information on less official but nevertheless important sites. These lists are updated from time to time, but a substantial amount of survey and analytical work is needed and it may be that the conservation bodies faced with a proposal to develop a particular area will wish to initiate a specific survey to determine the importance or otherwise of the site concerned. Areas or local features of particular scenic importance will be readily identified by Local Planning Authorities, who work in close liaison with the Countryside Commission.

A different situation arises where a new water feature, typically a new lake or reservoir, is being created. Unless entirely artificial in construction this can be expected to have some conservation value, and it will be important to agree with the conservation interests at the outset in what way and to what extent the new feature is likely to be of value and how this can be best achieved and safeguarded.

In deciding the location of, defining the boundaries of, or determining the acceptable degree of access to sites of scientific and ecological importance certain factors need to be borne in mind:—

(a) Wildlife needs a refuge into which it can retreat if necessary and remain undisturbed. Such a refuge may need to be the whole of a particular site or perhaps only a part of it, but the size will depend on the wildlife species concerned, the likely degree of interference, and the availability of other refuges nearby.

(b) The need to protect a refuge may vary according to the time of year and it may be feasible to reduce or necessary to expand its area at certain times. It is not always possible to be specific about the timing of such changes, however, as variations in seasonal weather can significantly advance or retard natural processes through the year.

(c) The more varied the environment in a nature reserve the more, in most circumstances, will it tend to encourage a wider diversity of species.

(d) The location of a reserve area may be determined by the distribution of significant species, or, if the species can be expected to tolerate any part of the site, by considerations of the area's susceptibility to unwelcome interference or disturbances. In the latter case, a situation naturally isolated from roads and other rights of way and from areas being used by other recreationalists is probably best, although it may have the drawback of affording less opportunity for people to see what is being conserved. The ideal is to provide reserve areas which are readily visible from public viewing points but not subject to physical disturbance. If this can be contrived, both objectives of conservation (to protect and to explain what is protected) can be realized.

Both the purpose and the location of a reserve area will have a bearing on how it should be managed. Management needs to be considered from the outset and the following questions must be examined:—

(i) What is the primary purpose of the reserve?

(ii) Could the reserve be left to manage itself?

(iii) Is it necessary to maintain the environment as it exists or to attempt to encourage particular species or to attract new ones by modifying their surroundings?

(iv) Are adjoining landowners likely to expect a form of management that will ensure that there is no infestation of their land by what they consider to be undesirable species?

(v) Are there any management practices that should definitely not be employed or limited to certain times of the year?

(vi) Does access need to be prohibited or strictly controlled?

(vii) Can access be allowed or even encouraged in particular areas at particular times?

(viii) Can provision be made for viewing the reserve from vantage points outside?

In some instances it will be more convenient for the undertakers owning the site to be responsible for the management of the nature reserve or other protected feature, drawing upon the advice of conservation bodies where appropriate. In other cases the land or buildings may be leased to a separate body or individual, or a management agreement entered into whereby the other party would undertake to manage the property in accordance with an agreed plan. The other party to a lease or an agreement can be a local authority, an existing voluntary body or group of such bodies, a specially constituted body, a charitable trust, a commercial undertaking, or a private individual, depending on the type of feature being conserved and the objectives of conservation.

It should be remembered that conservation is a specialist subject, and that it will normally be advantageous to seek outside advice from suitably qualified persons or organizations if such expertise is not available within the undertaking concerned. The earlier such advice is sought the better. The help that can be obtained includes assistance with survey, analysis, and evaluation; advice on protection, restoration, and continuing management; and grants and direct assistance with physical works. A number of voluntary groups exist specifically for the purpose of carrying out conservation and environmental improvement works. Provided that care is taken to ensure that there is effective direction and supervision (most groups now have their own qualified and experienced supervisors), such groups can make a most effective contribution in suitable circumstances.

An important aspect of conservation is to improve public awareness of its objectives. Whilst the need to protect particular features may tend to command much of the attention, it is also important to communicate the idea of conservation generally so that the recreational users of other parts of the site respect the protected areas. Against this background any literature provided for the general public should ideally be designed not only to help and inform, but also as a management aid to guide visitors unobtrusively away from the areas that are sensitive, whether for operational or conservation reasons.

7. TREES AND WOODLANDS

GENERAL

A wide variety of trees, woodlands, soils, and climate are likely to be encountered on waterworks sites because of inherent disparities in their locations and characteristics, the range of which can extend from hilly, high altitude moorland on remote gathering grounds to flat, low level amenity land in urban surroundings.

A proportion of the existing trees and woodlands pre-dates the use of the land for water supply purposes, its extent, tree species and condition reflecting the interests of the previous owners. However, the great majority was created subsequently through afforestation schemes undertaken at various times and for a variety of reasons by water supply interests, major examples being Derwent, Thirlmere, and Vyrnwy. In some cases, such schemes especially those on the margins of reservoirs, were perhaps favoured in order to reduce access by man and animals. In others the planting of trees may have been considered beneficial in smoothing out variations in run-off, reducing erosion, and inducing precipitation. More recent experiments have indicated that transpiration and interception may be greater than for other forms of vegetation. Large-scale afforestation for commercial timber production has also been criticized on aesthetic grounds, and therefore the tendency is now likely to be towards multiple land use. Smaller plantations, sited to provide a combination of shelter for farmland, landscape improvement, nature conservation and timber production are therefore likely to be more suited to current requirements.

Tree planting adjacent to water installations involves considerations not encountered frequently in the establishment of woodlands. Both water and electrical services may occur underground and overhead in unlikely situations and it is imperative that these are taken into account when designing a planting scheme. The growth of roots and branches over a considerable period may endanger essential services, either by penetration through cracks and joints causing blockages and enlargement, or by breakage due to the blowing down or uprooting of all or part of the tree. In this connection the ultimate size of any tree must be taken into account. Root spread is normally assumed to be at least equal to that of the branches. The planting of trees on earth dams is not recommended as they may obscure movements of drainage defects, make routine inspection difficult, and cause shrinkage of the clay core. The tendency for roots to follow and enlarge any small water seepage is equally important, as ultimately when the tree blows down or dies, a clear path for water may be formed.

OBJECTIVES

It is possible to place the more usual objectives into the following three categories:—

(1) Landscaping and screening.
(2) Protection and conservation.
(3) Timber production.

Whilst, in any particular set of circumstances, one objective may be dominant it is usually possible, due to the adaptability of trees and woodlands, to extend the benefits to cover at least one if not both of the other categories.

Landscaping and Screening

In the past, the landscaping of water installations was often concentrated either on forming visual barriers of trees, or to creating ornamental gardens with trees, shrubs, flowers, and lawns in what were often rural surroundings. The blending of structures into the countryside by the use of tree species indigenous to the locality and the careful design of belts and clumps to harmonize with the existing terrain and woodlands is, however, likely to achieve more satisfactory and acceptable aesthetic effects.

Expert advice should be obtained on the use of trees in such circumstances, but adequate information must be provided on existing or projected underground and overhead services, and the actual extent of land available for landscaping must be agreed. It is essential to bear in mind that, if satisfactory results are to be obtained, adequate provision must be made at the outset to accommodate the size of trees to be grown. Another aspect which is often overlooked is the long term problem of the ultimate replacement of the scheme without ruining its appearance. Failure to provide adequate space at the planning stage may make this extremely difficult. Grants for such works may be available from the Countryside Commission[33].

Physical problems may arise from the annual shedding of leaves by broadleaved trees, especially large leaved varieties such as Horsechestnut and Sycamore, in the

...idge reservoir, in Kent (Southern ...uthority).

The man-made "beach" at this ... completed reservoir. The dam ...aw-off tower and the dinghy ...s are shown in the background.

...his weather-boarded cottage has ...tractively restored, and is now ...the fishing lodge.

Above. Fish rearing cages at Draycote Wa
Severn-Trent Water Authority *(T. Schofield).*
Left centre. Fish stocking at a reservoir in W
(Welsh Water Authority).
Left. Example of a well designed and
structed notice board at the entrance to
North Meadow National Nature Reserve,
Cricklade in the Thames Valley *(Nature (*
servancy Council).

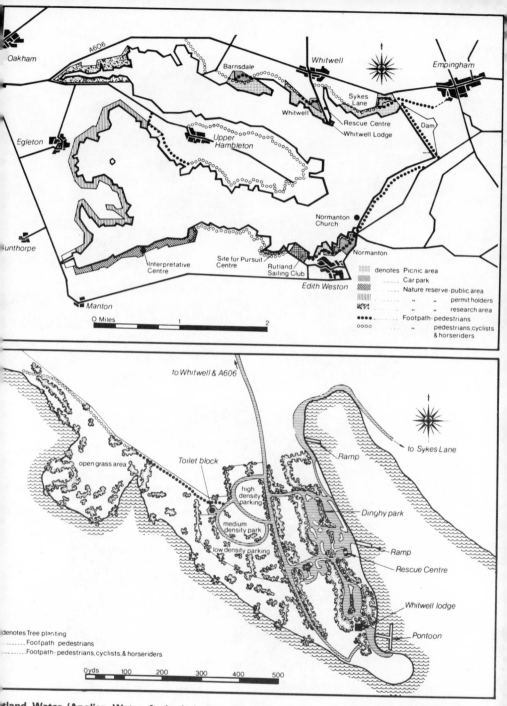

Top. General location of recreational facilities. **Above.**
Detailed plan of the Whitwell Peninsula.

Source Langford, P. R., 1979, Journ. I.W.E.S., 33, 117, "Leisure and sports facilities at Rutland Water".

Rutland Water (Anglian Water Authority).

Legend (top map):

denotes Picnic area
Car park
Nature reserve-public area
" " permit holders
" " research area
Footpath-pedestrians
" pedestrians, cyclists & horseriders

Labels (top map): Oakham, A606, Barnsdale, Whitwell, Sykes Lane, Empingham, Whitwell, Rescue Centre, Whitwell Lodge, Dam, Egleton, Upper Hambleton, Normanton Church, Gunthorpe, Interpretative Centre, Site for Pursuit Centre, Rutland Sailing Club, Normanton, Edith Weston, Manton, O Miles 1 2

Legend (bottom map):

denotes Tree planting
Footpath pedestrians
Footpath-pedestrians, cyclists,& horseriders

Labels (bottom map): to Whitwell & A606, to Sykes Lane, open grass area, Toilet block, Ramp, high density parking, Dinghy park, medium density park, low density parking, Ramp, Rescue Centre, Whitwell lodge, Pontoon, Oyds 100 200 300 400 500

Rutland Water (Anglian Water Authority)
Top. Normanton car park, picnic area, and public conveniences. *Above.* Interpretation Centre, at Sy
Lane car park.

autumn. The fallen leaves can cause blockage of filters or gratings and present hazards to vehicles or pedestrians when they rot and become slippery. This type of tree should not, therefore, be located in positions where it will overhang vulnerable installations, roads or car parks etc. Similarly, trees of any kind should not be positioned where they will obscure the view of drivers by blocking lines of sight.

The relationship of size of tree to the buildings to be landscaped has often been ignored in the past, although the matter of scale is by far the most important single factor in achieving success. The use of tall growing species, whose lower branches tend to die, is unsatisfactory if buildings and works are at a lower level. In addition, the extent of any new woodlands should relate to the scale of the existing topography and size of works. It must also be remembered that most broadleaved and a few coniferous trees lose their leaves in winter, and the use of a proportion of evergreen species may be necessary to maintain a partial screen during this season.

The size of young trees to be used in any planting scheme is open to discussion and will largely depend on how quickly a given effect is required and on the finance available. It is more usual to plant standard trees where wide spacing of individual specimens or small groups is required, for example within car parking and picnic areas, and to use forest transplants or whips where larger and denser clumps of woods are needed.

Replacement of trees in an old landscaped area is often difficult due to the even aged nature of the original planting, and the lack of consideration given to regeneration until a very late stage in its life. It is preferable for thought to be given at the planning stage to a partial replanting programme starting halfway through the life of the trees.

It is now considered important that larger scale plantings, including those primarily aimed at timber production, should also be integrated into the landscape. Information on the appraisal and design of such plantations is included in the Forestry Commission Booklet No. 44[34].

At times, it may be thought necessary, especially in urban situations, to establish formal lawns, flowerbeds, and shrubberies to convey an effect in keeping with the immediate surroundings of a particular installation. Costs of upkeep are high as regular grass mowing, weeding, and the annual replacement of flowering plants is very time consuming. The use of shrubs and perennial herbaceous plants requiring minimum maintenance is generally preferable in these circumstances.

Protection and Conservation

One of the direct benefits of tree planting to water supplies is the prevention of erosion on steep-sided catchment areas by the build up of soil and associated ground vegetation. This is brought about partly by the exclusion of grazing animals, but mainly by the binding action of the tree roots and the presence of overhead protection. These woodlands can also provide good conditions for nature conservation[35]. Management and maintenance is required to ensure the trees are kept stable and do not become too dense, thus destroying the ground vegetation previously built up.

In addition, many woodlands, especially on higher elevations, have been successfully planted to provide shelter to agricultural land. Advice may be obtained from the Ministry of Agriculture, Fisheries and Food[36] or from the Forestry Commission on such plantings, which are best located on steep or poor agricultural land.

Timber Production

All large planting schemes undertaken on catchment areas by water undertakers in the past, appear to have had timber production as a major objective, and the emphasis, especially in the uplands has been on coniferous trees. The majority of trees are capable of producing timber if properly managed, but the preference for coniferous varieties has resulted from their faster rate of growth, site tolerance, and ease of establishment. The growing of broadleaved species in such areas is generally more difficult and is often only made possible by the planting of coniferous "nurses" which are later removed.

The Forestry Commission has from time to time leased land from water undertakers for the purpose of afforestation, examples being Alwen, Bowland, and Goyt, or alternatively has assisted planting by grant payments under Deeds of Dedication. These were originally available under two systems termed Basis I and Basis II which are now closed and which have been superseded by Basis III covering areas of 10 hectares and over. Details are obtainable from local Forestry Commission offices[37]. Grants are made for initial planting and for long term management, and the requirements of the scheme are a properly prepared five-year plan of forest operations, and qualified supervision. Grants under the small woodlands scheme are available for areas of less than 10 hectares.

The management and maintenance of trees and woodlands is dealt with in Chapter 5.

8. REFERENCES

1. Langford, P. R., 1979, *Journ. I. W.E.S.*, 33, 117, "Leisure and sports facilities at Rutland Water".
2. Gibberd, F., 1961, *Journ. I.W.E.*, 15, 83, "The landscape of reservoirs".
3. Ministry of Transport, 1968, "Advisory manual: the layout of roads in rural areas", H.M.S.O.
4. Department of the Environment, 1977, "Design bulletin 32: residential roads and footpaths", H.M.S.O.
5. Road Research Laboratory, 1970, "Road note 29—a guide to the structural design of pavements for new roads", H.M.S.O.
6. Department of the Environment, 1969, "Specification for road and bridge works", H.M.S.O.
7. The Institution of Water Engineers, 1972, Report on "Recreation on reservoirs and rivers".
8. Huxley, T., 1970, The Countryside Commission for Scotland, Perth, "Footpaths in the countryside".
9. Ministry of Housing and Local Government, 1968, Report of the Footpaths Committee (Gosling Report), H.M.S.O.
10. The Countryside Commision, 1974, "Waymarking for footpath and bridleway", H.M.S.O.
11. French, S., 1977, *Jour. W.S.A.C.*, 11, 16, "Riding around reservoirs".
12. 1979, *Jour. W.S.A.C.*, 15, 23, "The newest jewel in Southern's crown".
13. Saxton, K. J. H., 1969, *Journ. I.W.E.*, 23, 425, "The recreational use of Grafham Water".
14. Beazley, E., 1969, "Designed for recreation", Faber and Faber Ltd., London.
15. The Countryside Commission, 1969, "Picnic sites", H.M.S.O.
16. Oliver, G. C. S., 1968, *Jour. I.W.E.*, 22, 129, "The development of a trout fishery on a lowland reservoir (Eye Brook)".
17. Halstead, P. E., 1954, *Mag. of Conc. Research*, 6, 93, "An investigation of the erosive effect on concrete of soft water of low pH value".
18. Adie, D. W., 1977, "Marinas—a working guide to their development and design", Architectural Press Ltd., London.
19. Mills, E. D., 1976, "Planning: buildings for administration, entertainment and recreation", Newnes, Butterworths, London.
20. The Civil Engineering Codes of Practice Joint Committee, 1951 Civil Engineering Code of Practice No. 2, "Earth retaining structures", The Institution of Structural Engineers, London.
21. British Standards Institution, 1967, Code of Practice CP 96: Part 1, "Access for the disabled to buildings. General recommendations".
22. Johnstone, D., and Brown, K. S., 1971, British Waterworks Association, London, "Report on the amenity use of reservoirs: a study tour of the U.S.A.".
23. British Standards Institution, 1965, Code of Practice CP 310:1965, "Water supply".
24. National Water Council, 1979 "Water Supply Hygiene: Safeguards in the Operation and Management of Public Waterworks in England and Wales", National Water Council, London.
25. Department of the Environment, 1972, "Building regulations", H.M.S.O.
26. British Standards Institution, 1968, Code of Practice CP 2005: 1968, "Sewerage".

27. British Standards Institution, 1972; Code of Practice CP 302: 1972, "Small sewage treatment plants".
28. Water Research Centre, 1979, Technical Report TR 107, "Septic tanks and small sewage treatment plants".
29. British Standards Institution, 1949, Code of Practice 302.200:1949 "Cesspools".
30. British Standards Institution, 1968, Specification BS 4324:1968, "Litter bins".
31. Sykes, J. et al 1979, "Designing against vandalism", The Design Council, London.
32. British Standards Institution, 1963, Specification BS 3621:1963, "Thief resistant locks for hinged doors".
33. Countryside Commission 1978, "Grants for amenity tree planting and management", H.M.S.O.
34. Forestry Commission 1978, Booklet 44, "The landscape of forests and woods", H.M.S.O.
35. Forestry Commission 1972, Booklet 29, "Wildlife conservation in woodlands", H.M.S.O.
36. Ministry of Agriculture, Fisheries and Food 1961, "Shelter belts for farmland: leaflet 15—Fixed equipment on the farm", H.M.S.O.
37. Forestry Commission 1977, "Advice for woodland owners", H.M.S.O.

Chapter 5

THE MANAGEMENT OF RECREATIONAL FACILITIES

1. INTRODUCTION

GENERAL

THE detailed planning and construction of various recreational facilities has been dealt with at length in the previous chapter. This Chapter is concerned with the management of those facilities.

The successful management of recreational developments requires the exercise of a considerable degree of skill, involving, as it does, the responsibility for a wide variety of tasks, including the maintenance and improvement of the site generally, the recreational facilities and associated services, the means of access, plant, equipment, furniture, etc., and the broad supervision of the recreational activities taking place. On the larger sites it is usual for a number of employees to be engaged full time upon this type of work but, on many of the smaller sites, which are presently in the majority, the recreational duties are normally combined with others, generallly of an operational nature. Regardless of the position in this respect, it is important to see that each site is maintained to a high standard so as to present an attractive appearance to the visitor and also to discourage vandalism. It is now generally accepted that a well-cared-for appearance and the prompt repair of any damage are the most effective deterrents available, against that kind of behaviour.

It is always useful, and indeed desirable, to have a reasonable insight into the likely reaction of visitors to any changes contemplated, before embarking upon improvements to recreational facilities. An understanding of probable responses can best be obtained by observation and monitoring of habitual visitor behaviour on each particular site, over a period of time. A pattern can often be discerned in this way, which will help in the planning of proposed modifications. Monitoring of behaviour patterns should, therefore, be considered an essential tool in the efficient management of the recreational area.

Arguably, in many instances, the most difficult managerial problem on a site is the amicable resolution of conflicts between participants in different sports or activities, and between the natural desires and preferences of visitors and the ecological or other constraints imposed on their activities by the characteristics of the site itself. Many stratagems have been employed to overcome these difficulties, the most commonly encountered being those involving the zoning of the conflicting activities on either a time or space basis and the restriction or prohibition of access to particularly sensitive areas of the site. The most suitable approach in each case will depend upon the particular circumstances prevailing at the individual site concerned. Whatever method may be adopted, however, a certain amount of friction is occasionally experienced. Much can be done to avoid this developing into a more serious situation if the site staff are encouraged to adopt a helpful attitude in their dealings with the parties involved, and enlightened management will seek to foster such an outlook amongst employees.

WASTE COLLECTION AND DISPOSAL

Arrangements for the collection and disposal of litter vary from site to site. In most cases the rubbish is collected by staff employed by the managers of the particular facilities concerned, with a frequency which will depend to some extent on whether the site is continuously manned or not. The rubbish is usually disposed of by incineration, burial, or where appropriate, tipping, or by storing it in dustbins or larger receptacles for subsequent removal by the local authority or a private contractor. Where there is an involvement on their part in the recreational provision, for example where the site forms part of a country park, the local authority may itself undertake the collection and disposal.

The responsibility for arranging the collection and disposal of refuse may vary between the owners of the site and of the premises and their tenants, depending upon the terms of the agreements between them. The collection and disposal operations themselves will normally be carried out by either the local authority or private contractors. the former have a statutory obligation to collect, but only where an agreement to pay their charges for the service is entered into. On large scale developments which justify the employment of permanent staff, refuse may occasionally be disposed of to a suitably screened tip on site. Where this practice is adopted care should be taken to ensure that tipping is carried out in a controlled manner in the interests of public health and amenity and of the minimization of nuisance from insects and vermin. A waste management paper issued by the Department of the Environment[1] sets out model conditions for the operation of landfill sites, a number of which may be of relevance, particularly on tips serving the larger scale recreational developments.

TOILETS

Public lavatories should always be kept in a satisfactory hygienic condition, since failure to maintain an acceptable standard of cleanliness can result in the visitors' enjoyment of the site being badly marred and may even have the effect of deterring them from making further visits. Considerable importance should, therefore, be attached to this facet of site operations and it behoves management to ensure, as one of its prime concerns, that frequent, thorough cleaning is carried out, preferably on a regular basis, and that consumable items such as paper towels, soap, and toilet rolls are continually replenished. On large sites which support resident staff, this can readily be done by employees on the spot, but, at unmanned sites reliance has to be placed on mobile gangs drawn from elsewhere.

2. SUPERVISORY AND OPERATIONAL PROVISIONS

GENERAL

Supervisory and operational provision varies considerably from one site to another, partly as a result of inherent differences in their respective circumstances, such as the size and characteristics of the site, the number, size and type of facilities and activities available and the intensity of use each receives, and partly because of differences in the managerial policies pursued by different water undertakers on such matters as manning levels, standards of accommodation and equipment, opening times, the imposition of entrance fees and other charges and, where appropriate, the protection of gathering grounds against pollution.

It may include boat certification and registration, fishery surveillance, information, warden and rescue services, together with provision for the issue of admission tickets, permits, etc., and for the sale of light refreshments. On sites containing clubhouses, outdoor pursuit centres or similar facilities, reception, training, catering and other domestic services may also be provided, augmented as appropriate, where overnight accommodation is incorporated. In addition, there are a further number of services which, although having a recreational dimension, are not primarily considered to be part of recreational provision, largely perhaps, because the requirement for them is relatively restricted. Lock-keeping and river policing, which are necessarily confined to navigable stretches of waterway, are examples of these.

As a rule, the larger and more intensively used the site and the wider the range of facilities and activities available, the more extensive is the provision made, so that extremely comprehensive services may well be found on major developments, in marked contrast to the position on smaller sites where the number and level of services can be minimal, indeed, in some cases, virtually non-existent.

There is a corresponding variation between sites in the numbers and types of staff engaged in the provision of these services.

It is generally only on a major recreational development that the employment of full time staff, exclusively on recreational duties, can reasonably be justified. It will be appreciated that in this context, such a development need not be confined to the area of a single large site but can embrace a group of smaller, individual sites situated in sufficient proximity to each other to enable them to be supervised and operated from a central base.

Typically in such a case, staffing may consist of a site manager, assisted as appropriate by a chief engineer and a recreation officer with their respective staffs, together with supporting administrative personnel. The designations of their posts may, of course, vary from undertaker to undertaker.

The site manager will normally have overall operational responsibility for all the undertaker's interests in the development, including such authority over the activities of members and personnel of other bodies associated with the site as may have been agreed, in addition to control of the undertaker's own staff.

The chief engineer will generally be in charge of the operation, maintenance and repair of buildings, equipment, plant and grounds, etc., and the recreation officer will be involved with recreational operations and supervision, supported by a complement of wardens, water bailiffs, information officers, instructors, ticket and permit clerks, catering and other domestic staff, rescue personnel, etc., as appropriate. Even on major sites the number of recreational personnel is usually quite small, at least initially, as illustrated by Gittins[2] and Langford[3] for two recent large scale reservoir-based developments.

WARDENS AND WATER BAILIFFS

Wardens and water bailiffs are probably the recreational personnel most universally encountered. The role of the warden can broadly be described as the general supervision of the site or of certain activities taking place on it, with the object of ensuring that conditions are maintained which enable visitors to obtain the maximum benefit, use, and enjoyment from the facilities and their surroundings. His duties normally include the provision of guidance, advice, and information to visitors, the promotion of cordial relations between participants in the various activities, the prevention of damage to installations and facilities, the enforcement of relevant byelaws and regulations, the promotion of safety and the control of malpractices such as the leaving of litter, the use of footpaths by motorcyclists, indiscriminate parking, the uprooting of flowers, the leaving open of gates, and the lighting of fires in dangerous circumstances. During the course of his patrols he should also observe and note visitor behaviour and monitor their enquiries so that the planning of improvements to facilities and information services, etc., can be carried out on a factual rather than a conjectural basis. Wardens on permanent staff are often employed on general repair and maintenance or minor improvement works during the winter months when recreational activity is at a low level.

Wardens are usually provided with some means of identification, which may consist of an appointment or authorization card preferably complete with photograph, a badge, an arm band or a uniform. In addition, they are frequently issued with a notebook, a pen and a whistle and occasionally on very extensive sites, with radio telephones and transport of some kind to increase their effectiveness and mobility.

The water bailiff has a broadly similar function in respect of fisheries to that normally performed by the warden in relation to other recreational activities. He is generally appointed by a water authority for the purpose of preserving and protecting the fisheries within its area and, in practice, is usually assigned to a specific water such as a particular stretch of river or an individual reservoir. He is responsible for the enforcement of fisheries byelaws, and of certain aspects of the Salmon and Freshwater Fisheries Act 1975, from which his powers are derived.

In carrying out his enforcement duties the bailiff has the same powers and privileges as a constable, and the special powers to enter on to any land for the purpose of examining obstructions and artificial watercourses, etc., to examine instruments, bait and containers, to search for and seize illegal fish and instruments and, under certain circumstances, to arrest people. As a general rule, he is not concerned with the question of whether or not a person fishing in a lawful manner with a valid licence is entitled to fish the water, as this is a matter for the fishery owner. He may however also act for the owner or lessee of the fishing rights by checking permits and membership cards. This is particularly the case with honorary bailiffs, who are usually members of the club which has rights in the stretch of water for which they are responsible.

Whilst on patrol the bailiff should make a point of learning as much as possible about the water within his jurisdiction, the types and habits of the fish population, points of access and vantage and obstructions such as fish passes, weirs, and gratings and how they work. He should also keep a lookout for pollution and new discharges to the water and for obstructions or breaches which might cause erosion and flooding and should note and report such observations immediately, together with other matters of importance affecting the water.

Those bailiffs who are employees of water undertakers usually have additional responsibilities which normally include giving guidance to honorary bailiffs, advising angling clubs and fishery owners on fisheries matters, carrying out fish surveys, supervising the introduction of fish or the restocking of waters, and organizing fish rescues.

As with wardens, water bailiffs are issued with a means of identification and, usually, with a notebook, a pen, a watch, a whistle and a good torch. Other useful equipment may include binoculars, polaroid glasses, and a litre size screw top bottle for taking water samples.

RESCUE SERVICES

The personnel with perhaps, literally, the most vital task of all on a major recreational development, especially one on which large scale water-based activities take place, with their consequentially greater risk of serious accident, are those engaged in emergency rescue work. Sailing clubs are usually made responsible for the safety of their own members and may occasionally agree to accept an obligation for rescuing boat anglers in difficulty. In these cases the rescue service is operated by the club itself and manned by club members. Where sailing and angling is run directly by the water undertaker, a separate service is necessary and this may be operated either by the undertaker or by other organizations on its behalf.

Ideally, such a service should be available at all times when these activities are in progress and should be equipped with high-speed patrol and rescue boats, complete with seat conversion stretchers, resuscitation and other rescue equipment, and direct radio links with local ambulance and medical services. The arrangements in operation at two major sites are described by Saxton[4] and Langford[3].

MANNING ARRANGEMENTS

In the smaller recreational sites, of which the medium-sized reservoir is generally representative, staffing is commonly confined to a single permanent employee, engaged principally on operational duties, who is responsible for the overall supervision of recreational activity. He may, depending upon the range and scale of the activities involved, be assisted by one or more wardens. Certain duties may also be undertaken by water bailiffs and, in respect of their own activities, by members of the clubs and other organizations using or operating the various facilities. Staffing on sites of intermediate size will, generally, lie between this level and that on major developments.

Manning arrangements on any particular site may vary throughout the year as a whole, in accordance with periodic fluctuations in the level and duration of the various activities taking place. In the British Isles these fluctuations are largely seasonal, with the demand for recreational services being greatest in summer, the peak holiday season, when the number of individual activities in progress is at its maximum and climatic conditions are more favourable to outdoor pursuits, with higher temperatures and longer hours of daylight. In the winter months, by contrast, demand is considerably reduced because of the often dramatic decline in the number of activities possible, fishing being prohibited by statute during this period in the close season and other diversions such as picnicking being effectively precluded by the unsuitability of the weather. Arrangements may also vary additionally, in accordance with daily and weekly peak demands.

In summer, with the advent of increased daylight, recreational sites are normally open for long hours every day, often extending, where angling takes place, from dawn to dusk during most if not all of the fishing season. The opening hours of specific facilities such as information and interpretation centres, those for public sailing, refreshment kiosks, etc., are usually, however, restricted to shorter periods of the day according to demand. For the same reason, some may only open on certain peak days such as weekends and bank holidays.

At this time of year, therefore, opening hours generally far exceed the normal hours of work in the water industry, with the consequence that a rota system of manning is usually essential in order to cover such times as early mornings, evenings, weekends, and bank holidays, except where low levels of activity render this unnecessary. The rota should be arranged to suit the established pattern of demand. It may, for example, be found by experience that visitor attendance is negligible early and late in the day, especially during the week, making it not worthwhile to deploy personnel during these particular periods. A similar situation may occur in respect of certain weekdays also. On the other hand, there will usually be a need for additional personnel to cover periods of peak demand. In this connection it is sometimes possible to accommodate daily peaks simply by overlapping the duty periods covering the earlier and later parts of the day, and weekly peaks by arranging a comparable overlap on the daily duty roster.

On large sites catering for a multiplicity of activities, compiling the duty rota can be a complex task. Apart from allowing for variations in opening hours and manning levels, it will often be necessary to accommodate several categories of personnel each with a different set of duties, and to take into account other factors such as their status, the extent of their availability and their ability jointly to provide adequate first aid coverage of the site at any time. On smaller sites with fewer activities the task is correspondingly simpler. At one medium sized reservoir in South Yorkshire, for example, catering principally for angling and sailing, where the site is manned every day from 07.00 hr to dusk in the trout fishing season (i.e., between 25th March and the end of September each year) by one full-time permanent and three part-time seasonally employed attendants under the overall control of a reservoir keeper, the rota provides for one attendant to be on duty at all times during opening hours throughout the week, with a second one supplementing his efforts during the middle of the day on Saturdays and Sundays to cater for the weekend peaks. In detail the arrangements are for the full-time attendant to be on duty from 07.00 to 16.00 hrs each weekday with one of the three part-time employees taking over between 15.30 hrs and dusk, and for all three part timers to cover the weekend, one from 07.00 to 15.30 hrs, the second from 15.30 hrs until dusk, and the third providing an overlap from 09.30 to 18.00 hrs, on both days.

In winter the days are shorter and it is often sufficient at this time of year for the site to be manned during normal working hours only. Weekend duties may, however, be necessary in addition, in cases where the level of recreational activity warrants such provision.

The status of the personnel engaged in providing recreational services can vary proportionally between different sites in accordance with individual circumstances. In Britain, full-time employees of water undertakers probably constitute an overall majority of those concerned. Some of them are permanently occupied exclusively on recreational duties whilst others carry them out purely on a part-time basis in conjunction with their other, often principal duties. Their numbers are frequently augmented during the summer months when the level of activity is generally at its height, by temporary staff employed for fixed periods, the duration of which usually varies with the types of activities involved. As an alternative, other operational personnel are sometimes seconded to recreational duties during peak periods, but this arrangement can be somewhat problematical because it is precisely at these very times that their own workload is at its maximum. This is particularly the case on elevated or exposed sites where adverse weather conditions commonly restrict operations during the winter. Where secondment is not practicable, it may still be possible to make use of the services of non-recreational employees especially those living on or near the site, on a voluntary basis, to cover periods outside normal working hours such as evenings, weekends, and bank holidays, at the very least on a standby basis to cover the absence of regular staff.

Another group which can comprise an appreciable percentage of the total number of recreational personnel servicing some developments, consists of the employees of outside bodies with interests in the site. Such bodies may include local authorities, other public enterprises like the Forestry Commission and private concerns such as catering and amusement concessionaires, sailing and angling clubs, and marina companies. Local authorities administering country parks may, for instance, employ wardens who patrol areas of a site lying within the boundaries of the park. In some cases, their duties may, by mutual agreement, be extended to cover the remainder of the site, possibly as a joint operation in conjunction with the water undertakers own staff.

In addition, on most sites, volunteers render invaluable assistance in the provision of supervisory and operational services, making a very important contribution to the smooth running of many facilities and thus to the enjoyment of visitors and of participants in the various activities. They may include in their ranks wardens, rescue personnel, water bailiffs, etc., drawn from a wide variety of organizations such as school groups, conservation societies, naturalist trusts, youth groups, sailing and angling clubs, the St. John's Ambulance Brigade, the Royal Lifesaving Society, and many others.

The terms and conditions of service of employed personnel depend greatly upon the type of work they do and upon the nature of the organization which employs them. Those applicable in the case of the staffs of the water industry, local authorities, and other statutory public bodies in this country, are usually the ones set out in the appropriate national agreements, subject, occasionally, to minor modifications to take account of the special circumstances or requirements of a particular post. These agreements cover, generally, matters such as rates of remuneration, periods of notice, superannuation, hours of work, payment for overtime and standby, leave and public holidays, allowances and expenses, injury indemnity and disciplinary and other procedures and tend to be fairly comprehensive in scope. Privately employed staff may be parties to similar agreements or may, alternatively, be subject to conditions negotiated with individual employers, preferably covering broadly the same details as those included in the public service agreements referred to above.

Virtually everyone engaged in recreational operation or supervision comes into contact with members of the public in the course of their duties. The manner in which they carry out their tasks can therefore have an enormous influence on public relations on the site and can, indeed, make or mar the enjoyment of visitors using the various facilities.

Because of this and its effect on the success of the project as a whole, and also because their conduct reflects upon the undertaking or organization providing the service, it is extremely important that the personalities of the individuals concerned should be compatible with the kind of role they are called upon to play. Suitability of temperament should, accordingly, be a prime consideration in their selection or appointment and management should constantly seek to ensure that the correct approach is adopted by all such personnel in their dealings with visitors. The personal qualities particularly apposite are friendliness and helpfulness, accompanied as occasion demands, by persuasiveness, tact, and firmness.

Medical services are not always readily available in the vicinity of recreational developments, because of their often comparatively remote locations. It is therefore highly desirable, if not indeed essential, that site staff, or at least a proportion of them, should also be competent in first aid and, where water-based activities are involved, in lifesaving and resuscitation techniques, in case of accidents. The necessary medical supplies, equipment and accommodation should be provided for their use.

3. MAINTENANCE OF BUILDINGS AND GROUNDS

A high standard of property maintenance is extremely desirable on any recreational development, for a number of reasons. In the first instance it helps to enhance the attractiveness of a site, thus making a considerable contribution to its success by adding to the enjoyment of visitors and encouraging their return. In the second place, it helps to project a favourable image of the organization managing the development and, thirdly, it has the beneficial effect in the long term, of minimizing the cost of repairs by preventing premature deterioration through neglect.

VANDALISM

In addition, efficient maintenance also plays its part, in conjunction with suitable supervisory measures, in combating the growing menace of vandalism. Extensive reference is made to this problem in Chapter 4 (Section 5, Ancillary Facilities, p. 119). It is now widely recognized that probably the single most effective way of discouraging this reprehensible type of behaviour is to ensure that both the buildings and grounds always look to be well cared for. This aim can only be achieved by making certain that the standard of routine maintenance of such items as paintwork and structural elements is kept consistently high and that any damage sustained is repaired promptly. A positive appreciation by site management of the psychological factors involved, accompanied by correspondingly expeditious attention to any necessary remedial works and rigorous adherence to a suitable routine maintenance programme, can markedly reduce the incidence of further damage and hence, ultimately, the scale of the problem. This type of understanding and approach is, therefore, generally to be encouraged as a matter of policy.

SCOPE AND RESPONSIBILITY

The number and scale of the items to be maintained varies considerably from one site to another, largely in accordance with the size and characteristics of each and the extent and magnitude of the facilities provided. On any particular site the list may include buildings such as those set out below; together with slipways, piers, quays, and jetties; water, drainage, and foul sewage systems; and such features as roads and footpaths, walls, fences and hedges, car and boat parks, and picnic and play areas:—

Information, interpretation and visitor centres
Outdoor pursuits centres
Administrative accommodation
Depots and stores
Staff houses
Clubhouses
Ticket offices
Toilet blocks and disposal points
Refreshment kiosks, cafés, and shops
Shelters and hides.

Responsibility for the maintenance of buildings and other facilities generally rests with their owners, although in some instances it may be passed on to the tenants under the terms of their lease. In Britain, water undertakers usually provide and accept the responsibility of looking after the general public recreational facilities on sites within their jurisdiction, together with the associated utility services, access arrangements, and staff accommodation. The position in respect of certain other facilities, to which access may be restricted either on a commercial basis or to specific groups of people, is often different. In practice, the most common examples of this type of facility are clubhouses used exclusively by club members, but others include outdoor pursuits centres, marinas, shops and cafés. In these cases the managerial body, whether club, local authority or commercial organization, may either own or lease the premises. Where such a body is the owner, maintenance is normally its own responsibility entirely, but where the buildings and their associated facilities are provided by a water undertaker and leased to the managers, as is sometimes the case, the usual arrangement is for the undertaker to carry out the maintenance work, the cost being either reflected in the rental charged or recovered directly. The most convenient arrangement will depend to some extent on the maintenance capability of the parties concerned and there is no reason why lessees should not be responsible for maintenance or conversely why the water undertakers should not maintain premises which they do not own, if this is mutually agreeable.

STAFFING

The employment of maintenance staff working full time on an individual site is really only feasible on the largest recreational developments where the workload justifies such an arrangement. The composition of a maintenance section depends largely upon the volume of work involved, the skills required, and the relative demand for each. In this connection, it must be remembered that in winter, outside maintenance is often interrupted or restricted by inclement weather, especially on elevated and exposed sites and work has consequently to be concentrated undercover as far as possible. In these circumstances it is difficult to keep all the staff concerned, effectively occupied. Because of this, decisions as to the optimum complement of maintenance personnel are matters of fine judgement, if overstaffing in winter is to be avoided. On such a development, the section may consist of a small number of building tradesmen from selected trades with unskilled support, together with a modest complement of general ground staff, under the supervision of foremen and engineering personnel, based upon a depot on the site. The trades in greatest demand are usually carpentry and joinery, masonry and bricklaying, since even on these sites there is seldom sufficient work to warrant the inclusion of other tradesmen such as electricians, painters, plumbers, paviors, etc. This type of work is generally carried out by personnel based at the nearest area maintenance depot, or central depot or by private contract.

On the smaller developments a certain amount of ground maintenance and of unskilled or semi-skilled building maintenance is often carried out by operational site staff as part of their normal duties. For work outside their capabilities, either on account of the skills required or because of the magnitude of the task, reliance is placed on central or area maintenance personnel whose services are called in as required.

4. PLANT AND EQUIPMENT

An enormous variety of plant and equipment is to be found on recreational sites in general, the level of provision at each depending upon the circumstances prevailing at the particular development concerned. Individual items may be classified very broadly into three principal categories; recreational, support services, and maintenance equipment. The first of these includes such items as notice boards, picnic furniture, ticket machines and barriers, playground equipment, boats, boat handling and lifting gear, landing stages, buoys and anchors, together with ancillary equipment such as outboard motors, bollards, fenders, etc. The second includes litter bins, mechanical water supply and sewage treatment plant, rescue craft and emergency equipment; and the third, such items as tractors, grass cutters, workshop equipment, and construction plant and equipment. The participation of recreational management in its detailed selection will usually vary in extent, in accordance with the type of item concerned but, more often than not, it will probably be greater with equipment in the first category than with that in the other two. Decisions in respect of certain items will inevitably need to be based upon the advice of appropriate specialists.

Because of the tremendous range of equipment involved and the continual introduction of new developments and improvements to much of it, it is practically impossible to deal adequately with the detailed requirements of individual items. There are, however, a number of basic considerations common to the generality of such equipment which must be taken into account in determining its suitability. Amongst these are economy, effectiveness, reliability, resistance to damage, ease of repair and maintenance, compatibility with the surroundings, safety, and the risk of pollution.

Economy is a consideration universally influencing the choice between alternatives. In the case of the equipment in question it should not be taken as being synonymous with initial purchase price as, almost invariably, other costs also enter into its overall assessment. These normally include the costs of repair and maintenance and of eventual replacement together with others which may arise, consequentially, in the event of an item becoming unserviceable. Such consequential costs may take the form of hire charges or fabrication expenses for temporary replacements; loss of income, for example, from ticket machines, boat rentals etc.; loss of output, through reductions in productivity, or additional operating costs, due to extra staffing requirements.

Effectiveness manifests itself in many ways in practice; precisely how depending both upon the type of item concerned and the circumstances in which it is to be used. This factor merits careful attention at the selection stage if the full potential of the equipment is to be realized. For instance, to be fully effective, a rescue boat needs to be fast, manoeuvrable and stable so that it can reach the scene of an incident quickly and, once there, can carry out a rescue with the minimum of delay and difficulty. Similarly, litter bins in exposed locations will not satisfactorily serve their purpose unless fitted with lids to prevent their contents being scattered over the site on windy days. By the same token, notice boards etc., will not fulfill their function properly unless their message can be easily and quickly read and assimilated, which means that it should be concise and where appropriate, interesting, and should be attractively presented.

The reliability of recreational plant and equipment is not only important because of its economic implications but also because it can affect the enjoyment of people using a particular item and even make a material contribution to their well-being and safety. Failure can cause disappointment, as for example when playground equipment is discovered to be unusable; inconvenience and annoyance where entrance barriers, winches etc., are found to be out of order when required; and apprehension where, for instance, engine failure leaves a powered boat drifting helplessly in midstream or in the centre of a large reservoir. In the latter eventuality the safety of the users may also be placed in jeopardy, which could easily be the case too, should breakdowns of such items as rescue craft, lifesaving and firefighting equipment, radio telephones etc., occur.

Resistance of equipment to damage whether from wear and tear, accident or vandalism, is of consequence for the same reasons as reliability. In considering this point account should be taken of such features as robustness of construction, type of materials used, and the absence of vulnerable projections. Many new materials have become available over recent years which are extremely strong and therefore difficult to damage or deface. In addition many designs now incorporate such features as smooth, uninterrupted surfaces and concealed fixings which further reduce the likelihood of damage. It is, therefore, advisable to ensure that the latest possibilities in these directions are investigated before a choice is finally made.

It is highly desirable, for obvious reasons, that equipment should be easy to repair and maintain, preferably by the type of labour generally available on site, which can often be unskilled or semi-skilled. As a corollary to this, on the principle of prevention being better than cure, it is also prudent to minimize potential maintenance requirements by, for example, a judicious choice of items which incorporate the maximum of rot and corrosion-resistant materials. An allied requirement is that spares should be readily obtainable and in this connection it is an advantage to standardize as much as possible in order to reduce the quantity, variety and cost of spares which it is necessary to hold. Such a policy also has the added benefit of reducing the numbers of different mechanisms with which the maintenance staff need to be familiar.

Equipment should, preferably, be compatible with the surroundings in which it is to be used so as not to offend the senses of visitors to the site and thus detract from their enjoyment of the facilities provided. In practice the only senses likely to be affected are sight and hearing and equipment should, therefore, generally be selected which will neither look nor sound out of place in its intended setting. So far as appearance is concerned, this consideration could for instance result in choosing rustic furniture rather than other styles, for picnic areas in informal rural locations. In the case of audible compatibility it could similarly lead, for example, to the selection of quieter four stroke inboard engines in preference to two stroke outboards to power motor driven craft on remote and tranquil sites.

Safety has recently assumed greater prominence in the selection of recreational plant and equipment than has sometimes been the case in the past. Advice is now usually sought from the undertakers' safety officer before purchasing any item which could conceivably present a safety hazard. In the case of workshop plant, local officials of the Health and Safety Executive may often also assist if consulted. The subject is far too vast to be covered here, but one example can perhaps, with advantage, be given of some of the relevant aspects to be considered in respect of one of the many possible items involved. Probably the most suitable one for the purposes of illustration is the hire boat. It is obviously vital that such craft should be inherently safe because the expertise of the hirers in handling them and their behaviour in emergencies are unknown factors which cannot readily be ascertained beforehand. The boats, therefore, need to possess stable flotation characteristics to prevent overturning and in this regard the ratio of length to beam is important. They also need adequate freeboard when fully loaded to prevent them becoming swamped in stormy conditions. Both these factors will vary in extent in accordance with the severity of the conditions likely to be encountered on the particular stretch of water on which the boats are to be used. Some indication of possible requirements in this respect can be gained from the fact that the boats in use on a large lowland reservoir in east central England[3] have a length/beam ratio of 2.8:1. Other important considerations are the thickness of the hull, which must be sufficient to prevent accidental holing, and the provision of adequate buoyancy to prevent the vessel from sinking in the event of a serious mishap. The latter objective is normally achieved by the incorporation of buoyancy tanks built into the boat which must, at least, be of adequate capacity to support the weight of the boat itself and that of the maximum number of passengers carried.

The danger of pollution is an important consideration wherever equipment is to be used in the vicinity of water. This is particularly the case on direct-supply reservoir sites, especially if the associated treatment plant is of an unsophisticated type. The greatest risk probably arises from the spillage of fuel oil on to the water surface itself, which most commonly occurs as a result of leakages from the engines of motor driven craft, or of losses during refuelling. In this respect the problem may be worse with the outboard than with the inboard type of engine. This point, however, needs to be balanced against other factors in comparing the two types[4]. An alternative well worth considering, where circumstances warrant it, i.e. where the consequences of potential pollution are sufficiently serious, is the use of propane gas in place of petrol propulsion. This type of fuel effectively eliminates the risk of pollution since any liquid immediately evaporates into the atmosphere.

It is virtually impossible at the selection stage, without prior knowledge of its performance in similar conditions to those in which it is to be used, to be sure that a particular piece of equipment will, in practice, prove completely suited to its purpose. There are, however, a number of ways in which the area of uncertainty can be reduced. One of these is to enquire from experienced users, their opinion of the equipment concerned, followed up, where appropriate, by visits to site to observe it in operation. Enquiries should preferably be made in terms specifically related to its intended location and use as well as in general ones, if the maximum degree of benefit is to be gained from the exercise. Another way of achieving the same object is to hire the equipment for a sufficient period to enable an accurate assessment to be made of its performance in its normal working environment. For expensive items in particular, it may sometimes be worthwhile combining the two methods in order to obtain the maximum practicable amount of information on which to base a final evaluation.

5. MAINTENANCE OF PLANT AND EQUIPMENT

The proper maintenance of plant and equipment plays a significant role in the success of any recreational development. There is nothing worse than wanting to make use of a piece of equipment, only to find it out of order simply because of lack of adequate attention to this essential detail. If this eventuality should occur in the case of a recreational item, for example, the visitor's pleasure may be marred, to an extent which will depend upon his degree of need at the time. With rescue equipment, the consequences for him could be much more serious, even leading perhaps in the ultimate, to loss of life. When maintenance equipment becomes unserviceable, operational efficiency and economy are usually the principal casualties, although, in some instances, there may also be secondary repercussions affecting the general appearance of the site, which can, in turn, reflect upon the enjoyment of visitors. In addition, poor maintenance generally increases the overall cost of equipment through the need for premature replacement of parts or of the whole item, brought about by unnecessary wear or, in extreme cases, collapse. For these reasons it is incumbent upon management to ensure that standards are kept consistently high.

The responsibility of water undertakers for the repair and maintenance of plant and equipment is normally confined to that which they themselves own, although, on occasion they may by mutual agreement, carry out this type of work for other owners on the site, usually on a rechargeable basis.

Mechanical equipment generally requires regular servicing. Some of the tasks involved can be relatively simple and well within the capacity of unskilled or semi-skilled labour to carry out unaided. These are normally undertaken by the various members of the site staff responsible for the operation of the individual items concerned. For example, wardens etc., may be responsible in the case of playground and similar equipment, drivers and attendants in that of vehicles and mobile plant and tradesmen in respect of their own workshop equipment. The same personnel may also carry out any minor adjustments and repairs found to be necessary from time to time. The less elementary routine servicing and repairs, as well as all overhauls, are almost invariably undertaken by fitters or mechanics, the vast majority of whom are necessarily based at area or central depots or at electrical, mechanical or transport workshops, off site. Only on the largest scale developments is it generally feasible to station them on site under the control of suitable local engineering staff, with their own workshop facilities. Where items of specialist equipment are involved, such as ticket machines, automatic barriers, fire extinguishers, radio telephones, television cameras etc., water undertakers often prefer the entire maintenance work to be carried out by the manufacturer concerned, on the basis that his staff should be much more conversant with the details of the equipment than their own could ever be and should, therefore, provide a more efficient service.

Non-mechanical equipment does not, as a rule, require servicing. Routine repairs are however occasionally necessary and these are commonly undertaken by recreational site staff supplemented, as appropriate, by carpenters and other tradesmen based at similar locations to the fitters and mechanics.

If equipment is to continue to perform at its maximum level of efficiency in the longer term, it is essential that it should receive periodic overhaul, preferably on a regular and systematic basis, in addition to routine servicing and repair. A suitable programme can usually be readily implemented on an annual basis in the case of items used specifically for recreational purposes, because of the largely seasonal nature of this type of activity. Accordingly most water undertakers take full advantage of the lull in activity, which in the British Isles occurs during the winter months, to carry out a thorough inspection and overhaul of such items, each year, as a matter of policy, in readiness for the busy season. In this way they can be reasonably certain that the reliability of the equipment is at its highest when most needed. An appreciable proportion of the work involved on a number of the items is relatively unskilled and can therefore provide useful additional, out of season employment for such personnel as full time wardens, who it may otherwise prove difficult to keep fully occupied at this time. A potential improvement in the balance of the overall workload on site is therefore an added advantage of such a policy. The remaining equipment is normally subject to a programme of overhaul not directly related to the level of recreational activity, but account should nevertheless be taken of this factor, where possible, in the formulation of a suitable strategy for the items concerned.

6. CLUBS AND ADVISORY COMMITTEES

An authority providing water recreation facilities will almost inevitably find itself faced with two groups of people: one representing users or prospective users of the facility, and the other representing local communities who might in some way be affected by the recreational activities. Both groups may be brought into the planning and management of the recreational facilities for any or all of three main purposes:—

(1) To enable them to make their claims, register objections, and provide advice and expertise not available within the promoting authority during the planning stages of the scheme.

(2) To provide a forum for an interchange of views between the various parties when the facilities are in operation. This should reduce the likelihood of conflict which more often than not arises because individual groups do not always appreciate the needs, problems, and practices of other groups.

(3) To shoulder, financially or otherwise, some or all of the burden of provision of facilities and their subsequent management.

The nature and extent of such involvement will depend on:—

(a) The nature of the water resources and the amount and variety of recreational use possible.

(b) The possible effects of this recreational use and associated traffic on the surrounding environment.

(c) The extent to which the promoting authority wishes to be involved in recreational provision and management.

In the fairly simple situation where a reservoir is used for trout fishing and dinghy sailing, usually zoned by time or space, a promoting authority has often found it more convenient to let the sailing to a club. Such a club would be allowed a specific area of water and have leased to it a piece of land on which would be constructed its own clubhouse, and parking and launching facilities. The fishing too might be let to a club, but frequently the promoting authority has preferred to control this use itself on a day or season ticket basis. Whichever course is adopted it may be useful to establish a committee or other means whereby the fishermen can present their collective views to, and be consulted by the authority.

The arrangement outlined above is comparatively simple to operate and will continue to be appropriate where the water can accommodate only a limited number of activities and where there is no likelihood of any substantial increase in levels of use. Where there is pressure and scope for extending the range of uses, and/or increasing the levels of use and especially where the resource is a new one, it is likely that something more will be needed. There is however no hard and fast rule and appropriate machinery must be developed to meet the local circumstances.

The promoting authority will find it useful to be able to negotiate with one or more clubs representing the participants in each sport at a particular site. As often as not a club will spring into being even before the water itself exists in the case of new reservoirs, and it may be convenient to recognize this club as the one to speak for its particular activity. It may, however, fall to the promoting authority to encourage the formation of a club either because none has developed spontaneously or because there are several in the field each competing for recognition. In the latter case it may be appropriate either to encourage the various clubs to get together and nominate one of their number as the focal point or to form a new combined club or yet again for the authority to promote a public meeting out of which an entirely new club may be formed.

Where there are several activities on a particular water it may be desirable to have several clubs and to link these in some form of advisory committee, formally or informally. A less common alternative, but one likely to become more appropriate as economic circumstances increasingly point to the sharing of facilities by participants in several different activities, is the formation of a multi-sports club responsible for overall control of all participants. An individual joining such a club could either become a member of the section of his choice or preferably would pay to join the club as a whole and be free to participate in any or all of its activities. In such a case there would be merit in arranging, from the outset, how clubhouse facilities may best be combined and how they are to be funded to provide a maximum of facilities at a minimum of cost but with an attendant degree of give-and-take between the parties concerned.

In the planning stages of developing a new water area for recreation the promoting authority will probably be under pressure to consult all the interested parties and even if not pressed, will probably find it both prudent and helpful to do so. The formation of an advisory committee preferably at officer level is probably the best means of meeting this need, and there is much to be gained from keeping it as informal as possible subject of course to any clear recommendations and decisions being properly recorded. Committees that are too large tend to be unworkable, and it is important not only to limit membership to those bodies with a definite interest in the scheme but to try to ensure that their representatives have both the competence and the authority to make a positive contribution to the proceedings. Groups and organizations likely to be involved fall into four main categories:—

(i) Those with a general promotional role whose interests cover a group of activities, for example the Sports Council (encouragement of sporting activities generally), the Countryside Commission (encouragement of informal outdoor recreation), and the Nature Conservancy Council (promotion of nature conservation). These are national bodies but contact will most likely be through their regional organizations. In some areas a local Sports Advisory Council composed of representatives of many or all local sporting activities may be in existence and able to offer help.

(ii) Specific user organizations, for example individual local sports clubs or, where none exist, the regional arm of the appropriate national body such as the Royal Yachting Association, British Water Ski Federation, Amateur Rowing Association, etc. This group also includes conservation bodies such as the local County Naturalists Trust, Royal Society for the Protection of Birds, etc.

(iii) Specific amenity organizations such as local civic and protection societies which are concerned not so much with the provision of recreational facilities as with ensuring that such developments do not adversely affect the surrounding environment and the local communities.

(iv) Local Authorities (Parishes, Districts and Counties) who have the dual role of promoting recreation and protecting the environment and who in any event exercise the ultimate control in so far as planning permission may be required for particular developments. Local Education Authorities in particular are usually keen to develop training facilities for schools and youth groups.

Whilst such advisory committees can be of real help during the planning and development stages, the question of whether they should continue and in what form once the facilities are operational, must be answered according to local circumstances. Certainly where there are several activities on or around the water, including conservation, regular meetings between the various group representatives on a fairly informal basis can be of real value as a means of sounding opinion on changes proposed by the providing authority, communicating such changes once decided, resolving conflicts between the groups, working out operating procedures, programming activities and events, and generally increasing mutual understanding. Whether or not it is necessary to extend the membership beyond these user groups will depend on the scope for, or likelihood of, significant variations in the pattern or level of use and the extent to which such changes could affect the surrounding environment. It may also be considered appropriate to include other bodies in order to reassure local opinion about possible implications of either current or future schemes to be promoted by the providing authority. This could only be decided in the light of local circumstances, but it must be remembered that the wider the consultation is spread and the more decisions that are made subject to advisory committee comment, the more difficult it will be to exercise the proper functions of management in responding to changing needs and circumstances.

There is no doubt, however, that in the right circumstances it can be extremely helpful to the providing authority to have a local committee of user groups at a particular site not only for advisory and consultation purposes but also to co-ordinate and initiate executive action within the policy guidelines set down by the authority. This could include the sharing of tasks such as safety cover on the water, supervision of parking areas, hygiene, and catering in shared premises and so on. Again, no hard and fast rules can be drawn, but where mutual interests can be served, economies in operation achieved and goodwill maintained, sharing of the load should certainly be given serious consideration subject always to the proviso that any sharing arrangement must be capable of being clearly understood by all the parties concerned.

7. FISHERY CONSIDERATIONS

FISH SPECIES

The geographical distribution of fish depends on the availability of suitable waters and the ability of fish to reach them, either by natural means or with the help of man. This is illustrated by the freshwater fish fauna of the British Isles, which contains a total of 51 species; of these 13, ranging from the common carp to the North American rainbow trout, have been deliberately introduced, leaving only 38 native species[5,6]. A further 13 species, including the eel, salmon, mullet, flounder, and sticklebacks, either spend only a part of their lives in freshwater or are equally happy in the sea, leaving only 25 truly freshwater fish in the British fauna. Compared with continental Europe[7], this number is low and is a consequence of the most recent ice age. When most of this country was glaciated or covered in frozen tundra the plants, animals, and fishes that are familiar today were displaced far to the south. However, when the ice retreated northwards, the newly exposed land was re-colonized, first by sub-arctic species and later by those which prefer a temperate climate, but this process was only partially complete when the English Channel was formed, after which time only those fish which could tolerate salt water were able to enter our rivers.

Although the British freshwater fish fauna is poorly developed, most of our species have been exploited for food until recent times and those which the cottager could not eat himself he fed to his pig or his cat. However, the demand for fresh-water fish declined as living standards rose and as fast refrigerated transport made sea fish widely available inland. Today only salmon and trout are widely eaten; eels are enjoyed by a few people, but species such as carp, pike, tench, grayling, and perch are a minority taste.

In spite of this, angling for pleasure is still a popular sport and there is great demand for access to any water which might contain catchable fish[8]. Anglers recognize three categories of sport, sea fishing, game fishing and coarse fishing, the first of which does not concern us here. The other two classes are distinguished by the species of fish sought, the acceptable ways in which they may be caught, and the historical mores of angling. In general, game fishing is for salmon or trout using rod and line with artificial flies or lures, and coarse fishing is the term which covers angling for all other freshwater species.

Game Fish Species

Salmon.—Only the Atlantic salmon is found naturally in British waters. At least two Pacific species have been introduced to continental Europe and may stray into our rivers, but are not considered here.

Adult salmon[9] enter our rivers from the sea in all months of the year, but peak migrations may occur in early spring, in mid-summer, or in late autumn. Salmon do not feed in freshwater although they may remain there for several months while migrating upstream to their spawning grounds, where they spawn in mid-winter, burying their eggs in excavations in the pebbly bed of the stream. Completed nests are known as redds and are recognizable as disturbed humps of gravel on the stream bed. The eggs are large, about 7 mm in diameter, and take one or two months to hatch, depending on water temperature. Even at this stage, the newly hatched alevins are not independent; they are about 1 cm long, without scales and having only rudimentary fins, and are attached to a large yolk sac which continues to nourish them for another month or so. Alevins lie quietly in the interstices of the gravel, swimming away from light when disturbed and do not emerge until they metamorphose into fry when all their food reserves are exhausted.

Salmon fry are about 2 cm long and are recognizable as small fish, having scales, fins, and a pigmented skin. At this stage they have to search for food for the first time and those which fail die. Those survivors which are not eaten by predators (including their brethren) establish individual territories and grow rapidly, being known as parr when they reach a length of 6 to 8 cm. Salmon parr have distinctive vertical black bar marks along their sides and at one time, before their life history was unravelled, were thought to be a separate species of fish. Parr spend up to three years in their native river, depending on their growth rate (this phase may be much longer in colder continental rivers), but migrate out to sea as smolts in the spring following the attainment of a critical length of about 15 cm. Smolts are adapted for marine life and are very sensitive to mechanical damage for as long as they remain in freshwater. They are recognizable by their uniformly silver colour.

Little is known about the habits of salmon in the sea. They are not found in British coastal waters, but do occur off the coast of Greenland, although tagging experiments have shown that this is not their only destination. After one, two, or more winters they return to the river of their birth and the cycle is complete. Fish returning after only one winter in the sea are known as grilse, whereas those which remain in the sea for two or more winters before returning are classified by anglers as "true salmon" and are usually larger. Fish which have spawned are known as kelts, those which survive migrate out to sea and may return to their parent river to spawn in subsequent years.

Salmon are usually found in upland rivers or chalk streams, being unable to survive at any stage in their development in waters much warmer than 25°C or with a dissolved oxygen content consistently below 70 per cent of the saturation value. They are sensitive to organic pollution and their eggs are rapidly killed if the flow of water through the redds is reduced or blocked by silt.

Brown Trout.—Brown trout[10] are indigenous to Britain and are found wherever the water quality is high and summer temperatures are not too great. Their requirements are similar to those of the salmon, but slightly less demanding so they are frequently found alongside other species such as dace, roach, or perch, although it is in upland streams that they become the dominant fish species. The trout population contains a migratory component, the sea trout, which has a similar life history to that of the salmon except that sea trout are less specific in returning to their parent streams, do not disperse so far in the sea, keeping mainly to coastal waters, and the survival of adults after spawning is better so that more of them return to spawn a second time. Returning adult sea trout may weigh up to 6 or 8 kg and are much sought after by anglers.

The resident component of the population, the brown trout, completes the whole of its life history in freshwater but may make an upstream spawning migration in the autumn. This is particularly true of trout in lakes, whose tributary streams are the nursery area for the adult lake population. Resident brown trout reach a weight of 1·5 to 2 kg in the wild, but much larger fish have been bred in captivity.

Other Trout Species[5].—Introduced species such as rainbow trout and brook char are reared extensively in hatcheries to supply recreational fisheries, but only occasionally form successful breeding populations in the wild. There are indications that brook char may be able to survive and breed in cold nutrient-poor lakes where even brown trout are unsuccessful, in which case they will be welcomed by anglers as a valuable addition to the British fauna.

Coarse Fish Species

Coarse fish comprise all freshwater species other than salmon or trout. The only characteristic they share is that they all (with the exception of the eel) spawn in spring or early summer rather than in the winter months. The group includes representatives from 14 of the 20 families of the zoological class of boney fishes found in Britain and covers a wide spectrum of habitats.

Grayling Family:—The grayling is a relative of the trout and salmon, but unlike them it spawns in spring or early summer. Grayling are found in similar rivers to those which contain trout, and are particularly plentiful where the water is hard and productive. Many anglers enjoy fishing for grayling during the winter months (when trout are out of season), using methods which they would otherwise use for trout.

Pike Family.—The pike is a familiar predator in lakes and slow-moving rivers, requiring clean, well oxygenated water but able to survive the summer temperatures found in lowland Britain. Pike breed in early spring, attaching large quantities of small brown eggs to the stems of water weeds. The eggs hatch within a few days, releasing fry which feed on microscopic plankton, insects, and eventually other fish.

Carp Family.—The carp family includes species such as the common carp, crucian carp, barbel, tench, bream, bleak, rudd, roach, chub and dace which are all important to anglers. Dace, roach, bleak, chub, and barbel are principally river fish, whereas the others are typically found in lakes and ponds. Common carp, tench, and crucian carp are very resistant to high temperatures and low levels of dissolved oxygen, but are at the limit of their geographical range in Britain. They are not common north of the Humber, and do not breed successfully in this country in cold summers.

Perch Family.—Perch are widespread and common in lakes and slow-moving rivers throughout Britain. They require clean water and breed in spring when they drape their eggs in strands on submerged vegetation. The related ruffe is found in the lower reaches of rivers in central and eastern England, and is an attractive fish to anglers.

Eel Family.—The eel differs from all other freshwater fish species found in this country in that it spawns at great depth in the Sargasso Sea in the central Atlantic and its larvae reach this country after some two years of passively drifting in the Gulf

Stream. Whilst still at sea, the larvae metamorphose into elvers which migrate into our estuaries in spring and probably penetrate to most freshwaters in the country. Adult eels spend about seven years in freshwater, migrating back to sea as silver eels in the autumn when they are mature. The eel is the only species for which there is a commercial fishery in freshwater. A crop is taken from the spring elver run on the river Severn, immature adult eels are fished for throughout the year using fyke nets and migratory silver eels are trapped on fixed grids in many rivers in the autumn.

FISH AND THEIR ENVIRONMENT

The most important pathway by which organic material is produced in nature is photosynthesis, the process by which green plants grow using sunlight as a source of energy to elaborate inorganic compounds into living material. Production continues via a web of food chains involving successive organisms, which typically increase in individual size as they decrease in abundance. Dead or waste material is re-cycled through the activities of micro-organisms which break down organic material into its inorganic components.

The amount of biological material present in a system at any one time is known as the *biomass* or *standing crop*. The amount produced over a period, typically a year, is the *production* and the amount harvested is the *yield*. *Primary production* relates to the activities of green plants in producing organic material; *secondary production* refers to the conversion of plant material to animal flesh by herbivores; and *tertiary production* is the process whereby carnivores convert one form of animal flesh into another. The concept of *terminal production* relates to the production of organisms such as fish which are directly used by man. The energy flow through a food chain and the relationships between the production and yield of the components of a community of animals and plants are amenable to mathematical analysis, which can establish a basis for scientific fish stock management[11].

In a closed aquatic system the absolute abundance of living material depends on the initial concentration of inorganic precursors such as phosphates, calcium, silica and nitrogen compounds and it cannot increase unless more inorganic materials (and energy) are added. Natural systems on the scale that can be managed by man are not closed, but lakes and ponds are sufficiently close to the model to be treated as closed systems in the short-term and it is true to say that the production of fish in these waters is ultimately governed by the availability of inorganic nutrients, together with such physical factors as water temperature and the availability of energy from sunlight.

Even though the total biomass in a lake may be regarded as being fixed, the relative abundance of the plants and animals which make up the living community and of the different age classes within each species, depends on the dynamic balance between the forces of reproduction, mortality, growth, predation, and competition. This results in a biological system which can make the optimum use of available resources, since only the most efficient organisms survive, but which has the flexibility to respond to changing environmental conditions, allowing new species to become dominant. It follows that, although biological systems can be manipulated and are robust in the face of change, the maintenance of a particular equilibrium state may be very difficult if environmental conditions are not constant.

The success of a fish species forming part of a larger community depends on maintaining a balance between mortality and reproduction. In the wild, British freshwater fish populations suffer a mortality rate which may be as high as 30 to 50 per cent each year, and even higher in the younger stages. Rather than devoting their energies to raising a small number of offspring under protected conditions, fish have evolved to meet this problem by releasing large numbers of eggs in the hope that a few might survive. A pair of brown trout may produce 800 eggs a year for three or four years and yet only two of these need to survive to maturity for the population size to remain stable. By ensuring that there is a surplus of individuals available at all stages of the life history, the species is always in a position to exploit the environment to the full. Conditions vary from year to year with the result that fish produced in good years may be more abundant in the population than those from poor years, but the requirements of individual fish change as they grow larger, so fish which were successful as fry may find conditions harder in subsequent years and have to compete against each other as well as against other species for the available resources. Limiting factors influencing population size include water temperature, chemical water quality, the availability of food or territorial space, predation by other species, and the incidence of disease.

The ability to determine the age of fish is an important tool in the management of fish populations. If absolute growth rates were known it would be possible to gauge age from the length of a fish alone, but nature is not this tidy, and indirect methods have to be used to estimate age. Fish continue to grow throughout life, so older fish tend to be larger than younger ones from the same population, but being cold-blooded their growth rate depends on water temperature as well as the availability of food. Both of these factors vary with the seasons so that fish in temperate latitudes follow an annual growth pattern which is rapid in summer and autumn but slow in the colder months. This results in a direct record of the age and growth of individual fish being preserved in their bony structures, rather like the rings on trees.

For many species, age and growth can be measured by examining detached scales under the microscope, as each scale consists of a thin bony plate enclosed in a projecting pocket of skin. Once formed on the developing fry, the number of scales remains constant throughout life and their growth is proportional to the growth of the fish as a whole. It follows that the radius of the annual growth zones on a scale is a measure of the growth rate of the fish and if both the length of the fish at capture and the radius of the whole scale are known, the length of that fish at each stage of its life can be estimated. If this information is obtained from a number of fish forming a random sample of the population it is possible to estimate the growth rate, mortality rate, and age structure for the population as a whole. When an estimate of population size is combined with this information the standing crop, annual production, and sustainable yield of the fishery can be estimated.

When a fish stock is first exploited by man the annual yield is high in proportion to the fishing effort expended, but as the harvest makes inroads into the fish stock, catchable fish become rarer and the catch per unit of effort falls. If the value of the catch falls lower than the cost of fishing, market forces will close the fishery, but if catch value remains high in spite of a diminishing yield it may be economic to exploit the fishery until the fish stock is extinct. This is clearly undesirable in the long-term and when such circumstances occur a policy of regulation is needed to produce a sustainable yield, representing the annual increment of growth of the stock, before the biological system collapses under the strain. In general, larger fish are more acceptable than small ones and tend to be removed from the population first when fishing begins. The age structure of an unexploited population is hyperbolic, with large numbers of young stages being continually reduced by mortality so that only a few older, larger fish survive. In an exploited population, the hyperbole is truncated as large fish are removed selectively. As the intensity of fishing effort increases the stock of fish becomes progressively smaller and younger. If a stage is reached where fish are being removed from the population before they are old enough to spawn, there is a danger that the population and the fishery will collapse. It is for this reason that size limits are applied to many fisheries, the size limit being related to the size at which the fish become sexually mature, but it is important that size limits should not be set too high or fish will die of natural causes after they have spawned but before they may be legally caught, thus reducing the potential yield of the fishery. Size limits are an important management tool, but need to be related to the biology of the fish stock and to the level of fishing pressure.

MANAGEMENT OF STOCKS FOR RECREATIONAL FISHING

The demands made on a recreational fishery are less clearly defined than those made on a fishery exploited for food. Individuals engaging in recreational activities, by definition, are not operating on the concepts of profit and loss which govern the viability of an operator producing fish for the market. Provided that they are satisfied with the experience most anglers are relatively indifferent to the cost of their sport and do not value their catch in money terms. Indeed, it is only the sea fisherman and the game angler who take their catches home, the great majority of anglers return their catch to the water at the end of the day's sport.

Angling has been described as the contemplative man's recreation; it depends on individual skill rather than team effort, even when practised as a competitive sport, and is not hedged round by closely defined rules. One of its attractions is that it gives scope to the individual to pursue his own path, with the result that no two anglers approach their sport with the same objectives. Some anglers are content only if they are constantly catching fish, others derive satisfaction from making their task as difficult as possible and then surmounting the self-imposed difficulties by the exercise of skill. An angler may spend months in pursuit of one record sized specimen fish, or hours snatching small fry from a canalized waterway in pursuit of competition prizes—another may use the sport to enhance his social prestige, or as an acceptable excuse for relaxing in pleasant surroundings away from home. Many of these aims are incompatible and not all of them can be provided from one fishery, so it is essential that the fishery manager should identify the segment of the angling market he hopes to satisfy and manage his resource to that end.

Natural Fisheries

Natural, unmanaged fish stocks can form the basis of successful recreational fisheries, provided that the level of exploitation is low, as in an upland trout fishery where the yield of fish taken is no greater than can be replaced by natural production, or in coarse fisheries where fish caught are normally returned to the stock and mortalities arising from the handling of fish are not too high.

Any new body of water in temperate latitudes will rapidly be colonized by fish from the catchment, introduced by man or arriving as eggs on the proverbial feet of ducks. Once present, they form part of an expanding but unstable community of plants and animals exploiting the new resource, with different species in turn rising to dominance and then declining in the face of more successful competitors. In the early stages of the development of a fish population, the growth rate of individual fish will be high as they are not limited by lack of space or food, but if the population is very sparse they may have difficulty finding one another to breed. Thus, if the initial population is below a critical density it will decline, even though the individual fish are healthy and grow well. Once this critical population density is exceeded, however, numbers will increase exponentially until the standing crop of fish is as large as the resources of the lake can support. At this stage the population will consist of a moderate number of fast-growing fish, including a high proportion of older, larger individuals. The fecundity of the population will be high and the mortality rate low. Such a population will be in peak condition and will appeal to the angler looking for "specimen" or record fish, but they may be difficult to catch on account of the moderate density of the population and the availability of natural foods with which the angler's bait has to compete for the fishes' attention.

Once a developing fish population has reached the optimum size which can be supported by the environment, further growth in the biomass is limited by the availability of food. In the absence of predators, the biomass will remain steady in future years, but reproduction will continue so that more and more fish compete for the available resources. Growth rates fall, mortality rates rise, few fish survive to old age and ultimately the population will consist of a large number of small, young, stunted fish in poor physical condition. Such a population is liable to a disastrous mortality from parasites, disease, or deterioration of water quality, leaving only a few individuals to carry the species forward to its next cycle of population growth and decay. Fish in overcrowded populations are numerous and hungry and are suitable for fisheries where anglers are looking for an assured catch but are not concerned about its quality. Such fisheries are common in enclosed lowland waters, particularly if they have been managed by the removal of predators such as pike or perch, or by over-stocking with the desired species, but their instability makes them unattractive as recreational fisheries.

Managed Populations

Where a natural fish population is unsuitable for exploitation as a recreational fishery, it can be artificially managed to produce the conditions anglers want, but management costs money and is only justified if it results in better use of the fishery or a higher income from fishermen.

Increasing the Food Supply

In a small fishery where production is limited by the availability of food, the standing crop of fish can be increased by feeding them. The resulting improved growth rate of individual fish can only be maintained as long as feeding continues, but if no fish crop is taken from the water, the biological community will become more and more unstable and prone to such unwanted side-effects as massive algal blooms as the level of nutrients increases. Feeding the fish in larger waters is expensive and impracticable as large quantities of food are needed and much is wasted when it is not possible to feed in such a way that the food can be seen to be consumed by fish.

However, where feeding is uneconomic, it is possible to increase fish production by indirect means by fertilizing the water with phosphates, nitrogen compounds, or lime, which promote plant and algal growth for conversion into fish flesh via the food chain. Even this approach may be difficult and expensive in large lakes, and it has the disadvantage of directly stimulating algal growth, which may be undesirable if the water is abstracted for public supply.

A fish population fed by the addition of resources from outside is by definition overcrowded and will suffer drastic changes if the external food supply is cut off. Competition for food will increase; individuals will starve; growth rates will fall, probably to zero; mortality will increase, and fecundity will diminish. When a new equilibrium is established the nutrients previously added will have been converted into a larger standing crop of small stunted fish which will be indistinguishable from those in the original unmanaged population.

POPULATION CONTROL

The population dynamics described in the preceding sections have assumed that food supply has been the factor limiting population size, but this is not always the case. Population numbers may be kept in check by predators or disease organisms, whose own numbers are in balance with the fish population, or by the availability of young fry entering the population to make up the loss of adults resulting from death, predation, or cropping. If spawning sites are limited or there is insufficient food for the young stages, the full reproductive potential of the population will not be realized; as a result, the adult population will be under-stocked in relation to its own food supply and will enjoy the virtues of high growth, good physical condition, and low mortality rates.

In a recreational fishery these conditions can be simulated by artificial means, although relatively crude management techniques cannot be expected to achieve the same fine balance as the subtle forces of nature[12]. The objective must be to lower the size of the population so that the available food is shared between fewer fish, which then have a better chance of survival. The most natural way of achieving this end is to encourage anglers to take a crop, as happens in a trout fishery, but this solution might be difficult to implement in a coarse fishery where anglers are reluctant to kill their catch. An alternative may be to introduce predators to the water, such as pike, but even this solution may be opposed by anglers and exotic species (such as zander) should be introduced only after consultation with local conservation bodies and the Nature Conservancy Council, who will be able to advise on the likely impact of the new species on the environment. Where anglers will not take a crop and predators are unacceptable, population numbers can be controlled by artificial means such as trapping, netting, or "electric" fishing.

Electric Fishing

Electric fishing[13] is the technique of catching fish by the application of an electric field which directly affects their nervous systems, resulting in temporary paralysis. The equipment is potentially dangerous, but can be operated safely by trained staff who *must observe a recognized code of practice* to minimize the hazards. The efficiency of electric fishing depends on the size of fish caught (larger specimens being more susceptible), the conductivity of the water, and the output of the machine, which may produce an AC, DC or pulsed DC field. In good conditions fish may be caught in 2 to 3 m of water, but the efficiency of the method is greatest in shallow streams and small ponds where fish are unable to escape the field. On larger shallow waters the area to be fished may be divided up with nets and each section fished separately. Electric fishing is particularly useful where underwater obstructions make other methods unusable. **On no account should mains power be used for electric fishing, as this is extremely dangerous.**

Seine Netting

This technique consists of laying a semi-circle of net, typically 200 m long and 5 m deep, and drawing the ends into the bank so that trapped fish are enclosed in an ever smaller volume of water. The efficiency of seine netting depends on the skill of the operators, and is greatly diminished if the water contains obstructions which prevent smooth operation of the net.

Gill Netting

Fixed nets suspended by floats will trap fish which run into them, but they usually die as the net prevents their gills from working. The efficiency of a gill net depends on the density of the fish population and the size of the fish. Small fish may swim through the meshes unharmed, whilst those which are too large will bounce off the net without being caught. Slim fish such as pike are more likely to be caught than deep bodied specimens such as bream.

Fish Traps

Fixed traps are effective for catching migratory fish populations which follow known routes, but they are expensive to build and to run. Portable traps such as perch cages are more commonly used in the management of recreational fisheries; they operate in a similar way to lobster pots, and are most effective in early spring when shoals of perch concentrate for spawning.

Culling Rates

The optimum balance between population size and the physical condition of the fish is achieved when the standing crop is just below the maximum that can be supported by the available food supply. In nature, this optimum occurs only as a transient stage in the development and decay of a fish population and would be difficult to sustain by artificial means. The manager of a recreational fishery should aim at a rather lower biomass to be certain that the food supply is not limiting the growth of his stock. Before fish populations are culled by one of the methods outlined above, it is essential that there should be a biological appraisal to determine standing crop, population number, age and size distribution, growth and mortality rates[14].

It must be remembered, however, that what is required is management information, rather than statistically proven scientific fact. Broad appraisals quickly arrived at are to be preferred to more precise, but delayed, information. As a rough guide, it has been found that overcrowded coarse fish populations in southern England can be effectively managed by removing one-third of their number, with repeated culls every second year, and that fish populations are sufficiently resilient to respond to this treatment by producing an acceptable balance between size and catchability of fish.

Stocked Populations

Where the size of an adult fish population is limited not by its food supply but by the availability of young fish entering the population to grow to maturity, the number and weight of adult fish in the water and the productivity of the fishery can be improved by introducing extra young fish to make up the deficit. Such a situation may occur in a lake trout fishery with inadequate tributaries where fish can spawn, or in a fishery where the fry rely on a specialist food supply which limits their number. The extreme case would be a fishery using an exotic species, such as rainbow trout, which grows well in our climate but which does not normally spawn unaided in the wild.

Although stocking originated as a way of making good the deficiencies of Nature, it has developed as a management technique to the extent that entirely artificial fisheries can be created overnight by stocking waters with large numbers of adult fish which are rapidly removed by anglers. In such a "put and take" fishery, the water is merely a medium in which the angler practices his art. The greater part of the food resource of the water is used by the fish to maintain their physical condition, with little left to allow them to grow, but as most fish are caught within a few weeks of stocking, this is of little consequence. The natural resources of a put and take trout fishery are devoted entirely to providing anglers with sport. The net production of food from such a system is negligible and there may even be a net loss, as a proportion of the stocked fish will die before they are caught, but its recreational value can be high and in water supply reservoirs the presence of a dense fish population voraciously devouring the plankton can have operational benefits in that organic material is being removed and disposed of by anglers rather than by the water treatment process.

THE MANAGEMENT OF PUT AND TAKE TROUT FISHERIES

The availability of put and take management methods has enabled trout fisheries to be developed wherever water conditions are suitable and there is a demand from anglers[15]. Limiting environmental factors are the dissolved oxygen content of the water, which should never be less than 50 per cent of the saturation value, and the summer water temperature, which must never exceed 25°C and which ideally should be below 20°C. In lakes smaller than 2 ha these conditions are satisfied, provided that the water supply is unpolluted, the water attains a depth of at least 2½ m, there are not too many water weeds or algal growths, and dissolved oxygen is not depleted by decaying mud on the bottom. Lakes shallower than 2 m warm up rapidly in summer and are not suitable for trout fisheries. Larger waters present fewer problems, but those deeper than 15 m are liable to become thermally stratified in the summer and may suffer from dissolved oxygen problems in their lower layers.

Trout are not the natural inhabitants of lowland lakes, whereas coarse fish such as roach, rudd, bream, perch, and pike will thrive under these conditions, competing with the trout for food and reducing their numbers by predation. When a trout fishery is started in a newly flooded reservoir, it is possible to slow down the development of coarse fish populations by stocking heavily with trout which prey on coarse fish fry, although coarse fish cannot be completely excluded in this way.

Any sudden change in the environment leads to instability in the balance between species and this is particularly so where water is concerned. New fisheries can be very productive, but may suffer from unusual and transient problems whilst the balance of nature is adjusting itself. Successive species such as algae, planktonic crustacea, or water snails may rise to dominance and then decline to relative obscurity, but are sources of potential trouble to the fishery manager whilst they are abundant. Algae can cause deoxygenation of the water in addition to being a nuisance at the treatment plant and crustacea and snails are carriers of parasites[16] which affect the fish. In this latter respect native brown trout are usually more resistant than exotic species and should be preferred for early reservoir stocking.

The success of put and take fisheries depends on economic rather than biological factors and provided a water is not grossly overstocked, it is economic factors which will determine its management[17]. The attractiveness of a fishery to anglers depends on price, the size of fish available, the likelihood of catching them and the overall quality of the environment, where factors such as seclusion, landscape beauty, and exclusiveness are important. From the point of view of the management, it is important to attract anglers, but in view of the expense of providing such a fishery, it is equally important that they should catch no more fish than they have, on average, paid for. This conflict of interests is particularly actue in the case of a fishery relying for its income on the sale of day tickets, where success depends on having a good reputation and so securing the repeated return of anglers during the course of the season. If prices are high and catch rates are low, there is a chance that anglers will not come in the first place, let alone return. However, if prices are low and catch rates are high the fishery is bound to run at a loss! It is generally considered that a trout angler will be satisfied and will return if he has a better than even chance of catching a fish during his day's sport. The stock density of the fishery should be adjusted to ensure an average catch per rod visit of at least 1 and preferably 1·5 fish. High catch rates will attract more anglers but will be uneconomic unless day ticket prices are adjusted to pay for them. Average catch per rod is obviously a very crude measure of angling success, as the novice may catch nothing whilst the expert scoops the pool. Nevertheless, anglers are prepared to accept such inequalities provided that a limit is placed on the expert's success. Bag limits of four, six, or eight fish are commonly imposed at day ticket put and take trout fisheries.

The conflict of interest between management and customers at a season ticket fishery is less acute. If a season permit holder has a blank day's fishing, he is generally happy to hope for better luck on his next visit. In such waters management is likely to benefit from an input of opinion and preference from the user, whose advice and views can usefully be sought before price structure and stocking programmes are finally determined.

Performance Indicators

No matter whether a trout fishery is run as a season permit or a day ticket water, it is essential that records should be kept of income, expenditure, fish stocked, fish caught, and the number of angler visits, so that the performance of the water can be monitored and compared with that of other similar waters. The following performance indicators can be derived from simple data and are invaluable as a management tool:—

Stock density	:	Number of fish stocked/ha/year.
Intensity of use	:	Number of rod visits/ha/year.
Available stock	:	Fish stocked/rod visit.
Angling success	:	Average catch/rod visit.
Efficiency of capture	:	Total catch for year÷total stock/year.

Stocking Policy

Control of the number of fish stocked is the most important tool in the management of a put and take trout fishery, but can be exercised effectively only on a long-term basis, unless the water is very small or very intensively used[18]. It is frequently the experience that no more than 70 per cent of the fish put in are likely to be caught by anglers; and this figure may be much lower for a water which is lightly fished.

In a case where the manager is aiming to produce a fishery with angling success of 1·5 fish per rod visit, he may need to stock two fish for every rod he hopes to sell. Intensity of use is inversely proportional to the size of a fishery, but for a water of about 100 ha within easy reach of a centre of population it could be expected to be of the order of 25 rods per day, so that for a season of 200 days 10 000 fish would be expected to be required, giving a stocking rate of 100 fish/ha. This figure would, of course, need to be reviewed and adjusted if necessary from year to year in the light of the performance of the fishery.

Even if a water is biologically capable of supporting a whole year's stock it would be a mistake to introduce all the fish in advance of the angling season, as this would lead to a situation where the available stock and catch rates would fall as the season progress: indeed, early birds would probably catch all the worms, leaving the fishery under-used once the catch rate fell below an acceptable level. This situation can be avoided by stocking not more than one-half the fish in advance of the season and the remainder at intervals as the stock is depleted.

One way in which this can be achieved is by growing a proportion of the fish needed on site, either in stew ponds or in floating cage nets. The manager then has the flexibility to introduce fish as he needs them, rather than being dependent entirely on the services of outside suppliers.

TROUT PRODUCTION FOR FISHERIES

Trout breed only once a year so trout production is a batch process taking 18 months in the case of rainbow trout (up to 30 months with brown trout) before the fish are large enough to stock in a put and take fishery. Demand for fish is high, but production is limited by the availability of suitable sites, so it is essential that the longterm needs of a fishery should be met by ordering stock fish well in advance.

Fish farming is a high risk business subject to flood, frost, drought, disease, and pollution, which can destroy a year's production in a matter of hours; these risks are recognized in the prices charged by fish producers, which are considerably higher than the bare cost of production. A fishery manager with suitable facilities, and who is prepared to accept the risk, can cut his stocking costs by producing his own fish. He should beware, however, of relying exclusively on his own efforts in case his own production is disastrously affected. Similarly, when placing outside orders, he should safeguard his supply by dealing with more than one producer.

The traditional trout farm relies on a flow of clean cool water to supply the fish with oxygen and to remove waste products before they build up to toxic levels. The available flow of water limits the quantity of fish which can be held at any one time, and hence the number which can be produced in a year. Absolute values for the volume of water required depend on water quality and temperature as well as the configuration and management of the farm, but the following figures may be taken as a guide. Eggs can be hatched in a flow of 250 l/day/1 000 eggs; fry need 1 000 l/day/1 000 fry, but larger fish require a minimum of 0·5 Ml/day per tonne of fish held.

Ideally, the water should be well oxygenated, free from silt and dissolved pollutants, within the pH range of 6 to 8, with a steady temperature of 10°C to 15°C throughout the year and should come from a gravity source uncontaminated by other fish populations to minimize the risk of disease. In practice it is difficult to fulfil all these requirements, but as a minimum the water should have a temperature of less than 20°C at all times, be free from visible suspended solids and toxic pollutants, and have a dissolved oxygen content of at least 75 per cent of the saturation value. Pumped water supplies involve both the costs associated with the power source and the risk of unreliability at a critical time. Borehole waters may, in their natural state, be deficient in dissolved oxygen or be supersaturated with nitrogen or carbondioxide, which could cause gas-bubble disease in the fish. These problems can be overcome by mechanical aeration before such water is passed through the farm, but other characteristics of natural borehole waters may require more complicated facilities for their treatment before use. Expert advice should be sought, if only to provide guidance as to costs to be taken into account if such processes are required.

It is generally assumed that when labour, food, and capital costs are considered, the smallest viable trout farm is one producing 25 tonnes of fish per year, but this figure is no more than a preliminary guide, individual circumstances varying widely. Such a farm would require 2 to 5 acres of land and a flow of 12·5 Ml/day of water. Provided that the flow of water is adequate, trout may be kept in ponds, channels, raceways or tanks, which may be excavated from the soil, lined with butyl rubber or plastic sheeting, or purpose-built from masonry, concrete, glass reinforced plastic, or steel. Individual ponds and tanks should be drainable and sited so as to be free from the risk of flooding. When pumped water supplies are unavoidable there should be a header tank with a capacity of at least 2 hr full flow to keep fish alive in the event of a power failure or pump breakdown.

When choosing the site for a fish farm consideration should be given to security against vandalism and theft. Various forms of remote sensing and warning devices are available, but their success is, clearly, dependent on personnel being available to respond to the warnings which they provide. If possible the farm manager should live on site so as to be available in emergencies and to deter poachers.

Fish Husbandry

Fish farming is a full-time occupation, every day of the year, and as it uses intensive rearing methods there is a constant threat of losses arising from disease or stress caused by over-crowding. Good husbandry, particularly strict hygiene, is required at all times. Waste or spilt food must be cleaned up immediately to avoid attracting vermin. Nets and equipment on the farm must be kept separate from those used for other purposes, and they should be sterilized regularly in 1 per cent sodium hypochlorite, 1 per cent sodium hydroxide in 0·1 per cent Teepol, or a proprietary iodophore. *Phenolic disinfectants must not be used on a fish farm.* No disinfectant should be allowed to enter any watercourse, equipment should be thoroughly washed in tapwater after sterilization, and the washings and waste solutions disposed of to land or in such other manner as may be acceptable to the appropriate water pollution control authority.

Concrete, plastic, or rubber-lined ponds should be brushed out daily to prevent the build-up of fish faeces, but earth ponds cannot be treated in this way without stirring-up mud from the bottom. Such ponds should be de-sludged annually, sprayed with sodium hydroxide/Teepol or covered with quicklime to kill pathogens and then left dry for a week. When re-flooded, no fish should be introduced for 48 hrs.

No matter how carefully a fish farm is managed, disease is always a potential problem. A daily record should be kept of the number of dead fry or fish removed from each pond or tank, and specialist advice should be sought from a veterinary surgeon or water authority fisheries department if mortalities rise suddenly. Certain diseases[16] are "notifiable" under the Diseases of Fish Act 1937 and if such a disease is found restrictions may be placed on the movement of live fish from the farm. The Act is administered by the Ministry of Agriculture, Fisheries and Food, whose fish disease laboratory at Weymouth is a valuable source of advice.

Trout are reared by artificially stripping mature adults and hatching the fertilized eggs in clean flowing water. Full details of the process are described in text-books[19,20,21], where it will be found that this stage of production requires very clean water, is labour intensive, and involves keeping adult fish throughout the year in preparation for the breeding season. For a small farm where it is not intended to experiment with breeding hybrids or specialist lines of fish, it is likely to be more economic to buy in newly hatched or feeding fry for rearing on. Where a farm has anything but a perfect water supply this policy is essential.

A modern development in trout rearing has been the use of floating net cages in open water to grow small fish to a size suitable for stocking. A typical cage may be 7 m square and 5 m deep, supported by a floating catwalk, and can be used to rear 1·5 tonnes of rainbow trout in a lowland reservoir. Higher stock densities are possible in colder, less productive waters, but under these conditions the fish will have a slower growth rate.

The siting of cage nets is critical: they must be in water at least twice as deep as the cage, they must be securely anchored in a sheltered position and yet there must be sufficient movement of water through them to keep the fish healthy. In nutrient-rich waters, algal growths rapidly choke the meshes of the net but can be controlled by raising each side of the net in turn, exposing it to the sun and air for 24 h and brushing off the dried remains. Treating fish diseases is more difficult than on a land-based farm, but by floating a plastic sheet under the cage and lifting the edges clear of the water, the fish can be isolated and treated with fungicides or antibiotics as necessary. After treatment the plastic sheet is withdrawn allowing clean water to enter the cage. Such a treatment method may not be acceptable if water is abstracted for direct supply from the reservoir where the cage is kept. If this is the case, fish must be removed from the cage for treatment in a dip-bath, but handling them increases the stress of medication and may result in higher than normal mortalities.

Cages are no less liable to attack by predators than are conventional fish farms. Herons can be excluded by stretching large mesh netting to form a closed box about 1 m high above the whole surface of the cage, but if the netting is not tight herons may sit in the centre causing it to sag below water level so that they are able to catch fish through the meshes. Some cage net operators report trouble with cormorants attacking trout through the side walls of the submerged net, or ripping the net and letting fish escape. This problem can be controlled by suspending vertical sheets of net around the outside of a cage, rather in the manner of torpedo netting around a battleship.

Cage rearing in reservoirs has been found to be successful for rainbow trout, but is not suitable for brown trout or brook char which are susceptible to bacterial diseases when kept under these conditions. Much has yet to be learned, however, about the long-term efficiency of cages. They are cheaper to provide than a conventional fish farm and, even though more difficult to operate, have the advantage of keeping a stock of trout on the fishery for release when required. Provided that the risk of loss is acceptable they offer a cheap way of raising rainbow trout at a put and take reservoir fishery.

Controls on Fish Farming

When the whole of the production from a fish farm is sold for food, rather than for re-stocking fisheries, the farm is regarded as "agricultural", a status providing some exemption from planning controls. Nevertheless, any prospective fish farmer would be well advised to consult both his local planning office and water authority before developing a new site. The use of water for agricultural purposes on land contiguous with a watercourse is exempt from the abstraction licensing provisions of the Water Resources Act 1963, but abstractions for other than "agricultural" use, or from underground sources, require the consent of the water authority under that Act. Any weir or dam to impound water requires consent under the 1963 Act and large impoundments of more than 25 Ml are subject to further controls related to the safety of the dams. Any work which involves construction in the flood plain of a statutory "main river" requires the water authority's consent under the Land Drainage Acts. All fish farm effluents are subject to control under the Rivers (Prevention of Pollution) Acts 1951 and 1961 and the Control of Pollution Act 1974. In England and Wales several of the regional water authorities have produced information leaflets about the relationship of their several functions (water abstraction, pollution control, fisheries management) to fish farming.

8. MAINTENANCE OF TREES AND WOODLANDS

Substantial areas of afforestation have been established over the years by many water undertakers and these commercial plantations should now form a substantial asset. Difficulties were often experienced in the past due to the small size of many such schemes, making it impossible to set up, economically, a fully equipped trained and properly supervised forestry gang. Often management did not progress beyond the establishment stage and in consequence much potential timber production was lost. The situation has changed now that the larger Regional Water Authorities have been established.

The management systems used to achieve the different objectives under which trees and woodlands were established (see pp. 129 to 132 of Chapter 4) will vary, but there are certain basic elements of establishment and maintenance which are common to all tree planting.

GENERAL ESTABLISHMENT AND MAINTENANCE

The choice of tree species suitable for the site and appropriate to the schemes objectives is a matter for specialist advice. This may often be available today from suitably qualified staff employed directly by water undertakers themselves, many of whose forestry operations are now of sufficient magnitude to warrant the engagement of such personnel. Alternatively, the Forestry Commission may be able to provide guidance, or to suggest suitable organizations or individuals in a locality capable of doing so.

If establishment and maintenance are to be carried out proficiently, it is usually essential to use trained labour which is fully engaged in forestry operations rather than to rely on the occasional use of inexperienced personnel normally occupied on other duties. The operations likely to be encountered are listed below, and are adequately described in the Forestry Commission Bulletin No. 14[22], and Booklet 46[23]:—

(1) Growing trees in nurseries.
(2) Preparation of land for planting (including vegetation removal, drainage, cultivation, and fencing).
(3) Planting and fertilizing.
(4) Weeding
(5) Brashing and pruning.
(6) Thinning, felling of mature trees, and timber processing.

It is unnecessary to describe these operations in detail here, but it is important to discuss the implications of some of them in relation to operations and general management in the water industry.

Tree Nurseries

The growing of trees from seed or cuttings in an economical way is a highly specialized operation involving considerable investment in equipment, buildings and land. As chemical weed control is also involved, care needs to be taken in the location of nurseries, particularly on gathering grounds, if possible pollution dangers are to be avoided. The differences in site conditions between the various woodlands and the multiplicity of objectives encountered within the water industry result in a requirement for an extensive range of species, numbers and sizes of trees, which is likely to vary from year to year. To ease supply and management problems, it may be preferable to obtain these requirements annually from large commercial nurseries.

Preparation of Land for Planting

It may be necessary to remove or control certain existing vegetation, for example rhododendron, in order to establish the required tree species. On the other hand, natural vegetation may sometimes help considerably in the initial stages by providing shelter or screening whilst the new trees are being established, and this is often more acceptable on aesthetic grounds in sensitive areas.

Drainage may be required in order to provide conditions suitable for tree growth, but it should be designed so as not to cause rapid run-off or soil erosion. Impeded drainage is often encountered on sites after major construction works have been completed, on parts of which it is usually necessary to carry out landscaping works to fulfil planning conditions. Sub-soil cultivation and surface rotovating is likely to be required before the satisfactory establishment of trees is possible.

The growth of trees on poor natural soils and peats has been found to be improved after the ground has been ploughed with special forest ploughs. Problems and criticism have resulted from their use, as the ground disturbance can appear considerable although only 25 per cent of the surface may actually be cultivated. Increased run-off and sediment loads have been found to occur, usually because no attempts have been made to limit them. The use of contour ploughing, catch drains, and sediment traps could effectively reduce such problems.

Newly planted trees may require protection in the form of fencing to exclude rabbits, sheep, cattle, horses and deer, more especially for the first ten years after planting. It is most important that such fencing should be adequate initially and that it should be maintained in a satisfactory condition continuously throughout this period. Even after that most trees are still vulnerable to damage caused by animals, especially if large herds are still involved, or if winter conditions are particularly severe. On balance, it is preferable to exclude farm stock from plantations at all times.

The increased use of sheep to control grass on reservoir embankments and surrounding areas can put at risk many trees, especially broadleaved varieties, unless they are adequately protected.

Planting and Fertilizing

The ultimate size of the trees to be planted must be appropriate to the circumstances of each site. For example, only small growing trees should be planted in inaccessible positions, unless it is accepted that considerable expense will be incurred in maintenance and ultimate removal.

It may sometimes be useful in areas of poor or compacted soils to aid establishment with tree mulch or fertilizer. Tree mulch usually consists of sedge peat, with small quantities of added nutrients, its aim being to encourage root growth and conserve soil moisture. Fertilizing of forests on a large scale is sometimes carried out to improve tree growth, using slow release fertilizers such as rock phosphate. The quantities used are small and applied infrequently in comparison with agricultural application. They should pose no problems to water supplies if the guidelines set out in the Forestry Commission Leaflet No. 63[24] are followed.

Brashing and Pruning

The pruning of side branches to a height of 2 m (brashing), although expensive, may be considered worthwhile to reduce fire danger to the plantations themselves as well as to adjoining installations. Opening up impenetrable thickets of young trees to allow inspection and management can improve their visual appeal when they are situated near to picnic areas, public highways, and rights of way. At the same time, this practice can discourage their use by the general public as rubbish tips.

Thinning and Felling of Mature Trees

It might be considered that the only reason for cutting down trees in a woodland was to produce timber, but the gradual reduction in the number of trees occupying an area of land also has very important silvicultural and management objectives.

The health, development, stability, and appearance of trees and woods can be improved by a properly managed thinning regime, which can at the same time produce timber. Trees that are grouped closely together are usually more susceptible to windblow, thus causing soil disturbance, and are unable to develop proper healthy long crowns or to grow valuable timber. This feature has been the cause of much adverse criticism of forests, especially those of coniferous species.

The maintenance of a regular programme of thinning over a five to ten-year cycle is the main element in the process of achieving the planting objectives in all woodlands.

Trees eventually die, become unstable, or are cut to produce timber depending on the main objective of the planting scheme. Any owner of trees has a responsibility in law[25] to practise good estate management and to ensure that his trees are not a danger to the general public or to his employees. Regular inspections should be undertaken to detect and remove dangerous and unstable specimens. However, if skilled supervision is employed and maintenance and replacement are practised on a regular basis, few problems should occur.

Certain regulations apply to the felling or lopping of trees in the U.K., but statutory water undertakers are exempt when the work is directly related to the operation of the works and to the safety of the water which the undertakers supply. In the case of non-operational circumstances, a felling licence may be necessary, and this can be obtained by making application to the Forestry Commission.

Specific trees and woodlands may also be the subject of tree preservation orders, in which case additional permission is needed from the authority issuing the order before work can be carried out. Trees located in conservation areas automatically fall under the same restrictions as do those to which preservation orders apply.

Although full time forestry staff are more likely to be efficient at undertaking commercial forest operations, if may be necessary to have a minimum of 800 ha of woodland to make a direct labour force worthwhile. Such an area would fully occupy the time of a suitably qualified head forester[26], supervising a staff of ten. One forestry worker is capable of maintaining 80 ha of woodland if he is using up to date techniques and equipment. A unit smaller than this may be over burdened with management overheads and machinery costs, making it more attractive to use the services of a forestry management company and contract labour.

Even in larger units, timber marketing may be a problem either due to the need to invest in expensive harvesting equipment, or to the impossibility of providing continuous supplies to specific markets. The sale of standing timber to firms specializing in harvesting and marketing has considerable advantages, but will still require specialist assistance to mark, measure, and present the timber correctly. Due to the relatively small quantities which are likely to be involved, the emphasis should be on the growing of quality timber rather than on the bulk production of poor grade material. The small and poor quality trees sometimes cut in early thinnings can usefully be sawn with inexpensive equipment by directly employed labour and used for estate maintenance or for local sale. Christmas trees can be a source of additional income, if properly managed and marketed.

9. REFERENCES

1. Department of the Environment, 1976, Waste Management Paper No. 4, "The licensing of waste disposal sites", H.M.S.O.
2. Gittins, J. W., 1978, *Journ. I. W.E.S.*, 32, 303, "Llyn Brenig: recreation and amenity".
3. Langford, P. R., 1979, *Journ. I. W.E.S.*, 33, 117, "Leisure and sports facilities at Rutland Water".
4. Saxton, K. J. H., 1969, *Journ. I. W.E.*, 23, 425, "The recreational use of Grafham Water (Great Ouse Water Authority)".
5. Maitland, P. S., 1972, Freshwater Biological Association, "Key to British freshwater fishes".
6. Varley, M. E., 1967, "British freshwater fishes", Fishing News Books.
7. Wheeler, A., 1969, "The fishes of the British Isles and North-West Europe", Macmillan, London.
8. National Angling Survey 1980.
9. Mills, D., 1971, "Salmon and trout. A resource, its ecology, conservation and management", Oliver and Boyd.
10. Frost, W. E., and Brown, M. E., 1967, "The trout", Collins, London.
11. Ricker, W. E., 1968, "Methods for assessment of fish production in freshwaters", Blackwell Scientific Publications, London.
12. Pratt, M. M. 1975, "Better angling with simple science", Fishing News Books,
13. Vibert, R., 1967, "Fishing with electricity", Fishing News Books,
14. Alabaster, J. S., 1977, "Biological monitoring of inland fisheries", Applied Science Publishers Ltd.,
15. Water Space Amenity Commission, 1977, Research Report 3, "The recreational use of water supply reservoirs in England and Wales".
16. Roberts, R. J., 1974, "Handbook of trout and salmon diseases", Fishing News Books,
17. Water Research Centre, 1978, Conference Proceedings, "Recreational freshwater fisheries: their conservation, management and development.
18. Crisp, D. T., and Mann, R. H. K., *Fisheries Management*, 8, 4, 101, "A desk study of the performance of trout fisheries in a selection of British reservoirs".
19. Hickling, C. F., 1962, "Fish culture", Faber,
20. Huet, M., 1972, "Textbook of fish culture-breeding and cultivation of fish", Fishing News Books,
21. Sedgwick, S. D., 1976, "Trout farming handbook", Seeley Service and Co.,
22. Forestry Commission, 1978, Bulletin 14, "Forestry practice", H.M.S.O.
23. Forestry Commission, 1978, Booklet 46, "Managing small woodlands", H.M.S.O.
24. Forestry Commission, 1975, Leaflet 63, "Fertilizers in the forest", H.M.S.O.
25. Arboricultural Association, 1976, Leaflet No. 6, "Trees and the law".
26. Department of the Environment, 1978, Pamphlet No. 81 (Forestry), H.M.S.O.

Chapter 6

SAFETY AND PROTECTION

1. INTRODUCTION

REGIONAL Water Authorities and Water Companies in England and Wales as statutory water undertakers have a positive duty under the Water Act 1973 to make their waters and associated lands available so far as is reasonably practicable for recreation, and it is likely that other water catchment owners throughout the British Isles may wish to do the same. This use, superimposed on the original purpose for which the reservoir area was created, will involve considerations of safety both on and off the water. Whatever the legal position may be, proprietors will feel themselves to be under an obligation not to invite people to expose themselves unwittingly to danger. Unfortunately, risks are largely "written out" of most people's scenario for living, but when they depart from daily routines and seek recreation they meet with situations where their personal actions gratuitously invite or remove danger. It must be assumed that most people are not particularly well tuned to recognizing danger, and that no amount of careful planning and equipping on the part of the landowner can protect people from the results of their own bad judgement.

This chapter is not concerned with the subject of safety at work and the requirements of the Health and Safety at Work etc Act 1974, which is referred to in Chapter 3 of Book 1 in this series[1]. It is concerned, primarily, with the safety of those who take part in the many and varied recreational pursuits on water and land associated with water, and with the safety of staff where they come into contact with the recreationists.

Recreation on reservoirs and water catchments has been a scene of widespread and successful development in recent years and no doubt this will continue. In this relatively new field of activity there are few textbooks or tables to which the designer may refer, and he is then forced to rely on experience. Theory and abstract calculations have less to offer. This Chapter therefore seeks to deal with practical issues. It does so in the general context that there are no absolute standards of safety where the very act of going onto, or into, or near water must involve a degree of risk which is implicitly accepted by those so doing. Were we to aim at absolute safety, no recreational activity at all would take place.

2. WHOSE SAFETY AND PROTECTION?

PERSONAL SAFETY

Everyone on the site must be considered when issues of safety arise. The question should automatically be asked when any proposals are considered—"could this be made more safe?" Visitors will usually arrive at the site by car and they may park the vehicle and then remain inside until they leave the site. Alternatively, they may leave the car but remain close by, or move to an adjacent area, or head off for a long walk or towards the base of some specific activity. Children may escape from control at any of these points. Visitors may enter premises to buy permits or to change into sailing clothes, and then push further on to the water itself by way of hired or owned

---

I.W.E.S., Recreation: Water and Land, 1981, Chapter 6.

boats. There is thus a widening series of actions each of which of itself or by its interaction on others can involve a degree of risk.

Staff on the site may be affected by these behaviour patterns, and by the passage of vehicles. There are few instances where they are likely to be actually endangered, but where they are closely involved with, for example, fishermen they must beware of the careless use of fishing tackle, especially hooks, and when handling boats they must do so in a safe manner.

PUBLIC AND PRIVATE PROPERTY

Visitors may bring with them, as well as their cars, personal items of equipment which may be worth considerable sums of money, and clearly these possessions should, as far as possible, be protected from the risk of damage or loss. There is also the question of the protection of private property which may adjoin the site, and the control of visitor activities should be adequate to avoid danger or damage to this.

ENVIRONMENT

It is not possible to conduct any activity on a site or to make any changes in practice without causing some impact on the environment. Recognition of this important fact is crucial, so that action can be taken to preserve selected aspects. This subject is far-ranging.

PUBLIC HEALTH

It must be assumed that the health of the whole community concerned is a primary consideration, and will act as a constraint upon all visitor activities.

3. STATUTORY REQUIREMENTS AND ENABLING POWERS

GENERAL

There are two Acts of Parliament which have an important bearing on the duty owed by the site owner to the visitor. First there is the Health and Safety at Work etc Act 1974 which, whilst dealing in the main with the issues implied by its title, is also concerned with persons not at work who may be affected by an employer's undertaking. Section 3 of that Act spells out the duty which an employer has in ensuring that no working practices take place which could endanger members of the public.

Whilst for many reasons, including safety, it will be normal practice to separate the recreational public from operations on site, it should be the aim to separate them by a margin suitable to the circumstances. Potentially dangerous equipment or materials must be kept out of the way.

The second Act which is of importance in this context is the Occupiers' Liability Act 1957. The main relevant provision in this legislation is that the occupier must take "reasonable" steps to ensure the safety of visitors to his land or premises. This duty is particularly onerous where children are concerned. There are indications that the Courts are taking a stern view of the duty of care which the occupier owes not only to visitors but to trespassers as well. It is advisable, particularly in the light of the judgement given in the case of *Herrington v. British Railways Board* (1972), and the case involving Swindon sewage works (*Wells v. Thames Water Authority* (1976)), to look with an imaginative eye on possible hazards.

Where the site owner provides facilities, these must obviously be safe in all respects, and all equipment must be suitable for safe use. Just as it is not thought to be necessary to draw attention to obvious danger, it is advisable to ensure that hidden dangers such as steeply shelving, or slippery, or unstable underwater shores, are indicated and, where possible, fenced off. Anything which renders hazards more difficult to perceive should be guarded against.

There is no duty to protect people from the results of their own ill judgement or wilful abuse of facilities or equipment. Nor, should other people be endangered as a result of such behaviour, would the site owner normally be expected to shoulder responsibility.

Life-saving apparatus, to a "reasonable" standard, should be provided. There is no clear guidance on what would constitute an adequate level of provision, and this is again a matter where the word "reasonable" must suffice. But it is obviously prudent to provide a lifebuoy at or near places where visitors are concentrated close to deep water, such as landing stages. In the case of a long shoreline, it is virtually impossible to have completely adequate safety provisions, since the odds are against a rescuer finding a lifebuoy sufficiently close to an emergency to be of any use. But, again, any such safety equipment must be suitable in design and must be adequately maintained.

Where boats are provided for recreational use, they must be of a safe and suitable design and, if there is any danger of swamping, they should be of an unsinkable kind.

Life jackets or buoyancy aids should comply with recommended standards, and should be in good condition. It is not universal practice to require these aids to be worn by boat fishermen, in view of the resistance of some anglers, but it is prudent for the site owner to have them available and to ensure that this fact is advertised.

There is no legal obligation on the part of the site owner to make visitors conduct themselves safely. Similarly, the law does not seem to compel the site owner to ensure that life jackets should be worn, but various safety organizations advise this.

Civil liability can to some extent be passed on to, for example, a tenant club, but liability for negligence resulting in death or personal injury cannot be avoided by exclusion clauses, or declarations to that effect on permits, notices, etc. (Unfair Contract Terms Act 1977).

Once visitors are allowed near work areas a new perspective in reviewing operating practices is necessary. Normally, visitors and operators will be separated in the interests of both, but there are occasions when this is not possible. For example, the cutting of grassed areas. Modern grass-cutting machines can, if not adequately screened, project stones with considerable force, and an accident to a visitor from such a cause would probably fall within the purview of Section 3 of the Health and Safety at Work etc Act 1974.

BYELAWS

These may be made under the powers contained in Section 22(6) of the Countryside Act 1968. Codes of byelaws exist for a number of reservoirs, and their main purpose is for the preservation of order, the prevention of damage, and for ensuring that visitors so behave themselves as to avoid spoiling the enjoyment of others. Clearly, the maintaining of a reasonable standard of order is conducive to safety and to the prevention of damage. This latter also comes under the heading of protection. It should be noted that prosecutions under such byelaws are very few; the main advantage of them is that they provide a "wall" to get one's back against, and they underpin the authority of wardens. Byelaws under the Countryside Act require the confirmation of the Secretary of State for the Environment, and to obtain this confirmation they do not usually depart very much from model byelaws produced by the Department.

4. SAFETY FOR RECREATIONALISTS AND IMMEDIATE SPECTATORS

GENERAL

Section 20 of the Water Act 1973 does not limit the obligation to use waters and associated land for water recreation only. A wide range of sports and pastimes may be practised and indeed encouraged on " . . . any land associated with water". Varying degrees of risk arise, and these are for the most part dealt with in codes of practice or rules of the governing body of the sport concerned. Since the experience of the organization in indentifying risks and suggesting or requiring practices to meet them is expressed in these rules or codes, a summary of them gives a useful guide to those with responsibilities for providing such facilities.

Water-centred activities include fishing, sailing (including board sailing), rowing, canoeing, motor cruising, power boating, water skiing, sub-aqua diving, swimming and bathing, and model boating.

Although intended primarily for those going to sea, the booklet "Seaway code"[2]. published by the Department of Trade and Industry, provides a useful primer to many of these sports. Another Department publication which contains a wealth of sound advice and information is "Safety on small craft"[3]. The "Water sports code"[4], produced by the Sports Council, is another useful publication, and the Council, together with the Water Space Amenity Commission and the Royal Society for the Prevention of Accidents (RoSPA) have issued advisory notes on water safety, provision in inland areas[5]. The RoSPA booklet "On the water—in the water"[6] is also a helpful guide.

It is recommended that all those who allow their waters to be used for recreation seek to ensure that, where the governing body for a particular activity lays down safety procedures, these should be adopted. One way of ensuring this is to require that user clubs or individuals are members of the appropriate affiliated body, or that they undertake in some other way to follow a strict safety code, departure from which could be a ground for exclusion, or suspension from the water.

Good management of recreation areas may be reflected in a number of ways, one of which is to ensure that adequate notices are available. A useful arrangement is to place at public car parks and access points "master" notice boards which show the reservoir, and outline the footpaths, access and no access areas, warden's post and any emergency points, telephones, etc. These notices may also, with advantage, be backed up by information located at strategic points referring to the items shown on the master noticeboard. Where visitors are requested to report accidents or emergencies, this fact and where to report them should be clearly shown.

WATER-CENTRED ACTIVITIES

Fishing

None of the national bodies which either govern or influence the safe conduct of this sport has produced a safety code as such. The managing authority of the water being used is expected to lay down the necessary rules to govern personal safety of the participants. Boat fishing is acknowledged as the branch of the sport with the most risk, and it is perhaps a reflection of the excellent safety record of boat fishing in reservoirs and lakes that the national bodies have not thought it necessary to produce a safety code.

An angler falling out of a boat is clearly at risk, especially if he is alone. If there is more than one fisherman in the boat, then the risk is reduced, and some authorities require at least two persons in each boat, and some—although very few—insist that fishermen should wear personal buoyancy aids (see section on "Safety Equipment" p. 181). Boat anglers are not, for the most part, used to wearing such aids, and it is a management judgement whether, in view of the low risk involved, it is desirable to make the wearing of aids obligatory. It is recommended that aids are made available on request, and that this fact is brought to the attention of all boat anglers. It may also be desirable to require, or recommend, that children and non-swimmers should wear these aids. It is further recommended that the wearing of thigh boots in a boat is forbidden. Knee boots are less dangerous, in that close-fitting ones will hold relatively little water on immersion, and loose ones can be kicked off. The wearing of ordinary shoes is much to be preferred in boats.

Boats themselves should be unsinkable and should be stable enough to allow the maximum designed number of people to move freely about without excessive heeling, and this will normally mean that the boats will not heel dangerously when anchored clumsily in breezy conditions. The sole (floor) of the boat should be uncluttered, apart from stretcher boards, and the boats should not float so high in the water when empty that a person in the water cannot reach the gunwale. Bailers should be provided and these should be attached to the boat in some way.

It is noted that, despite advice tendered to the contrary, fly fishermen often stand up in a boat to cast. Boats for this use should therefore be as stable as possible.

On reservoirs a drifting boat will eventually drive ashore at some point and, apart from incidental damage to the hull, this should not result in danger to the occupants. There are, however, circumstances where this is not the case. A craft which is out of control can drive downwind on to a vertical dam wall and pound until seriously damaged or capsized, or a boat might even pass over a spillway. In these circumstances it might be difficult for the occupants to reach the safety of the shore. The decision on whether boats should be allowed to go out in breezy conditions is important. At least the risks should be made known to boat users. It is useful to maintain a regular listen-in to wind and weather forecasts. The telephone directory will list meteorological forecast offices, usually at airports, where advice can be obtained on wind forecasts. Winds over Force 5 on the Beaufort scale (this scale is reproduced as Appendix A, p. 191) can create difficult conditions for rowing boats. A strong wind can cause a boat to be blown towards a hazard; local features will determine which wind force and directions are dangerous.

Oars and rowlocks must be adequate, not only for normal use but for the "desperate heave" of a strong oarsman trying to clear a lee shore. Some modern rowing boats are provided with somewhat ladylike spruce oars, but ash although heavy is preferable. A broken oar at the wrong time is a possible risk. Rowlocks should be fixed to the boat in some way so that they are not lost.

Risks to anglers are not confined to boat fishing. Slippery or crumbly banks, and soft mud or hidden holes in wading areas can be dangerous, especially to an angler wearing thigh boots. Any angler wading, even in a reservoir, is well advised to carry a landing net with a long stout handle which can double as a wading staff. This, of course, is up to the angler, but where wading is permitted he is entitled to expect safe wading conditions. Likewise, any dangerous areas should be adequately marked. It is important to consider whether an angler who has slipped or fallen could regain the shore when wearing thigh boots which have become full of water. If he would be unable to reach safety, then wading should not be allowed in that particular area.

Staff and visitors alike must realize that the back-cast of a fly fisherman can extend 30 m behind him, and that the fly is travelling very fast indeed as it reverses direction at the limit of the cast. Injuries from this cause are not uncommon, and are complicated by the barb on the hook. In some cases where the hook becomes embedded deeply, it is necessary firstly to cut the nylon cast near the fly and, secondly, to cut the hook itself with pliers so that the barbed end may be withdrawn from the flesh point-foremost. The hook may carry mucus or blood from a fish and this in turn may harbour bacteria. Hook wounds should be treated as potentially infective.

Sailing

The Royal Yachting Association produces a number of publications which give authoritative guidance upon the conduct of all aspects of sailing including the one most relevant to safety, i.e. "Safety boat handling"[7]. The accent on safety boats and their handling stems from the nature of the most popular type of inland sailing, namely, the racing of centreboard sailing dinghies or similar craft.

Unlike fixed-keel sailing boats, these boats will capsize when overstressed by the weather or unbalanced by errors in sailing technique. These errors are not infrequently made in racing or learning situations[8]. The design of sailing dinghies, whilst their lightness and speed are conducive to capsizes, makes them for the most part easily righted. These boats are buoyant to the extent that they cannot sink, and float high in the water with their crew even when swamped. The need for a safety boat is to assist crews who for some reason are unable to cope or have become exhausted.

Crews themselves are normally, or should be, obliged to wear personal buoyancy aids when sailing[9]. Winter sailing is now commonplace and many clubs insist on sailors wearing wet suits when water temperatures are at 5°C (41°F) or below. Immersion in cold water can cause sudden death[10], and the shock of immersion makes it difficult to breathe normally.

Given these factors, the basic safety devices are sailing boats buoyant to a satisfactory degree, personal buoyancy and, in cold conditions, wet suits. If these conditions apply, there is less need for safety boats on confined waters because a capsized vessel is soon going to reach the shore even if it cannot be righted. The safety boat is the long stop, essential to prevent capsized vessels drifting into danger near dams and spillways, and to recover crews when they become exhausted or injured. For this reason the provision of safety craft is virtually universal on inland waters, and it is desirable that a prerequisite of sailing starting is for the safety boat to be manned and on the water.

Sailing commonly takes place not only in cold but in gusty conditions. Because of the usually short fetch (length of exposed water) on reservoirs, dinghies can handle stronger winds on inland waters than on an exposed estuary or at sea. It is usually part of club organization to restrict or prohibit sailing when conditions are such that rescue services are likely to be unable to cope. All sailing has to be controlled by a person who is responsible for making this judgement.

The Beaufort scale of wind force has been accepted internationally and is used in communicating weather conditions. The scale is reproduced as Appendix A, p. 191.

Where sailing is directly administered, arrangements will depend upon whether visitors bring their own boats or hire these at the waterside. In the former case, buoyancy fixed in the boat and personal buoyancy must be scrutinized, and staff must be briefed to recognize safe buoyancy, security of fastenings in the case of buoyancy bags, and apparent airtightness and freedom from cracks or holes in the case of built-in buoyancy. It is also usual to require owners to produce certificates of third party insurance to a suitable amount. Most dinghy policies include at least £100 000 third party cover, some £250 000 at the time of writing (1980). Where boats are provided these items will already have been taken into account. Any hazards must be pointed out to visitors, and any marks on the water for their guidance must also be indicated. They will be expected to know, and follow, the rule of the road for preventing collisions in giving way to other vessels when this requires. It is recommended that copies of this rule are on display in simplified form insofar as they affect sailing boats. Crowding is not usually a hazard in itself, and conditions due to high density of craft become unattractive to sailors before they become unsafe. Boats are, for instance, in very close proximity before the start of a race.

Rowing

Competition rowing is rare on reservoirs, which by reason of their size and shape offer hostile conditions in breezy weather. There are some rowing clubs on such waters and the Amateur Rowing Association has drawn up a Code of Practice for safety[11]. This deals with the appointment, in a club, of an appropriately trained safety officer. Active club members must be able to swim, and in addition coxswains should wear life jackets. All rowers, coxswains, and coaches should learn capsize and accident drills, and should be encouraged to learn life saving and resuscitation techniques[12,13,14]. Adequate supervision is recommended. In addition to the safety code[11] there is a further code for regattas and for equipment[15]. These cover largely the maintenance of the rather delicate racing craft, checking of buoyant compartments, and the use of easily released clogs or straps which secure the feet of the rowers.

The existence of a safety code for rowing emphasizes the vulnerability of narrow lightweight racing craft of specialist design compared to the stablility and strength of the rowing boat used for fishing. The Amateur Rowing Association prefaces the safety code[11] with the words: "The primary responsibility for personal safety rests with the individual who is also responsible for ensuring that his or her activities do not harm others".

It is clear that the Amateur Rowing Association regard the safety code as a developing project. It contains a requirement that all cases of accident involving injury or damage to equipment which could have resulted in injury shall be reported to their Headquarters.

Canoeing

The British Canoe Union recognizes grades of proficiency tests, taken before an examiner appointed by the Union. These tests cover kayaks and Canadian canoes. They are: start test (this replaces the "elementary" test), inland proficiency, sea proficiency, inland advanced, and sea advanced. These are also described as the five star tests. Capsize drills are covered in the "elementary" test, which is a basic assessment of ability at the end of a beginners course. The "proficiency" test is aimed at ensuring that the candidate can be considered reasonably safe in a kayak or Canadian canoe under "normal" water conditions. The proficiency level is that of a member of a group, with a leader. These tests also contain non-safety elements, and require some ability to swim. The "advanced inland" test is for leaders of small groups of canoeists. The test includes rescue and "eskimo roll" techniques. The "advanced sea" test requires demonstration of a deep sea rescue with partners, and of an approved method of resuscitation. A bronze lapel or cloth badge indicates a holder of "proficiency" level, and a silver lapel badge indicates "advanced" level.

The British Canoe Union advises the wearing of a particular pattern of life jacket, to British Standard Specification No. 3595. This provides for 13·2 lbs buoyancy at all times and in addition can be orally inflated to give further buoyancy to a total of 35 lbs. A life jacket inflated, or containing buoyant material, which will provide the 35 lbs of positive buoyancy which is standard, is generally too cumbersome for safe or effective canoeing.

It is to be noted that although experienced canoeists will wear warm clothing, according to conditions, it may be necessary to agree whether, or when, wet suits may be required. Although a wet suit provides some buoyancy, it is recommended that life jackets should also be worn.

Canoes, especially those designed for slalom or other competitions, are liable to capsize. Throughout training, therefore, capsize drills to cope with this situation, together with instruction on the construction of the canoe and all equipment are given careful attention. Capsizes should not therefore lead to danger. It is essential, however, that canoes proceed in parties under the leadership of a certificated instructor, or holder of an "advanced" certificate (5 star). There is no reason for a group to split up (unlike sailing where boats become scattered over wide areas), and a minimum of three canoeists is accepted as providing appropriate safety. Where production of a certificate is required, canoeists should be warned of this. An appreciation of this safety and training structure will indicate what conditions should be imposed on canoeists using reservoirs. In some cases there may be a requirement for specialist training, such as race training or competitive racing.

Canoe races will usually be over distances of 500 and 1 000 m, and since canoes when racing will necessarily be ungrouped the safety arrangements to be made for actual races may require discussion.

Elementary training in capsize drills and more advanced training in Eskimo rolls, and rescue, require frequent immersion. Although this is not usually thought to be unacceptable in a reservoir, it may be considered preferable in some instances to keep immersion to a minimum. In such instances it can be a requirement that such training takes place elsewhere, for instance in a swimming pool. Some encouragement may be desirable for open water practice in such techniques, however.

The British Canoe Union also issues a general code of conduct[16].

Water Ski-ing

Safety and protection problems which can arise from this sport are associated with:—

(1) impact on the environment and upon the visiting public;
(2) impact on other water users;
(3) safety of participants; and
(4) possible effects on water quality

Impact on the Environment and Visiting Public.—This mainly stems from noise, wash, stirring up of the water, and the intrusion into what would otherwise be a tranquil setting. The main "protection" rests in the segregation of the activity by allocating space where any possible adverse consequences will be minimized.

Although water ski boats can unleash considerable power, their effects quantitatively can be restrained by good design, construction, and maintenance. The Noise Advisory Council's guidelines[17] require certain noise levels not to be exceeded, tested under standard conditions. Test conditions include speed and distance from the measuring instrument; for instance, in straight runs past an instrument 25 m distant, the noise level should not exceed 75 dB(A), as an arithmetic mean of four runs. A variety of boats have been tested against these requirements, ranging from 80 hp outboard to 225 hp inboard engines. Indications are that it is possible to keep within the noise recommendations; indeed, with the newer designs of boats and engines figures of less than 60 dB(A) have been recorded under standard conditions.

Waves generated by craft rarely exceed 15 cm, a train of five or six waves being common, at 25 m. There has been little work on the effects of turbidity resulting from the stirring action of the propellor wash. This action is dissipated within the top 2 to 3 m of water, and can stir matter into suspension at lesser depths. The resulting increase in turbidity will reduce light penetration into the water and suppress aquatic plant growth. It may also cause treatment complications in the case of a direct-supply reservoir.

Impact on Other Water Users.—can arise from the above, as can the disturbing effect of relating a fast moving sport to a slower one. Segregation of activities is advisable, and where this practice is adopted the zones should be clearly marked off and understood by all other users. Segregation should extend if possible to launching and "take-off" points. Such ski lanes are frequently marked with buoys.

Safety of Participants.—This is assisted by certain established practices. Limiting the number of craft on the water is much more important than in sailing. Prescribing a circulation direction and laying down a control station signal routine are also essential. Water skiers and boat crews should wear personal buoyancy, and life jackets or waistcoats conforming to S.B.B.N.F. standards are often worn. The latter, also recommended by the British Canoe Union Committee for certain events, give greater body protection. Water skiers can hit the water hard in a fall, particularly when jumping or when the skier is starting his run and they should wear a jumping safety jacket as approved by the British Water Ski Federation. The skis themselves are buoyant and will therefore afford some assistance to a skier in the water.

A minimum depth of water of 1 m, is recommended for ski-ing, and there should also be two people in the boat, one to handle the craft and the other, who should himself be a competent skier, to observe the person who is ski-ing. Water skiers have a recognized system of hand signals for communication. It is also recommended that a lifebuoy and fire extinguisher should always be carried in the boat.

Possible Effects on Water Quality.—There should be no adverse effects, if the organization of the sport and equipment are good. The question of turbidity has already been mentioned. Fuel spillage from boats is a factor, but boats fuelled by Liquid Propane Gas are now in common use which should help to alleviate the problems. Exhaust emission from boats has been measured but is apparently so minor that effects cannot be demonstrated, even when ski-ing is being undertaken to saturation intensity.

Sub-Aqua Diving

The British Sub-Aqua Club (BSAC) has recognized from the early days of underwater swimming in the U.K. that the sport uses a wholly hostile environment, and the activity is most strictly controlled concerning the training of divers. Divers who are members of a branch of the BSAC have to progress through a series of tests. These usually begin in a swimming pool, and pass on to tests on open water diving of increasing complexity. Every diver maintains a log book in which his progress is recorded and countersigned by the branch officer: in addition, divers are required to attend lectures on the technical aspects of diving. The whole progress of a diver is strongly safety oriented, and the sport has no place for the "loner" or the diver who takes chances. The use of the right equipment and the care of it plays a vital part in the training.

The safety record of divers conducted under BSAC rules is extremely good. Every diver is controlled by a dive leader, and no diver may dive alone. In addition to a foam neoprene free-flooding wet suit, or waterproof dry suit (rare), every diver carries a quick-release weight belt, and a self-inflating life jacket. Compressed air is carried in one or more metal cylinders discharging via a reducing valve and "demand" breathing valve. This is used under water, and a "snorkel" tube is used when swimming on the surface. The risks involved in this activity are:—

Drowning, by reason of some circumstance which prevents the use of the breathing apparatus, due to damage, injury, or exhaustion of the air whilst trapped under water. Vomiting or coughing under water can have serious consequences.

Rupture of lungs (pulmonary barotrauma) caused by retaining air in the lungs whilst ascending. The reduction in external pressure is in these circumstances not balanced by a corresponding reduction in pressure within the lung. Ear damage can also result from the change in pressure on descent or ascent.

"Bends", due to ascending too quickly after a long period at depth. This is not likely to happen with the breathing apparatus in normal club use, due to the limited capacity of the cylinders, but repeated dives can build up nitrogen in solution in the blood under pressure, which emerges in bubble form when pressure is reduced. Small bubbles may block capillaries to the brain, etc. Re-pressurization in a pressure chamber will usually cure this problem.

Heat loss—hypothermia—leading to exhaustion and impaired judgement which may in turn cause an accident. The capacity of a wet suit to retain heat is not unlimited.

Black-out, or sudden loss of consciousness, due to holding the breath under water for too long.

A well trained diver will usually be in no danger under water if he keeps to the recognized procedures. Risks are more noticeable on the surface when waves and the awkwardness of swimming when unbalanced by cylinders and other equipment may disorient a diver and interrupt his normal breathing.

Means of dealing with these risks are built into BSAC training progress schemes and dive procedures, and sub-aqua swimming under the auspices of this club may be regarded as a safe sport within the overall control of sports using water. The same does not apply to non-BSAC clubs, whose safety produces may not have been evolved from the same exhaustive analysis of experience and advice. If such clubs are to be allowed to dive at reservoirs, their safety drills should be examined carefully. They may be perfectly acceptable, but on the other hand they may not.

The range of a diver under water is limited; 200 m is quite a long way, and divers do not as a rule embark on under water "journeys". Their aim is normally to conserve air by keeping the use of energy to a minimum. By the same token, a diver who finds himself in a strong current has limited power to fight against it, even with the swimming capacity derived from the "fins" which he wears on his feet. Reservoirs with under water draw-offs which are in operation will exert a pull over a distance of 10 m or more, and an adequate distance between dive sites and draw-off points is necessary, and limits must be set, and made clear to the club concerned. Reservoirs can, however, be safely used for diving where draw-off is small in relation to the volume of water in the reservoir, and where the geography allows a long horizontal separation. To give a "feel" for what distances should be regarded as safe—really safe—managers should discuss on-the-spot conditions with the diving officer of the local branch of the BSAC.

Long Distance Swimming

This sport is usually conducted, at competition level, in straight-line courses, but

Above. Derwent reservoir (Sunderland and South Shields Water Company), showing the dam, draw-off tower, and overflow spillway. The reservoir can impound 50 000 megalitres of water and, in addition to its main function of water supply, provides excellent sailing and fishing facilities.

Left. The Iver potable water supply treatment works of the Three Valleys Water Committee. The works, which has an ultimate capacity of 320 megalitres per day, treats water taken from the river Thames at Sunnymeads for distribution to the Colne Valley, the Rickmansworth and Uxbridge Valley, and the Lee Valley Water Companies.

Above. Grafham Water (Anglian Water Authority). Washing plant for the disinfection of equipment such as boats, trailers, diving apparatus brought to the reservoir from other locations.
Right. Rutland Water (Anglian Water Authority). Preparing for the day's sailing.

this is not essential. Open-water swimming venues, where the bacteriological conditions of the water are acceptable, are much sought-after and on occasion consideration may be given to the use of reservoirs for such events. Championship organization embodies the following arrangements with safety in mind. Each competitor is required to submit a medical certificate stating that they are fit to compete, together with a certificate from a competent official confirming that they can cover the distance of the event (from one to 40 km) in open water. During the swim, every competitor will be accompanied by a rowing boat containing at least two people, one a competent oarsman and the other competent in life-saving techniques. Each rowing boat carries an inflated inner tube with a line securing it to the boat. A large plastic bag is also carried, to be used to protect a swimmer from the elements and to keep him warm if he has to give up the swim. There are usually some launches in attendance, one of which will carry the referee: he will check the competitors and may order a swimmer to retire who appears to be in trouble. Also in attendance will be other officials who will be holders of certificates of competence in pilot life-saving, oarsmanship, life saving, and swimming. In all such events the rowing boats will fly international[15] flag "A" which, as in the case of driving escorts, means "keep clear".

The above comments apply to large, open-water swimming events such as the 16 km contest on Lake Windermere. In more sheltered waters canoes may be used instead of rowing boats. For individual long distance swims the escort arrangements are similar, and emergency services are notified.

In those swimming events in which children between 12 and 14 years old are taking part, a pilot life-saver must be in attendance. There is no such requirement for training swims, but where these are organized on reservoirs, the above championship arrangements may be a helpful guide.

Land—centred Activities

General

Land-centred activities from time to time occur on reservoir catchments. Most of them, like water-based activities, are controlled or advised by a nationally based body. The safety aspects must be considered in the same light as those of water-centred activities.

Car-borne Visitors

The roads used by visitors to reservoirs will usually be public highways but some will be owned by the operators of the sites. In the case of the latter kind, reasonable regulation of the traffic should be designed into the system. Experience will show whether speeding is a problem and this can be controlled by the use of speed ramps or "sleeping policemen". Advice on the use of these ramps is available from the local highway authority and their "severity" and frequency will depend upon the degree of control necessary. The ramps should be marked, and a warning notice displayed.

For the most part, visitors arriving in cars will park them and leave them for destinations within the site. The paths by which they do so should not cross "blind" vehicle ways and should, if possible, be arranged so as to lead people away from moving vehicles. Children are particularly at hazard.

Good design of parking areas can eliminate problems of runaway vehicles, and baulks or ditches can provide a means of preventing cars from running out of control and possibly into the reservoir. It is suggested that it is safer to park vehicles across exposed slopes rather than on the line of them. It may well be that such safety barriers are necessary only where vehicles are likely to be heading directly towards nearby water, and cannot be held, in the event of brake failure, by the nature of the ground or the presence of other obstructions.

It will be desirable, in the case of some large paved areas, to eliminate the risk of spilt oil reaching the water surface. Oil or petrol spillages in any quantity likely to cause problems as a result of the normal use of a carpark by vehicles are virtually unknown, and the quantities used by normal vehicles would probably be easily absorbed by ground lying between the car park and the water. The main concern from oil would arise from quantities such as fuel oil for heating buildings, club-houses and the like and it is important that these should be bunded-off. As in all else, the scale of the threat is the consideration.

Picnicking

Picnicking presents no especial hazards, but regular clearances of litter and, particularly, broken glass are necessary. Wasps in late summer can be a real problem and nests should be destroyed where possible. Some people react violently to wasp stings and a few can become seriously ill as a result. Picnic areas must be carefully maintained and tidied, and litter bins, if provided, should be emptied frequently.

Camping and Caravanning

Where this is backed by acceptable toilet and litter collecting facilities, then from the safety and protection point of view there are few problems. Casual tenting has been acccepted in many reservoir catchments, but there are sometimes reservations about sites close the water, and about caravanning. The Caravan Club (which has a membership of 200 000), caters for mobile caravanners, and requires them to observe a published code of practice[18]. This includes a requirement to dispose of all rubbish by the means provided at the individual site, and to collect waste water in a receptacle so that it does not foul the ground. There is also the requirement to dispose of the waste water in the manner provided, and on casual sites to minimize risk of fouling by distributing along hedges, etc. Chemical closets must be provided and emptied as provided for.

There is no reason why, if properly sited, caravanning or camping should pose any greater risk of pollution than is likely to arise from casual visitors, since appropriate sanitation arrangements must be provided for both groups. Since the effluent from chemical closets is likely to be treated after reception, the Caravan Club recommends the use of formaldehyde-based fluids for these closets, as they are relatively harmless to biological treatment processes.

Orienteering

This is the competitive sport of finding one's way on foot across rough country with the aid of a map and a compass. The British Orienteering Federation gives guidance on safety, whilst acknowledging that accidents are rare. Injury and exhaustion are hazards and are potentially serious because assistance and medical aid may not be readily available. The Federation publishes safety Rules[19] also maintains a third party insurance scheme to cover its organizers against claims for negligence. The landowner is co-insured under the same policy.

In the case of young and inexperienced competitors (i.e. boys under 15 and girls under 17 years of age), the Federation recommends that they should take part in pairs or groups, and this is particularly important at night. Each participant should at all times carry a compass, watch, and whistle. Organizers must ensure that competitors are sufficiently experienced to tackle the proposed course and that they have been given appropriate safety instructions—these normally include a closure time, with instructions on how to find the route to the finish for those competitors who are still on the coarse when the closure time has elapsed.

A search procedure is included in the safety rules[19] to find competitors who are considered to be missing. Landowners should be consulted on all possible sources of danger, such as quarries, bogs, shooting areas, etc.

Courses will be of different standards of difficulty and exposure and events can also take place at night. Where "tough" courses are used, heat exhaustion in hot weather and hypothermia in winter are hazards; the safety rules include detailed instructions in the recognition of these hazards and their causes, symptoms, and treatment and prevention. Organizers are, or should be, able to handle events without risk of these effects, and should be able to cope with such problems if they arise.

Agreements should include an undertaking on the part of those permitted to use water catchment areas that they will organize events in accordance with the rules of the British Orienteering Federation.

Gun and Field Sports

Wildfowling and game shooting are traditional forms of countryside recreation and the risks involved are the obvious ones of injury from gunshot. Arrangements should secure that any shooting is let to responsible tenants, who must satisfy the operators that they are competent. The shot sizes in normal use for game and wildfowl shooting are small, and carry for a limited distance only. It is unusual to use the larger shot size such as "BB" which is about the same diameter as a ·177 airgun slug, although it is sometimes used for geese. Lethal ranges, against game, are calculated on the basis of a striking energy of ·87 ft/lb. They vary from 35 m for the small No. 8 shot used for snipe, to 70 m for No. 4 shot used for duck, and 130 m for BB shot. Pellets will carry much further than this, and can still injure at three times these ranges. Shooting areas should be allocated accordingly and their use co-ordinated with the access of other users. The Wildfowlers Association of Great Britain and Ireland (WAGBI) publish an excellent shotgun safety code[20], which contains essential advice on how to handle a gun in the field.

For safety reasons it is desirable for all responsible shots to know the lethal potential of their weapons. They should have been fully instructed in the "rules" of the sport. These include never allowing a gun, loaded or unloaded, to be pointed at anyone; never shooting where one cannot see (i.e. into cover); and always guarding against accidental discharge of one's gun by removing the cartridges when approaching other persons, or crossing obstructions. Of all sports, shooting is the most able to endanger persons other than the participant, and must be dealt with accordingly.

Shooting with rifles is a different matter because these are capable of killing at very long ranges—1·5 km in the case of a ·22 rifle and over 3 km in the case of heavier calibre weapons.

Some forest areas harbour deer, and under special arrangements these may be shot, indeed culling may be essential to keep herds within limits to avoid excessive damage to woodland or crops. It is illegal to use ·22 rifles or shotguns to kill deer and heavier calibre rifles will be used. Normally such shooting is only carried out under the direct supervision of the forester, warden, or stalker, and he will not allow shooting on dangerous lines or angles.

It should be possible by sensible management to meet the safety requirements of shooting and to ensure that all shot, or bullets, will fall to the ground well short of any other person (except, of course, other members of the shooting party). Agreements to allow shooting should include boundaries which allow for this, and time schedules as well.

Archery

Dangers from the accidental discharge of arrows are very remote, and adequate range discipline should ensure safety. The range of target bows is limited to about 250 m at extreme range, but at normal shooting elevations arrows, allowing for ricochets, will not go further than about 100 m. An arrow has a surprising power of penetration and is a dangerous missile. There should be no danger with responsible archers, and the usual arrangements for control by a club will be adequate. Specialized forms of shooting, with crossbows or long range "distance" bows merely require more room but the above remarks otherwise apply.

Hang Gliding

Fatal accidents do occur in this sport, and although by far the greatest risk is to the pilot, he may crash on other people, or where his forced landing can do serious harm. The British Hang Gliding Association issues a booklet containing a code of good practice, flying recommendations, and flying rules[21]. The code is a commonsense summary of points to observe in the way of normal courtesy and consideration to the landowner, farmer, and the public at large. The flying recommendations begin, refreshingly, with the sentence "Any fool can fly a hang glider—but not for very long"! The recommendations cover the design, construction, and checking of the glider, its suitability for the user's physical build, other equipment and clothing, and recommendations as to general approach, training through a school or club, and progress through conditions of increasing difficulty. Lone flying is discouraged, and the use only of recognized sites and observance of their rules are recommended. General flying recommendations aim at keeping clear of other fliers and spectators, and adopting a predictable flight path which fits in with other fliers. As in some other sports, accidents involving injury must be reported to the governing body.

Flying rules are brief, but govern observation, alterations in course to avoid collision, a rule of the road as to which keeps clear, how far apart to fly, and how to overtake.

The Association has introduced a pilot rating system, ranging from student pilot through to pilot 1, 2, and 3. Only pilots who have completed their training and logged experience up to pilot 2 level and thereafter obtained the "Delta Bronze" qualification and then the F.A.I. sporting licence may take part in certain competitions and record attempts. The Association, as does the British Sub-Aqua Club, builds safety into a progress in prestige and privilege. There is an elaborate stairway of tasks to be completed in progressing up the pilot grades.

All British Hang Gliding Association members are covered by public liability insurance while flying.

Motor Sport (Motor Cycle Scrambling, Trials, Car Rallies)

Car rallies in particular are under the control of the Royal Automobile Club, and are rigidly controlled as to organization. Risks are to spectators as well as to competitors but this is well recognized and spectator control figures prominently in their rules.

5. SAFETY FOR THE PUBLIC

GENERAL

The preceding Section of this Chapter dealt with the hazards and safety requirements for the various activities which can take place on water and associated land, both from the point of view of the participants and the immediate spectators. This section is concerned with general hazards and with some of the safety equipment which can be made available at sites.

HAZARDS OF SITE

Risks should be assessed by a careful inspection of all parts of the site to which visitors can gain access. One of the first considerations is a reasonable standard of site maintenance. A half-buried length of barbed wire, broken glass, unsafe walls and the like could all cause personal injury. Steep banks with insecure footing, old quarries, etc., may well require safety fencing and suitably worded notices. These must be inspected regularly and kept in good repair. Worse than no fence is a fence which gives way when called upon to do its job. Site safety is paramount and must not be subservient to considerations of appearance, although clearly it must be made to look as attractive as possible.

Adequate segregation of visitors from the specialist users calls for measures which are not always popular. This may be because of the dangers which are not always apparent, or appreciated, and which can arise at sites which cater for many types of user.

Most organized sports are, or should be, conducted under a code of practice or rules which cover foreseeable accidents, and it is possible to ensure that such accidents will be dealt with by a drill. Casual visitors may not behave sensibly, but a prime consideration is that notices are displayed at strategic locations which will direct visitors to the point where they can get help. It is useful if notices can encourage members of the public to report accidents so that these can be properly investigated at the time and the particulars recorded; this can be most important.

It will be normal practice to segregate visitors from operational areas as much as possible. Considerations of security of the water supply in the case of a reservoir will prevail in any event, particularly where dangerous substances are handled, such as gas in cylinders, which must be kept away from all visitors. This entails measures of security over and above those which are need in the case of trained staff.

The Health and Safety at Work etc Act 1974 will apply where working practices endanger the public. All working practices and visitor access must be viewed in this light.

6. SAFETY EQUIPMENT

LIFEJACKETS AND PERSONAL BUOYANCY AIDS

A useful leaflet is published by the Royal Society for the Prevention of Accidents[9], under this title. It explains the life expectancy of individuals when immersed in water at varying temperatures, and since these vary upwards from exposure of less than an hour at temperatures around freezing, it is apparent that marginal effects leading to unconsciousness can develop in inland waters in winter. This is the reason for the wet suit rule usually imposed on many sports where the participants can be exposed to cold conditions.

"Life jacket" is the term given to equipment approved under BS 3595[22]. It provides positive flotation, and is self-righting. They are recommended for sea going use. The jackets may be foam-filled orally inflated, CO_2 gas inflated, or two-stage, i.e. part inherent and part oral inflation.

"Personal buoyancy aids", as approved by the Ship and Boat Builders National Federation (SBBNF), provide immediate buoyancy, minimum maintenance, and minimum cost. They are not necessarily self-righting, but will support the wearer in a vertical, or backwards-of-vertical posture. Different sizes are available to suit different body weights, and the buoyancy developed, and hence the bulk, is less than that of a life jacket.

WET SUITS

These are variants of a skin of neoprene foam, normally about 6 mm thick. A nylon stockingette lining makes them easier to put on and take off. There is some variation in pattern depending upon the sport involved, but the principle is the same. Suits are designed to flood on immersion, but to fit sufficiently close to the body to minimize the amount of water entering. Once flooded, there is little exchange of this water and it rapidly warms to body temperature. The insulation provided by the wet suit reduces loss of this heat. Wet suits do not keep the wearer warm indefinitely, but the better the fit and the more complete the cover, the more effective is the suit. Considerable chilling will occur after the wearer has been immersed in cold conditions for about ½ hr and this continues when the wearer is thereafter exposed to cold wind. Sailors usually wear further layers of clothing over their wet suits to reduce this effect.

DRY SUITS

These are worn by a few divers, mainly professionals, and are being developed for other activities, for example water skiing. They provide a completely waterproof seal, under which warm clothing is worn. They keep the wearer warmer for longer than a wet suit but are costly and vulnerable, being useless if punctured, and dangerous if flooded. Unlike wet suits, which are often home made, dry suits are normally professionally made.

LIFEBUOYS AND HEAVING LINES

Standard lifebuoys are 75 cm in diameter, and can support two people. They are difficult to throw far and they are cumbersome to handle. They are also expensive. The pattern now recommended is 50 cm in diameter, which is still effective in use and which is much easier to handle and to throw to a person in difficulty. (It is important to appreciate that a person in serious difficulty is unlikely to understand instructions, or to make a co-ordinated effort to reach a lifebuoy.)

Specially made heaving lines are very portable and cheap. They can be thrown a distance of about 40 m and are used to pull a person to safety. They are not usually regarded as a complete safety device, but rather as a very useful supplement. They can be placed on stands round a shoreline and, perhaps more appropriately, carried in vehicles on site. Their relative cheapness, and portability, makes them a useful supplement to lifebuoys.

It is recommended that lifebuoys should be placed at key locations where persons are especially likely to fall into deep water, such as landing stages. It is clearly impracticable to place them at all locations where the waterside can be reached. Experience suggests that adequately secured lifebuoys are not especially vandal-prone. Heaving lines can, because of their cheapness, be placed at more locations, but are often stolen for their useful rope, or vandalized.

7. SAFETY FOR STAFF

HAZARDS ARISING FROM THE PRESENCE OF THE PUBLIC

In the first instance, an understanding of the types of recreation catered for on site is important for all staff likely to come into contact with the activities. This will help to ensure that needless risk are avoided. It should also mean that where members of staff require to approach recreationalists they will be able to do so in a manner which is likely to involve no risk to either party. It is also necessary to extend this familiarity to the equipment used in the particular activity. Much the same considerations arise as those which apply when ensuring that no danger is caused to members of the public.

There may be occasions when members of staff have to rescue, or assist, members of the public who may be in difficulty or danger. There is obviously a chance of running into danger in doing so, and training in safe rescue techniques is essential.

It is not only to render assistance that staff may require to approach visitors, but a necessary part of staff activities will be to ensure that rules are obeyed and orderly conduct is maintained. It is inevitable that, on occasion, a warden will be alone when faced with difficult situations, and he must be mentally equipped to deal with them. It is always a mistake to "look for trouble", or to attempt to tackle a difficult situation without help, if this can be readily summoned. But a warden is not effective unless he is capable of exerting his authority, and the better he is trained for this the less chance there is of physical violence. Cultivating the right way of approaching people is a protection in itself.

Any site where visitors are received must be organized in anticipation that there will be some members of the public—a very few—who are prepared to cause trouble. These are usually persons who are on site without proper authority, and poachers after fish or game are not uncommon. Indeed, many sites are regarded as prime targets for poachers and thieves who may be after attractive items which accumulate by reason of the development of recreation or amenity. As well as fish, or game on surrounding land, young trees (especially plantations of Christmas trees in their season) and indeed almost anything portable and saleable may come in for attention.

Especially attractive is the cash collected from those activities for which a charge is made. It is useful to arrange as far as possible for cash to be collected and handled off site. This is not always feasible and it must not be forgotten that violence is associated with raids for cash. The wise rule is to minimize the amount of cash held on site, and to avoid a regular routine carriage of money.

8. VANDALISM AND THEFT

VANDALISM

The growing problem of vandalism and some of the measures which can be taken to combat it have already been referred to in other Chapters. The presence of visitors on a site will clearly provide opportunities for vandalism, but unless site security is otherwise extremely tight the hazard would be present in any event. Opportunities for vandalism must rise as potential vandals are brought into contact with suitable targets.

The pattern of visitors to sites is not the same as the patterns associated with serious vandalism. These usually occur in urban areas, and targets are frequently buildings or other things which are apparently superfluous or in a run down state. The "gang" instinct has been identified as a source of destructive behaviour, when parties of youths collect together for some purpose and find themselves with a ready made target and companions who may be impressed. British Rail report that the scale of damage has doubled in the past ten years. Vandalism to telephone kiosks is also common. Other authorities consider that the pattern of vandalism where newer or in-use buildings such as schools are concerned is of sporadic, unpredictable, and localized occurrence.

Visitors to reservoir sites and gathering grounds will generally have gone there by choice and, unless the site lies close to a centre of population, they will have travelled some distance to do so. Their motivation is unlikely to contain destructive components, and they are unlikely to be present during the hours of darkness. Wholesale vandalism is most unlikely, but sporadic damage is possible. There is seemingly nothing that can be done to eliminate this problem altogether. Protection of obvious targets is useful especially derelict or unoccupied buildings, and the immediate repair of vandalised items is important.

Defacing and minor damage to facilities, graffiti, and wilful damage in toilets does occur. The best defence is to keep these facilities looking cared for. Vandalism can sometimes be an expression of annoyance or disgust with poor facilities. It should thus be apparent to visitors that property is cared for, and it must also be made apparent that surveillance is kept. At one large Midlands reservoir where all visitors are present by permit only, there has been virtually no vandalism to recreational installations or buildings in a period of ten years. At the other end of the scale, on "open" sites near towns, damage to notices and the like occur quite frequently.

There is probably no structure, which can be reached, which is wholly immune from unpredictable vandalism, sometimes hinting at a surprising determination and force. The problem appears, however, to be entirely divorced from recreational use.

Vandalism and theft are especially upsetting when they are directed at safety apparatus. For some reason it seems that the large traditional type of lifebuoy, cumbersome and expensive though it is, is considerably less prone to interference than the far cheaper heaving line. Experience is beginning to suggest that lifebuoys may be superior as fixed installations for this reason, whereas portable heaving lines may be most useful when carried in vehicles.

ORGANIZED THEFT AND PETTY PILFERING

One hazard which requires attention and which has been referred to earlier, is the collection and holding of substantial sums in cash at reservoir sites. This is mainly collected in permit fees and a significant proportion of those same fees is absorbed in protecting them against theft, and preventing them from becoming an attraction to thieves who may well include violence in their attempts to steal them.

Cash and attractive items can certainly invite thieves: outboard engines, radios, and even small boats have been stolen by visiting thieves. Commonsense precautions are to minimize the amount of money kept on site at any one time and to fit alarm signals and other deterrents where appropriate. The police will advise on systems to minimize risk, the most serious of which is the exposure of staff to armed attack. Some risk is quite clearly a consequence of the day permit system whereby reservoir facilities are made open to the casual, as opposed to the season, visitor. Generally, cash boxes and cash reception systems such as automatic ticket vending machines afford reasonable security, since the latter have been developed for, and are successful in, exposed urban car park sites. They have the attraction of eliminating the human target for would-be thieves. Generally, locks, chains and the like in effect buy time for the owner during which an alarm system may be effective.

9. PROTECTION OF THE ENVIRONMENT

GENERAL

In the past gathering grounds were traditionally left undisturbed as part of the "defence" of the water in storage against pollution. Modern thinking suggests that reservoirs, the water from which subsequently receives adequate treatment, do not require strict isolation from public use and so there is a trend to opening up adjacent lands and gathering grounds for recreational purposes. Even within the requirements of pollution prevention, this opening up may be of such a scale as to change an entirely undisturbed area into one which has frequent disturbance. As well as the protection of visitors and staff, the actual effects of public use on the reservoir and gathering grounds requires consideration.

Not only has a water undertaker a statutory responsibility for recreation, which results in some degree of visitor access, but the Water Act 1973 includes, under Section 22, a requirement that due regard shall be had to the desirability of conserving wildlife, and other natural or historic features.

The requirement as regards wildlife needs careful interpretation, since taken to is conclusion it would preclude the use of the site for any purpose whatever apart from the plants which could grow upon it and the animals and birds which could use it. The extent to which protection is needed will depend upon the objectives which the site has to fulfil. These have to be decided first. The techniques of protection can be obtained from a variety of reports and textbooks dealing with the considerable range of problems which can arise. The reading list appended will be useful in dealing with specific problems of management.

DEMARCATION OF BOUNDARIES OF PRIVATE PROPERTY ADJACENT TO A RECREATION SITE

The admission of visitors to a reservoir site may or may not have been foreseen when the area was first developed. The new factor may upset previous responsibilities as to providing or maintaining boundary fences. The maxim that good fences make good neighbours has the further force that it is not livestock but visitors that are at issue.

The issue is no less sensitive because reservoirs and gathering grounds have frequently been built only after Parliamentary powers have allowed acquisition of what is often agricultural land. There may have been reluctance to part with this land even for the self-evident social purposes of water supply. Now that the part of the land surrounding the reservoir may be used where practicable for purposes of recreation, the importance of ensuring that there is no encroachment onto privately owned land adjacent is self-evident.

The means of demarcation are a matter of good sense, and this applies equally to parts of the land onto which, whilst owned by the operator, visitor access is not practicable or desirable. It is not usually necessary to fence with more than five-strand wire, and security fencing is not usually required. Fences should be supplemented by appropriate noticeboards.

OPEN GRASSLAND

Where these areas are seeded, they will stand up to public use best if well drained, and seeded with a hard wearing mixture of meadow grasses and plants. In fact, only a proportion of the "grassland" plants are actual grass. The mixture chosen will only remain in stable form if handled as designed. A grazing mixture will remain only so long as it is either grazed or mown. If it is not, stronger growing plants which are not resistant to grazing will take over. Tussock grasses can take over a smooth pasture and render it almost useless for walking or picnicking if the area is left ungrazed or unmown. Pastures grasses are usually reasonably resistant to trampling, but are only as strong as the soil. Very peaty soil is soon squashed, particularly if ill drained, to a point where grass disappears and a muddy mess remains. Protection may lie in frequently changing heavily used points such as stiles and gates or reinforcing them. Paths may need building up or draining in low lying parts. They are unlikely to stand up to horse riding, and horse trails will need reinforcing or closing at times, in many cases, depending on use.

FIRE

Where grassland has been allowed for some reason to become fully grown without grazing or mowing, fire can be a hazard. This is mainly the case when growth has ceased and the season is especially dry in the late summer or, more usually, when the winter's moisture has been dried out in spring but before the season's growth has started. Grass and undergrowth of the previous year is a fire hazard during spring. The extent to which access by public constitutes a fire hazard must be taken into account.

The Forestry Commission freely admits visitors to most of its plantations (apart from nurseries), and experience has been such as to suggest that their presence helps in the early detection of fires, rather than adding to the risk.

BIRDS AND WILDLIFE

Visitors inevitably disturb wildlife. It is generally held that little and often is bad so far as disturbance to wildlife is concerned. Wildlife will tend to leave an area where they are frequently disturbed, but it is not so affected by occasional disturbance even if this is much greater. This is germane to the handling of events as opposed to the siting of footpaths.

Advice should be sought as to whether gathering grounds contain any really important wildlife assets which need especial protection, the objective being to avoid unintentional damage.

Birds are vulnerable so far as the protection of nesting sites at nesting time are concerned, and wildfowl using water areas for nesting in the autumn and winter are easily frightened by persons or boats approaching too close. Even reservoirs which are extensively used for sailing or other recreational purposes often harbour large numbers of wildfowl, and the effects of disturbance are not yet fully understood.

POLLUTION RISKS

It is taken for granted that no compromise is acceptable of the requirements to put wholesome water into supply (see Chapter 2). These will be sufficiently exacting, in respect of direct-supply reservoirs, to cover other effects on water quality, but also for consideration are gathering grounds and reservoirs used for river regulating and compensation purposes.

The principal causes of pollution of water in reservoirs adjoining recreational areas are referred to in the next section of this Chapter and in Chapter 2. Safeguards can clearly be relaxed in regulating and compensation reservoirs without serious harm. There is no reason to exclude soakaways from septic tanks in gathering grounds for such reservoirs but calculations are needed to ensure that no unacceptable change in water chemistry will result.

10. PUBLIC HEALTH

Attention is drawn to the National Water Council (NWC) publication entitled "Water supply hygiene"[23], and in particular to the section on "Protection of sources of supply" and to the bibliography. It is stated that:-

"Where water supplies derived from rivers are subjected to comprehensive treatment, recreational activities in and around regulating and compensation water reservoirs discharging solely to these rivers are unlikely to constitute a significant additional pollution hazard. In such circumstances, decisions on public access will normally be guided more by considerations of public safety and amenity than by water quality and hygiene.

"Where, however, a reservoir is one from which water is taken directly for treatment and public supply, different considerations apply. Public access and recreational use may involve a risk of pollution, but the significance of the risks and the extent to which such activities can be permitted will depend upon the characteristics of the reservoir and on the treatment given to the water. Restrictions and control will be needed for most kinds of recreation and they should be designed to be adequate to safeguard the water supply."

The NWC publication refers to the 1972 Report of The Institution of Water Engineers on "Recreation on reservoirs and rivers"[24].

The public health aspects of the recreational use of reservoirs and gathering grounds is dealt with in more detail in Chapter 2.

11. LIAISON WITH EMERGENCY SERVICES

Although an understanding of the likely hazards attending the use of the reservoir for public access and recreation is an essential prerequisite for preventing accidents, or for handling them when they occur, it cannot be assumed that the resources available will be sufficient to deal with their every emergency.

It must be assumed that at some time one or other of the public emergency services may have to be summoned to an incident and it is necessary to give consideration to the details of the particular site which the service will require in order to be as effective as possible in dealing with the incident.

The services most likely to be involved are the Police, the Ambulance Service, and the Fire Brigade. When contacted they should be given all relevant information, but advance liaison is most important. The first requirement will be an accurate map of the site showing all access points from the public highway: these should be named and the names shown on the map. All routes leading from them which are capable of accommodating the vehicles of the emergency services should be marked, together with any necessary notes on gates, conditions, etc. Copies of the map should be issued to the emergency services as required, as they will enable them to be directed to the most useful location. In the case of a large reservoir this can save considerable time.

A concise statement of the activities which take place at the site, and the locations used by visitors, is the next step. This will assist in the assessment which the services will make of the likely situations. Time schedules, attendances, and possible route obstructions are also essential items of information. Maps should show the locations of telephones, buildings, water points, and first aid equipment.

Liaison must be established with the heads of the relevant services, who should be supplied with the basic information referred to above. The services will, in turn, be able to supply such details as the time that they would expect to take in reaching a site and the kind of information which they would need to be given in the initial stage of any emergency. These details should be displayed in note form, together with a map of the site and the telephone numbers of the services, at strategic locations throughout the works close to telephone points. The requirements and the action to be taken should be discussed with all full-time and temporary staff so that in an emergency employees will be able to give the alarm to the best advantage.

This kind of liaison will enable the right help to be summoned to the right location in the minimum time. Advice from the services will ensure that the appropriate action will be taken by the site staff.

The above routines should ensure that emergencies requiring outside help can be handled promptly and efficiently. It cannot be too strongly emphasized that, however good the liaison which has been set up, it will not stay that way. At least once a year emergency arrangements should be reviewed and, whenever necessary, revised and updated.

12. TRAINING AND EDUCATION

Chapter 5 deals with the day-to-day management of the recreational facilities afforded at different sites. A prime contribution to safety is made by the presence on site of staff who can advise visitors where necessary, and who can ensure that all equipment, notices, fencing, etc., are kept in first class order. Nothing less that this is acceptable.

TRAINING OF STAFF

Special training is needed to ensure that all staff on site can assist with emergency routines if they have to. They must know what these are and their information must be renewed and updated regularly. Persons new to the site should also be instructed along the same lines.

Wardens and others who are regularly responsible for on-site recreation and visitor control and reception will need training in the requirements referred to in this Chapter, and in particular with:—

Rescue techniques—from shore.
Recognition of danger situations.
Action to be taken in such cases.
Resuscitation.
First aid—especially in cases of hypothermia, hyperthermia, removal of fish hooks, etc.
Boat handling.

The Royal Life Saving Society[25] and others have devised simple rescue techniques which should be applied in cases where people are in danger in the water. These may be summarized as follows:—

Stop and think—do not dive straight in.
Normally it is better to rescue from the bank without entering the water.
Reach—with a stick, or clothing.
Throw—a rope, or float
Wade—testing the ground
Row—a boat is the ideal safety gear
Learn resuscitation—artificial respiration.

Courses in these techniques and others are available from time to time, or they can be set up using advice from safety organizations.

Early recognition of potentially dangerous situations is important. On occasions the wind velocity and direction can be critical factors. The Beaufort wind scale (reproduced as Appendix A, p. 191) is the recognized reference, and it is important to remember that the local Meteorological Offices (which are listed in the local telephoned directories) provide weather forecasting services.

It is suggested that an essential ingredient of on-site training is an understanding on the part of staff of the recreational activities which will be taking place. Staff will then know what can be expected and what action can be left to the recreationalists. The aim is to ensure that staff can deal effectively with emergencies and, perhaps more important, are sufficiently knowledgeable to anticipate trouble, and to take appropriate action to guard against it. This aspect of training, and indeed the approach generally, must be stressed time and again.

Attention should be focused on possible needs, but these are likely to vary with the site. The details of the various types of activity in the foregoing pages will have given some idea of the ways in which hazards arise, and what they are likely to be. The common causes of problems will be asssociated with injury, exposure, drowning, heat exhaustion, and burning.

The principal bodies which provide advice and training in first aid, rescue from water, and resuscitation techniques are:-

British Red Cross Society
Royal Life Saving Society
St. John Ambulance Brigade and Association
Surf Rescue Association

The resuscitation techniques taught by the St. John Ambulance Brigade are now at a stage of development where they are easily mastered. Certain water authorities themselves organize courses for personnel who attend water recreation sites[26].

At best, the emergency help which will be available at a reservoir site will be confined to that which can be provided by the resident staff who will have had some training in coping with the immediate effects of an incident and who will be able to supply such needs as warmth, shelter, and bandages. This will need to be swiftly backed up by help from the established emergency services, as discussed earlier.

If circumstances permit, mock exercises can be carried out, where these are likely to be helpful. This will assist in building up the confidence of the resident staff and in drawing attention to any shortcomings in communications or elsewhere.

A specimen checklist of requirements for staff training in safety at recreation sites is given as Appendix B, p. 192.

TRAINING OF VISITORS

In the normal course of site management, notices should indicate the whereabouts of the warden services, telephones, and the like; they should also indicate particular hazards which might not be appreciated by the visitor. Obvious or normal hazards should not be indiscriminately signposted as this devalues the system. Display of an appropriate site plan can assist in both these respects.

It is a matter of choice how much further the site owner should go in seeking to "train or educate" visitors and indeed there is little that can be done apart from strategically placed signs and other information material.

It is essential that visitors know where emergency services and equipment are located, and where to summon help or report incidents and dangerous objects. Encouragement to report possible hazards is a useful investment in site safety.

13. REFERENCES

1. The Institution of Water Engineers and Scientists, 1979, Water Practice Manuals, Book 1, "The structure and management of the British water industry".
2. Department of Trade and Industry, "Seaway code—a guide for small boat users", H.M.S.O.
3. Department of Trade and Industry, 1973, "Safety on small craft", by G. Cole, H.M.S.O.
4. Sports Council, "Water sports code".
5. Sports Council, Water Space Amenity Commission, and the Royal Society for the Prevention of Accidents, "Water safety provision in inland areas".
6. Royal Society for the Prevention of Accidents, "On the water—in the water".
7. Royal Yachting Association, 1974, "Safety boat handling".
8. Royal Society for the Prevention of Accidents, "Sail surely-dinghy sailing".
9. Royal Society for the Prevention of Accidents, "Life jackets and personal buoyancy aids".
10. Royal Society for the Prevention of Accidents, "Cold water can kill".
11. Amateur Rowing Association, 1979, "Code of practice for water safety".
12. Royal Society for the Prevention of Accidents, "Could you cope with the kiss of life?".
13. Royal Life Saving Society, "Emergency resuscitation".
14. Royal Life Saving Society, "Life saving—water safety".
15. Amateur Rowing Association, 1980, Code for regattas and for equipment.
16. British Canoe Union, "The canoeists code of conduct".
17. Noise Advisory Council, guidelines re water ski-ing.
18. Caravan Club, "Code of practice".
19. British Orienteering Federation, 1979, "Rules—S7 Safety, as appendixes A.B.C.".
20. Wildfowlers Association of Great Britain and Ireland, "Shotgun safety code".
21. British Hang Gliding Association, "Code of good practice; flying recommendations; flying rules".
22. British Standards Institution, 1969, BS 3595, "Life-saving jackets".
23. National Water Council, 1979, Technical Paper No. 2, "Water supply hygiene: safeguards in the operation and management of public waterworks in England and Wales".
24. The Institution of Water Engineers, 1972, Report on "Recreation on reservoirs and rivers".
25. National Westminster Bank Ltd., and the Royal Life Saving Society, "Rescue skills scheme; illustrated guide to teachers".
26. Severn-Trent Water Authority, 1979, "Water safety code".

APPENDIX A: BEAUFORT SCALE OF WIND FORCE: SPECIFICATIONS AND EQUIVALENT SPEEDS

Beaufort Number	Description of wind	Specifications for use at sea [1]	Specifications for use on land	Equivalent speed at 10 m above ground [2]						Beaufort Number
				Knots		Miles per hour		Metres per second		
				Mean	Limits [3]	Mean	Limits [3]	Mean	Limits [3]	
0	Calm	Sea like a mirror	Calm: smoke rises vertically	0	<1	0	<1	0.0	0.0-0.2	0
1	Light air	Ripples with the appearance of scales are formed but without foam crests.	Direction of wind shown by smoke drift but not by wind vanes.	2	1-3	2	1-3	0.8	0.3-1.5	1
2	Light breeze	Small wavelets, still short but more pronounced—Crests have a glassy appearance and do not break.	Wind felt on face; leaves rustle; ordinary vanes moved by wind.	5	4-6	5	4-7	2.4	1.6-3.3	2
3	Gentle breeze	Large wavelets. Crests begin to break. Foam of glassy appearance. Perhaps scattered white horses.	Leaves and small twigs in constant motion; wind extends light flag.	9	7-10	10	8-12	4.3	3.4-5.4	3
4	Moderate breeze	Small waves, becoming longer; fairly frequent white horses.	Raises dust and loose paper; small branches are moved.	13	11-16	15	13-18	6.7	5.5-7.9	4
5	Fresh breeze	Moderate waves, taking a more pronounced long form; many white horses are formed. (Chance of some spray.)	Small trees in leaf begin to sway; crested wavelets form on inland waters.	19	17-21	21	19-24	9.3	8.0-10.7	5
6	Strong breeze	Large waves begin to form; the white foam crests are more extensive everywhere. (Probably some spray).	Large branches in motion; umbrellas used with difficulty.	24	22-27	28	25-31	12.3	10.8-13.8	6
7	Near gale	Sea heaps up and white foam from breaking waves begins to be blown in streaks along the direction of the wind.	Whole trees in motion; inconvenience felt when walking against wind.	30	28-33	35	32-38	15.5	13.9-17.1	7
8	Gale	Moderately high waves of greater length; edges of crests begin to break into spindrift. The foam is blown in well-marked streaks along the direction of the wind.	Breaks twigs off trees; generally impedes progress.	37	34-40	42	39-46	18.9	17.2-20.7	8
9	Strong gale	High waves. Dense streaks of foam along the direction of the wind. Crests of waves begin to topple, tumble and roll over. Spray may affect visibility.	Slight structural damage occurs (chimney-pots and slates removed).	44	41-47	50	47-54	22.6	20.8-24.4	9

Notes: 1. Where there is no swell and the fetch is not limited by proximity to land, the specifications describe the fully developed sea generated by steady winds of the forces indicated. There is always a lag in the response of the sea to wind speed changes, heavy rain appears to flatten the sea, and in shallow waters both water depth and tidal streams affect the sea state. Account should be taken of all these factors when estimating the wind force from the appearance of the sea.

2. Approximate corrections for wind speeds at other heights are: 2 m *subtract* 30 per cent; 3m *subtract* 20 per cent; 6 m *subtract* 10 per cent; 15 m *add* 10 per cent; 30 m *add* 25 per cent.

3. For finding the Beaufort number corresponding to a recorded mean, or range of mean speeds, and *vice versa*.

4. The scale applies to mean speed only. There is no equivalent for gusts.

5. The descriptions of the higher Beaufort numbers, which relate to storm, violent storm, and hurricane conditions are not reproduced here.

6. At the conditions pertaining to Beaufort number 6 sailing becomes a matter for experts, and rowing boats become difficult to pull against the wind even with strong oarsmen. Under Beaufort number 7 conditions it becomes difficult to sail a dinghy at all.

APPENDIX B: SPECIMEN CHECKLIST FOR STAFF TRAINING IN SAFETY AT RECREATION SITES

Type of activity	Hazards	Information needed by all staff
All	Various	Area used by each activity. Access by users in each case. Method of organization. Base or centre of activity—if any. Method of liaison with each type of user—how to contact. Liaison arrangements with emergency services. Action agreed in each type of emergency. Whose responsibility in each case (i.e. tenant, club, etc.). Arrangements for visitors and users to report incidents.
Fishing (a) bank	Relatively few. Falling in. Hooks in face or body of angler or bystander.	Treatment for exposure—rescue and resuscitation. Method of removal of barbed hook, first aid to be applied.
(b) boat	Falling in. Driving ashore on dam or over spillway, or capsizing—in stormy weather.	What rescue is available? When wind force and direction are beyond ability of users. Beaufort scale of wind force [reproduced as Appendix A, p. 191]. Signals to use to prohibit boats going out, or to recall them. Availability of buoyancy aids.
Sailing	Capsize—swamping. Crew trapped under boat. Boat insufficiently buoyant. Exposure. Spillways, etc.	Rescue services available. Conditions when these are likely to be inadequate. What scrutiny of buoyancy is routine. Treatment to give for exposure. Wind conditions, directions and force—when these are especially dangerous.
Canoeing	Capsizes leading to exhaustion. Rescue overwhelmed by weather. Exposure.	See above. What conditions the canoeists can cope with; rescue methods used by canoeists; where to land and treat victim.
Water ski-ing	Impact injuries, sprains. Exposure.	First aid—medical liaison.
Sub-aqua diving	Exposure. Rupture of lungs. 'Bends'. Drowning.	Treatment needed. Nearest medical emergency services. Nearest liaison arrangements— this is a highly specialized matter. Resuscitation—emergency liaison.
Orienteering	Exposure, cuts, sprains.	As above, both heat exhaustion and exposure to cold may be encountered.
Shooting	Gunshot wounds.	First aid—emergency service available.
Rock climbing	Exposure, cuts, sprains, more serious injuries due to falls.	Liaison needed with rescue services in the event that patient is immobilized.
Hang gliding	Crashes of all kinds. Cuts, bruises, fractures.	First aid—emergency services. Availability of stretchers, quickest access to all parts of reservoir area, best rendezvous points for ambulance, etc.

Chapter 7

ECONOMIC AND FINANCIAL CONSIDERATIONS

1. INTRODUCTION

RECREATION: ENCOURAGEMENT OR ACCOMMODATION?

THIS chapter purports to provide no more than an indication of the interplay of economic and financial factors within the recreational field. Such factors can, at times, be accompanied by political and emotive considerations. Separate chapters in Book 1 of this series of Water Practice Manuals[1] deal, specifically, with economics and with finance in the wider field of the British water industry, but it was not felt that the breadth of the recreational field justified dividing the two subjects into separate chapters in this volume.

The reader is referred to Book 1[1] for further information in relation to the whole field of water services; here in Book 2 his attention will be directed to the apparent paradox that recreation is hard work . . . at least for those concerned with its planning and administration! At the outset it has to be noted that, in supplying recreational facilities to the public, the water industry is not in the same monopoly situation that applies to the provision of a water supply, or to sewage or land drainage services. The customer is free to choose for himself whether or not he makes use of the recreational services provided by a public body whose primary role is that of providing the recognized water services. There will often also be available to him for the purposes of recreation commercially provided services of a similar nature, although it must be remembered that commercial operators seldom have such expanses of water available to them as those provided by a large reservoir. In addition, other public bodies also provide the means by which a potential customer can be lured away either to other similar facilities or to different forms of sport and recreation.

Therein lies an initial difficulty as far as references to the regional water authorities and other public water supply bodies are concerned, and the text hereafter refers to regional water authorities or water authorities on the understanding that the principles and philosophy which follow apply where appropriate to other statutory bodies able to provide water-related recreational facilities. The Water Act 1973 includes a permissive power to water authorities to provide recreational facilities on water and associated land but requires also that reasonably practical steps should be taken to obtain the best recreational use of their own waters and associated land. The question then arises as to whether or not recreation based on inland waters in public ownership should be confined simply to accommodating traditional and well-established water-related activities. Arguments can be advanced for positively encouraging an expansion of such activities and broadening them to encompass non-water-related activities also. Whatever course of action is determined (and it may well be influenced by practical water supply and treatment considerations) questions will inevitably arise as to what charges should be levied on those who make use of the facilities.

The public at large, not appreciating the true extent of the situation, may believe that the land and water in the ownership of a water authority has been bought at a cost to the public purse which is already reflected in the charges being paid for the "water" services giving rise to that ownership. Any charge therefore is likely, initially at least, to be regarded by the public as an additional and unwarranted imposition on charges for the monopoly services of the water industry. The fact that recreational activity and public access to water facilities requires an often elaborate infrastructure of roads, car parks, toilets, and supervisory staffing is frequently overlooked. In these circumstances it becomes desirable for the owning authority to embark on processes of public education, and necessary to consider whether any element of infrastructure costs might properly be regarded as a rate to be levied on the generality of water service customers.

The matter is not capable of simple resolution because the aspects to be considered range between wide extremes. On the one hand arguments are advanced that the whole objective of the recreational provisions in the Water Act 1973 was to ensure that the public at large might be able to enjoy the recreational benefits lying latent in the land and water held by water authorities. There is then an inference that costs may properly fall on the public at large, irrespective of whether or not their own circumstances and inclinations actually lead them to make use of the facilities made available.

CHARGES: WHERE SHOULD THEY FALL?

The Water Act 1973, however, also contains provisions which carry the broad implication that there should be as little cross-subsidization in the use of individual water services as is possible. The principle of an individual class or category of user subsidizing the services enjoyed by another is therefore no longer appropriate. The other extreme of the range of considerations therefore is that, although an element of rough justice is acceptable (for purely practical reasons) in the incidence of costs falling within categories of water service users, there is no reason at all why recreational users should not meet in full the appropriate costs of the facilities which they enjoy. This concept involves marginal cost pricing as described later in this chapter. There is no difficulty in identifying those who actually make use of the recreational facilities provided by water authorities. They identify themselves by their very presence and, with due regard to the practicability and cost-effectiveness of collecting every last penny, they can readily be charged fully for the costs which their presence is imposing on the owner of the facilities.

The purpose of this present chapter therefore is to examine how the recreational infrastructure costs might be met, together with a number of practical issues relating to the physical handling of the cash flow thereby generated. To do so, however, it is necessary to have regard to the economic factors which lead both to people having time for recreation and the disposable income to devote to its pursuit. The recreationalist can display a somewhat illogical approach to the pursuit of his hobby. He is prepared to allocate significant sums from his disposable income to the apparatus and transport needed for his recreational pursuits yet is, apparently, reluctant to recognize that he should meet other costs arising through the provision of public facilities. It has to be appreciated, however, that his disposable income is finite and also that the corresponding element of a water authority's budget is similarly constrained and, at least in regard to capital expenditure, is subject also to a greater conflict of priorities. In the hope that it will contribute to a better understanding of the nature (and availability) of the personal income base required to support charges for recreational provisions, attention will be directed initially to the economic considerations referred to earlier. Thereafter, the reader will be led forward into the considerations which lead to the actual determination of the sum to be printed on the admission ticket or season permit.

2. THE ECONOMICS OF WORK, WEALTH, AND RECREATION

RECREATION IN INDUSTRIAL SOCIETY

Clawson and Knetsch[2] define recreation as "the activity or activities (including inactivity if freely chosen) engaged in during leisure time. Leisure is time, recreation is activity." They divide recreation, thus broadly defined, into indoor and outdoor types, and take outdoor recreation as their subject. They note that outdoor recreation needs areas of land and water, often large ones, and that this need competes with other uses of the same resources. This is the framework for discussing the economics of recreation.

On the need for recreation, they note that modern life is "more ordered in terms of time" than in earlier economies. People in modern societies can consume more and live better because an industrial economy is more productive of material goods. But the price of this prosperity is living by the clock: work has to be done at agreed times, and leisure fitted into the interstices of life. This can cause emotional stress and tension, which in turn may call for some form of recreation to get rid of the strains of modern urban living.

Negative causes of the demand for recreation can be over-emphasized; the stresses of life in industrial economies may well be different, but they are probably not greater than those in traditional economies. It is undeniable, however, that the crowding and planning inseparable from urbanization necessitate the separate provision of resources and facilities for recreation; that the general prosperity flowing from industrialization has given most people the means and the energy to enjoy and to demand recreational activities; and that the gradual fall in the length of the standard working day, week, and life in the advanced stages of industrial development provide the opportunity for recreational activities.

In the next section we leave these generalities to consider some specific aspects of the demand for recreation. Discussions of the sociology of leisure in industrial societies can be found, for example, in the work of Kaplan[3] and Cheek and Burch[4].

DETERMINANTS OF RECREATIONAL ACTIVITY

The General Household Survey (GHS), which is undertaken by the Office of Population Censuses and Surveys (OPCS), interviews a sample of the population during each week of the year on a wide variety of topics. During 1973 and 1977 the surveys included questions on recreation, and the following subsections discuss some of the 1977 findings.

Informants (aged 16 and over) were asked what they had done in their leisure time in the four previous weeks, and how often. School activities were excluded as many of them are compulsory. Tables 7.I to 7.IV show the results for the most popular quarter, because annual averages understate the popularity of seasonal activities. Most of the following information has been abstracted from the OPCS[5]. There is a useful summary and comparison with the 1973 GHS in Birch[6].

The subsections which follow concentrate on water-based and countryside recreational activities. To put these in perspective, Table 7.I shows the participation rates in some other popular recreational activities compared to water-based and countryside ones. "Field studies" include birdwatching, nature study and collecting, conservation, archaeology, and guided walks. It will be noted that home-based recreation has vastly greater participation rates than out-of-home activities, indicating the influence of the money and psychic costs of travel.

TABLE 7.I. Some Leisure Activities (1977)

(Participation rates (per cent), most popular quarter)

Watching television	98.0	Betting/pools	20.4	Boat trips	1.7
Visiting and		Visits to country-		Field studies	0.9
entertaining	92.0	side	8.9	Sailing	0.7
Walking 2 miles		Fishing	4.0	Rowing/canoeing/	
or more	22.1	Camping/caravanning	2.4	punting	0.4

Sources: Office of Population Censuses and Surveys (OPCS)[5], Tables 7.1-3, and Birch[6], Tables 1 and 2, Crown Copyright.

The most popular recreational activity involving water is swimming, with a participation rate of 13 per cent. It is not shown in Table 7.I because it is probably unimportant as an outdoor activity in inland waters. Excluding swimming, the most popular water-based activity is fishing, with a participation rate of 4.0 per cent. Walking is, of course, not an activity confined to lands held in conjunction with water, but provision is usually made for walkers at water industry recreation sites if only because Enabling Orders provide at least for existing public rights of way to be replaced.

The following subsections take fishing and walking 2 miles or more as the two activities upon which to illustrate the effects of each determinant of recreational demand.

Age and Sex

Table 7.II shows participation rates as the percentage engaging in each activity in the four weeks before the interview, by different age groups.

TABLE 7.II. Participation Rates Per Cent by Age Group (1977)

Age	16-19	20-24	25-29	30-44	45-59	60-69	70+
Fishing	4	3	3	3	2	1	—
Walking (2 + miles)	16	19	20	20	17	18	9
Total: outdoor sports	43	39	35	33	24	22	11
Open-air outings	15	19	20	18	14	14	10

Source: Office of Population Censuses and Surveys (OPCS)[5], Tables 7.10-12, Crown Copyright.

The average ages of those involved in the activities listed in Table 7.II were: fishing 36; walking 42; outdoor sports 38; and open-air outings 41.

Fishing was much more popular among men than women in all age groups. In no age group did the participation rate of women exceed 1 per cent; their average participation rate was 1 per cent and their average age (if they fished) was 33. Men's participation rate declined gradually from 5 to 6 per cent up to the age of 45 to 1 per cent above 70. Women also participated less in all outdoor sports taken together (21 against 35 per cent men), but about equally in walking (16 and 18 per cent respectively) and open air outings (16 and 15 per cent respectively).

Another dimension in which engaging in an activity was measured was the mean number of days in which those who participated in an activity did so in the four weeks before the interview. Table 7.III shows the mean number of days by age group.

TABLE 7.III. Mean Number of Days by Age Group
(Participation during four weeks before interview, 1977)

Age	16-19	20-29	30-44	45-59	60+
Fishing	3.3	3.5	2.9	3.4	4.6
Walking (2+ miles)	5.9	5.5	6.2	7.5	10.7
Visits to the countryside	3.4	2.9	3.2	3.7	4.2

Source: Office of Population Censuses and Surveys (OPCS)[5], Table 7.15, Crown Copyright.

The effects of the availability of greater leisure time at different stages of life are clearly visible in Table 7.III, particularly in relation to walking. However, walking may also be favoured by the elderly as the easiest and simplest active pursuit outdoors. The mean number of days in which they engaged in fishing is markedly different between men and women, being an average 3.4 for men and less than 0.5 for women. For walking and visits to the countryside the difference between the sexes is negligible.

Income

Table 7.IV shows the participation rates and mean number of days by income groups in 1977, when the average gross weekly household income was about £93.00. It will be noticed that higher income groups tend to have a higher proportion of numbers participating, but that in general they do so on fewer days.

TABLE 7.IV. Selected Recreational Activities by Income Group (1977)
(1977 Average gross weekly household income, £93.00)

Income group, £	Less than 40	40-60	60-80	80-100	100-150	More than 150
	(a) % engaging in activity in 4 weeks before interview					
Fishing	1	2	3	3	2	2
Walking (2+ miles)	12	15	16	19	19	22
Total outdoor sports	14	22	26	31	33	41
	(b) Mean number of days engaged in activity; 4 weeks before interview					
Fishing	6.1	4.1	3.1	2.6	2.9	3.6
Walking (2+ miles)	11.0	8.3	6.8	6.6	6.3	6.0
Visits to countryside	4.2	3.7	3.3	3.9	3.3	3.2

Source: Office of Population Censuses and Surveys (OPCS)[5], Tables 7.16 and 7.21, Crown Copyright.

Socio-economic Group

Birch[6] shows that manual and non-manual groups have noticeably different participation rates in different activities. Whereas the proportion of non-manuals participating in outdoor swimming, walking 2 miles or more, and countryside activities is about one-and-a-half times to double the proportion of manuals, the situation is reversed in the case of fishing with the non-manual participation rate being only 0.5 to 0.9 times the manual participation rate.

Education

The GHS shows that, by and large, people with higher qualifications participated more in recreational activities, but OPCS[5] points out the interdependence of the different determinants:

". . .(the) better qualified tend to be male, young, in non-manual occupations, and enjoying higher incomes. All these factors are reflected in their participation rates . . ."

Holidays

The OPCS[5] also shows (in Table 7.40) that a large proportion of recreational activities takes place during holidays; for example, 90 per cent of camping and caravanning, 23 per cent of visits to the countryside, 21 per cent of fishing, and 16 per cent of walking 2 miles or more, took place on holiday.

MOTIVATIONS FOR RECREATION

A recent example of a motivational study is Hawes[7], which also refers to previous papers in this area. Hawes conducted a postal survey of the heads of households in the United States of America, in which he listed 50 recreations and 32 "satisfaction statements" or reasons for doing the activities, and asked them to match the satisfactions with the recreations they took part in. He analysed replies from 603 female and 512 male heads of households.

Women found the most important satisfactions, over all activities, to be peace of mind, learning about new things, and getting the most out of life. Men generally agreed, but they found learning about new things an unimportant recreational satisfaction, and preferred adventure and excitement instead. Escape from family pressures was important to women but less so to men.

Hawes also analysed the favourite recreations of those surveyed so as to find the clusters of satisfactions that were most important to each sex. A brief summary of his findings is given in Table 7.V.

TABLE 7.V. Analysis of Favoured Recreations

Cluster	Women	Men
1	Newness Relating to people	Physical activity Competence-seeking
2	Mental activity Independence, control, mastery	Recognition Understanding self
3	Physical activity Body orientation	Outdoor-orientated, contemplative introspection
4	Contemplation Passivity	Nostalgia Living full life
5	Seeking unknown Overcoming challenges	Seeking unknown Overcoming challenges

Hawes treated fishing and hunting as one recreation. For the women who included this in their three favourite recreations, the strongest satisfactions from it were strengthening family ties, enjoying nature, and escape from pressures. For the men their strongest satisfactions were adventure and excitement, enjoying nature, and being alone in a quiet spot. This provides an intriguing problem for fishery managers seeking to satisfy both kinds of customer.

The managerial implications of this study are stated by Hawes to pertain mainly to segmenting the market and positioning the product in relation to the satisfactions derived rather than just the pursuit *per se*. He suggests that a tennis facility might emphasize different features for men and for women. For women it could be marketed as a social outlet where women could make and renew friendships, receive instruction, and take part in large doubles leagues. For men, marketing should emphasize physical exertion, skill development leading to mastery and control, and singles tournaments providing maximum competition.

3. ECONOMIC TRENDS IN RECREATION

RECENT U.K. TRENDS

Tables 7.VI and 7.VII extend certain trends in leisure pointed out in Vickerman[8]. More detailed discussion of each trend will be found at the appropriate place in Vickerman, whose Table numbers are given here as sources.

Expenditure

Table 7.VI below is derived from the annual "Family Expenditure Surveys"[9] undertaken by the Department of Employment.

TABLE 7.VI. Household Expenditure on Leisure-related Items
(£/week at current prices; %)

	1. Expenditure on leisure-related items, £/week	2. Total expenditure, £/week	3. 1 as a percentage of 2
1957	2.58	14.27	18.1
1972	9.17	35.06	26.2
1977	18.27	71.84	25.4

Source: Vickerman[8], Table 2.I, Macmillan, London; and Family Expenditure Survey[9], Crown Copyright.

Expressed in 1975 prices, the expenditure on leisure-related items was £7.41 in 1957, £14.42 in 1972, and £13.53 in 1977. In real terms, therefore, leisure expenditure grew by 4.5 per cent a year between 1957 and 1972, but fell by 1.3 per cent a year between 1972 and 1977. Leisure expenditure, in fact, reached a minimum of £13.32 (in 1975 prices) in 1976, so there was a slight recovery to 1977.

Writing on "The economics of leisure" in Smith *et al*[10], Parker took another rough estimate of leisure expenditure from the annual "National Income and Expenditure"[11] and found that this increased from 19 per cent of national expenditure in 1960 to 21 per cent in 1970, but that the increase was mainly due to the expenditure on motor cars. In real terms the increase was 2.4 per cent a year over ten years, only slightly faster than the rate of increase in total expenditure. He noted that there was a similar tendency in the United States of America, namely that leisure expenditure was not increasing faster than total expenditure. The latest expenditure figures available at the time of writing, i.e. those for 1977, generally confirm Parker's findings, and also show the effects of the changed economic circumstances in the U.K. since 1973. In 1967 Parker's rough measure of recreational expenditure was 19.7 per cent of total expenditure; by 1973 this proportion had increased to 20.3

per cent but by 1977 it had fallen to 19.4 per cent. Between 1967 and 1973 nearly 25 per cent of the increase in recreational expenditure was caused by motor cars, etc.; between 1973 and 1977 they accounted for only 13 per cent of the increase (at current prices).

In real terms (at 1975 prices) leisure expenditure grew at 4.4 per cent a year between 1967 and 1973, during which years total expenditure grew at 3.1 per cent a year. Between 1973 and 1977 leisure expenditure fell at 1.4 per cent a year while total expenditure fell at 1.1 per cent a year. It would thus seem that leisure expenditure grows somewhat faster than average in good times and falls somewhat faster than average in hard times. This is what one would expect for expenditure on an item which, in the ultimate analysis, must be considered something of a luxury.

Weekly Hours of Work

Table 7.VII shows recent changes in the average working week in manufacturing industry.

TABLE 7.VII. **Average Weekly Hours Worked in Manufacturing and Certain Other Industries**

Year	Men	Youths	Women		Girls
			Full-time	Part-time	
1947	45.0	46.3	43.7	41.5	42.0
1956	46.6	48.5	44.9	41.5	42.5
1966	46.0	42.2	38.1	21.5	38.7
1976	44.0	40.5	37.4	21.2	37.5
1978	44.2	40.6	37.4	21.1	37.6

Source: Vickerman[8], Table 2.2, Macmillan, London; and Monthly Digest of Statistics[12], Crown Copyright.

This shows that the long-term trend towards a reduction in the weekly hours actually worked has continued during the 1970s. There are indications that this trend will continue, possibly accelerating with the advent of such new technologies as the micro-chip. Trades Unions seek reductions in the standard working week, but this does not of itself necessarily mean that the hours actually worked will fall by an equal amount. Nor should it be forgotten that whatever the technological possibilities of startling reductions in average hours worked may be, the psychological, social and economic probabilities point to a reluctance to reduce hours too significantly.

Vacations

As recently as 1961, 97 per cent of manual workers were entitled to annual paid holidays of two weeks or less. By 1977, 99 per cent had holidays of three weeks or more (Vickerman[8], Table 2.3, and Social Trends[13], 1979 edition, Table 5.19). The example of continental countries suggests that this trend will continue.

Economic Activity

The Office of Population Censuses and Surveys[5] points out three trends that are noticeable among the economically active (excluding full-time students, but including the involuntarily unemployed) between 1971 and 1977:-

(1) a decline in economic activity among men aged 60 and over, due to a trend towards earlier retirement;
(2) a decline in economic activity among non-married women; and
(3) more married women entering the labour force, a trend which has continued since the Second World War.

The increasing proportion of married women at work may suggest that economic necessity is leading to a decline in the leisure time available to that section of the community. It may, however, be a pointer towards an enforced leisure in individual isolation in the home being unattractive.

Income

In economics the measure of expenditure in a society is also a measure of its income. Hence, some indication of the trends in income, which is a determinant of recreational demand, were implied in the sub-section above dealing with Expenditure (p. 199). A good measure of spending power is real personal disposable income per capita, which is published in the monthly "Economic Trends" and its Annual Supplement[14]. Expressed in the value of 1975 prices this has grown as follows:-

Growth in Spending Power

Year	£	Growth Rate, percentage per annum
1950	716	—
1960	936	2.7 over 10 years
1970	1137	2.0 over 10 years
1973	1326	5.3 over 3 years
1977	1305	-0.4 over 4 years
1978	1391	6.6 over 1 year

The growth rate from 1970 to 1978 is 2.6 per cent per annum, showing that the perturbations of the 1970s, which are large when considered over short periods, tend to smooth out to a more stable rate, not very dissimilar to previous decades, when taken over longer periods.

RECENT RECREATION TRENDS

Comparison of the General Household Survey's recreational findings in 1973 and 1977 should have enabled us to derive trends in recreation during this very interesting recent period. However, as Birch[6] points out, the comparisons for fishing, etc., were invalidated by changes in method, and other changes were so small as to be within the range of sampling fluctuations.

Of the validly comparable activities related to water, major changes occurred for field studies (0.9 vs 0.3 per cent) and visits to the countryside (8.9 vs 15.6 per cent, although the latter included boat trips for which the 1977 participation rate was 1.7 per cent). Camping/caravanning (2.4 per cent) and sailing (0.7 per cent) had exactly the same participation rates in 1973 and 1977.

The Annual Report of the Countryside Commission for 1977-78[15] gives a summary of trends in countryside recreation. The commission also states that first examination of the 1977 GHS "confirms many of the findings of our national survey, for example the high popularity of countryside recreation, although an initial assessment of the data from the 1973 and 1977 surveys suggests that there was little or no increase in countryside recreation between those years.''

In summary, the general trends of recent years appear to be a continuing increase in leisure, but little growth in recreation.

4. THE FUTURE OF RECREATION — ECONOMIC FORECASTS

GENERAL

This section makes no attempt to forecast the demand for recreation, whether in general or for specific pursuits. It is concerned, rather, with the methods that may be used for making such forecasts. The first subsection is concerned with forecasting general recreation demand, and the second with forecasting the demand for specific facilities.

A word of warning about forecasting may be appropriate. Anybody can, and many people do, make forecasts but it requires some skill, training, and experience to minimize the subsequent probability of regretting having done so. Particularly in these days when even pocket calculators have built-in regression packages, it is necessary to emphasize that the most important ingredient of a forecast is understanding rather than method. Having made the forecast it can, at best, be an indicator enabling judgement decisions to be taken about the extent, type, and location of future facilities. At the worst those decisions will appear, in retrospect, to have been ''in error''; nevertheless, they will have avoided the greater ''error'' of not having attempted to anticipate a situation.

FORECASTING GENERAL RECREATIONAL DEMAND

Chapter 7 of Clawson and Knetsch[2] is a brief overview of the available methods of forecasting demand. They list five main methods:-

(1) extrapolating past trends in demand;
(2) extrapolating past trends in the determinants of demand;
(3) setting ceilings on future demand;
(4) using forecasts of the determinants of demand, and
(5) judgement.

The advantages of extrapolating past trends are cheapness and simplicity. Hardly anybody can resist the temptation to squint along a line of dots representing a time series, or to use a ruler or an equation, and persuade himself that extending the line into the future is an act of reasonable prudence. There are two main disadvantages: that trends over different past periods tend to go in different directions, and that when underlying causes change then trends can change without warning.

The advantages of extrapolating past trends in the determinants of demand are, in addition to cheapness and simplicity, that some understanding of the demand has been deployed, and that there is some chance that over-estimates and under-estimates of different determinants will fortuitously tend to cancel out, leaving a fairly good forecast of the demand itself. Also, a change in the trend of a determinant should give some warning of a change in the trend of a demand. The disadvantages are, obviously, that different trends fit different periods and that errors may be mutually reinforcing rather than self-cancelling.

The setting of ceilings on demand follows from the evident fact that particular growth trends cannot go on for ever. For instance, recreation can take no more than

100 per cent of the total time available to the population and will probably take very much less on any reasonable estimate of how many hours work and chores will occupy in the future. Hence, many demands are forecast to follow "logistic" curves, i.e. have increasing growth rates early in their lives, stable growth rates in their middle years, and falling growth rates in their maturity, reflecting the patterns of biological growth. Reasonable though this approach appears, it faces a number of difficulties. For instance, how to forecast when the trend will start changing, i.e. the "point of inflexion"; how to forecast what the saturation level will be; and how to forecast technological changes that will set off the next cycle beginning with fast growth. Despite much statistical apparatus, these forecasts are usually based on judgement.

Using forecasts of the determinants of demand has the advantage of seeking to benefit from the expertise and computational resources devoted to forecasting important economic and social measures, such as national income and household size. However, this will be an improvement on using trends only to the extent that the chosen forecast is better (i.e. turns out to be more accurate *ex post*) than the trend; there is some controversy about whether sophisticated econometric models perform any better than naive ones. The assumption in this method is that the relationship between the determinant and the demand being forecast will continue unchanged into the future.

In using and interpreting forecasts managers would be wise to bear in mind the limitations and the strengths of the particular forecasting method used. The more uncertain the future, the more prudent it is to "keep options open" as long as possible by staging works, postponing commitments, and considering whether earlier decisions need to be reviewed against a changed frame of reference.

FORECASTING DEMAND FOR PARTICULAR FACILITIES

Most of the work that economists have done in the area of recreation has been in the application of the "Clawson method" of forecasting demand for particular facilities. This literature is cited and reviewed in Gibson[16], which is short, sound, and relatively accessible to non-economists. In this section the intention is to explain the use, not the techniques, of the Clawson method.

The first point to bear in mind is that the Clawson method is a sharp and delicate instrument, unsuited to use by amateurs. In addition to Gibson[16], those interested in its many pitfalls and imperfections, even after two decades of intensive work on it, may wish to peruse Ulph and Reynolds[17]. The second point is that followers of particular pursuits are often (and rightly) enthusiasts, and tend to believe that new supplies of facilities will automatically evoke new demands. The Clawson method provides a more objective check on such claims.

The Clawson method shows demand as a "distance decay function"—fewer trips are made to a facility from more distant districts. This shows what one might expect, i.e. that the higher the costs people have to incur the less they demand of anything, including recreation. The fact emerges clearly from all empirical work that the demand for recreation falls away steeply as its costs rise, but it is often difficult for enthusiasts to accept this. It should, ideally, be evaluated for each facility and borne clearly in mind by planners and managers.

The benefit of trying to estimate demand as best we may is that the exercise clarifies thinking about objectives. Making the best use of resources means different things to different people, and deciding is particularly difficult when lobbyists believe that their favourite activities are not just economic goods, but "good for" people, society, and humanity. There is always choice about what activities to cater for at a recreational site, and measuring potential demand for each may increase the ratio of light to heat in the arguments preceding the decision. Particularly when faced with the argument that willingness to pay is not an appropriate measure of benefit or return to society, measurement helps the decision by making more precise the amount of subsidy that is being implied.

However, these arguments for objectively estimating demand as a help to decision-making must not be taken to imply that quantitative methods will solve all problems. Quantification verifies facts and clarifies assumptions and arguments, but hardly ever gives clear guidance on policy. The ultimate management decisions must still be based on judgements about the fuzzy relationships between objectives and resources, behaviour and technologies, and the past and the future.

5. ECONOMIC FACTORS AFFECTING CHARGING POLICY

MARGINAL COST PRICING

Reference has already been made to the diversity of factors capable of influencing the detailed structure of the charges applied to activities using recreational facilities provided by water authorities. General economic principles suggest that "marginal cost pricing", or charging the full additional cost imposed, leads to the greatest social welfare in a society. The theory is explained, for instance, in the papers in Part One of Turvey[18]. It is also, at first sight at any rate, equitable that those whose enjoyment is increased by the use of a facility should bear the extra cost of providing it.

The objection to this principle is that it is based on an assumption that money has the same value to different people. The distribution of income and wealth in society, however, leads to money being valued differently by different individuals. The argument can then be advanced that the recreational facilities made available by water authorities will thus, under a "no-subsidy" policy, be used only by a particular class in the community. That class then acquires, by inference, a privilege assumed to apply to those whose value and possession of money enables them to meet the marginal cost of indulging in what is attractive to them. Arguments as to whether or not a recreational charging policy should include an element of subsidy then begin to introduce questions of social welfare and the distribution of wealth, which the water industry has hitherto not regarded as falling within its statutory remit. Government-introduced measures such as the water charges equalization procedures which, introduced in 1977, had the effect of abating the incidence of water supply charges in Wales and elsewhere, have brought the industry's managers into contact with social policy matters unrelated to the real business of supplying water services. The 1978 White Paper on the Nationalized Industries (Cmnd. 7131) had something to say on the subsidy situation, i.e. "When help has to be given to poorer members of the community, it will be given primarily through the Social Security and taxation systems and not by subsidising nationalized industry prices."

The charges made for the basic elements of the water services reflect, by having been long established, a significant element of low historic cost. Recreational charges, however, have to take into account the current high cost situation which is therefore more closely akin to the marginal costs of recreational development. The water industry is, however, moving towards new charging structures for the basic services which it provides. Charges therefore seem likely to contain an element increasingly related to the provision of the "next increment" of capacity or service.

This will assist in removing any apparent inconsistency between the basis of charge as between recreation and the basic water services.

PUBLIC REACTION TO RECREATION

Another factor to be taken into account is the attitude of different sections of the public to proposals relating to the recreational use of, say, a new reservoir or to extending the traditional use which has been made of an existing one. Whilst it is possible for the promoters of a new scheme to have specific recreational interests present evidence about the need, and hence the apparent volume of future use, for given types of recreational facility that evidence tends to strengthen the opposition of those who are opposed to the new development *per se*. Experience has shown that such opposition is often transformed by the passage of time into acquiescence and finally into enthusiasm for what the completed scheme makes available recreationally and environmentally. Nevertheless, any established policy of subsidizing recreational use through charges raised on the generality of water service customers is likely to strengthen rather than diminish any initial opposition to proposals containing any element of recreational use.

The situation can be given an added twist when it is considered that the ability to offer preference in recreational availability to persons directly affected by the basic proposals is, in effect, making a subsidy available to those who happen to live closest to the affected site!

MOBILITY

A further factor to be taken into account, and one which probably would not have been entertained prior to the impact in 1973 of real fuel price increases on the economy, is that of travel to a recreational venue. Where facilities already exist and are patronized largely by "travelling" recreationalists there may be an argument for not raising recreational charges to the point where, on top of fuel costs, they could represent the last straw and lead to the under-utilization of expensive provisions. In the case of new proposals the scales might well be tilted by the proximity of the new development to large centres of population and to possibilities for making use of public, rather than private, transport to provide access to the site itself.

FISHERIES AND FISHING

The regional water authorities carry statutory responsibilities (Section 18, Water Act 1973) to maintain, improve and develop the fisheries in their areas and it will be apparent that, without a fishery, there could be no angling. That must be so whether the fishery is in a natural state or, as with some rivers and most reservoirs, fish are introduced on a "put and take" basis to provide an appropriate degree of sport and encouragement to the angler. There is a distinction, however, between use of a water as a specific recreational angling facility available on payment of an appropriate charge, as at a reservoir, and use for angling in a more general sense.

In the reservoir many of the fish which are introduced survive only for a relatively short time . . . not because they are diseased or because the water is polluted but because they are taken by anglers. In other waters the well-being of the fishery is, together with the well-being of aquatic flora and fauna generally, an indication of the well-being of the water itself. In such circumstances it is appropriate to regard part of the cost of meeting the regional water authority's fishery responsibilities as a proper charge on the environmental services account, the fishery being the equivalent of the coal miner's canary. That element of the fishery expenses not recovered in this way is met by charges raised for rod licences and, as is shown later in this chapter, the holders of such licences thereby receive fishery services to about double the value of the payments which they make.

GRANT AID

In all that has been said above about subsidies it has been assumed that the water authority will be looking to the recovery of its recreational costs after deduction of the available grant provisions referred to in other parts of this book. The purist might well argue that any such grant is itself a subsidy, coming as it does from funds raised from society as a whole and used to provide benefits for only part of that society. Those involved in the planning and provision of water-related recreation have, above all, to be practical in their outlook and would suggest to the purist that the bodies providing such grants do so as part of their nationally recognized function of encouraging specific aspects of recreation! Nor has it been assumed that each and every recreational activity at a particular site, or even within the area of a specific water authority, will be the subject of a separate debit and credit account. It may well be possible to recover from a given category of recreational user rather more than the costs attributable to them. In such circumstances the "profit" is generated by recreational use and it will be for the individual managing body to determine whether it is proper to apply such funds in supporting a less profitable activity within the overall definition of recreation. The purist, again, may express concern, but equally may be persuaded that without any policy of providing for recreation the activity which produced the surplus would not be taking place under water authority jurisdiction.

6. FINANCE AND RECREATION

In the preceding sections of this chapter much has been said about policy factors applicable in devising a financial structure which recovers, from one source or another, the costs of providing recreational facilities. In the ultimate the policy decisions actually reached will be political ones in the sense that the members of the public bodies concerned will determine how and where the charges should fall. It remains therefore to consider the financial officer's approach both in advising members as to the options open to them and, subsequently, in devising and operating the charging structure.

RECOVERY OF COSTS

Since the Water Act 1973 and the legal case of *Daymond* v *South West Water Authority* (1975), it has become clear that water authorities can for the most part only make charges on those persons who are provided with a service or make use of a facility, as set out below in the reference to Section 30(4) of the Act.

Nevertheless, there is an exception to this statutory policy in the continuation of the precepting arrangements for the financing of the land drainage service. Also, by virtue of the Water Charges Act 1976, the Environmental Services Charge may be recovered from all rated properties irrespective of whether a service is provided or facility used. The Environmental Service Charge is intended to recover the net costs of recreation, amenity, fisheries, water quality, and pollution control. The Water

Act 1973 made a fundamental change in the water industry's financial policies with regard to the recovery of costs by way of charges to consumers. The following Sections of the Act are particularly relevant:-

(Section 29(1))   "It shall be the duty of every water authority so to discharge their functions as to secure that, taking one year with another, their revenue is not less than sufficient to meet their total out-goings properly chargeable to revenue account."

(Section 30(4))   "In fixing charges for services, facilities or rights a water authority shall have regard to the cost of performing those services, providing those facilities or making available those rights."

(Section 30(5))   ". . .it shall be the duty of every water authority to take such steps as will ensure that, as from a date not later than 1st April 1981, their charges are such as not to show undue preference to, or discriminate unduly against, any class of persons."

It can be seen therefore from the above obligations that water authorities need to:-

(a) equate their revenue expenditure with revenue income and therefore cannot as a deliberate policy make losses or what could be regarded as unjustifiable surpluses;

(b) relate charges to both the costs involved and to the actual provision of services to categories of customers, with the exception of the environmental services charge; and

(c) ensure that by April 1981 charges for a service broadly reflect the costs of providing that service.

STATUTORY RESPONSIBILITY FOR SPECIFIC FUNCTIONS

There are three principal areas of statutory responsibility which are placed upon the water industry and, having an impact on water recreation, therefore lead to consideration of the detailed allocation of resources and the recovery of the costs of providing facilities. These responsibilities are:-

(i) Amenity and recreation. Under Section 20 of the Water Act 1973 water authorities and statutory water undertakers have a duty to take such steps as are reasonably practicable to make the best possible use of their rights to water (and associated land) for recreational purposes. This requires the allocation of resources to meet the statutory duty and with it the need to consider recovering the costs of those resources.

(ii) Fisheries. Under Section 28 of the Salmon and Freshwater Fisheries Act 1975 the water authorities have a duty to maintain, improve and develop fisheries and to regulate fishing by means of a licensing system. The detailed financing of the fisheries service is considered later.

(iii) Navigation. In some areas on 1st April 1974 the industry inherited responsibilities for navigation previously carried out by the former river authorities under the Water Resources Act 1963. Again, the discharge of this responsibility provides, by the maintenance of navigational channels on rivers, for the movement of craft and for those whose recreational inclinations lie afloat. Again, consideration needs to be given to recovering the costs of providing the necessary resources.

It has to be considered, therefore, in determining a financial policy for recreation, whether the policy should be to recover, through specific charges raised on the recreational users, those costs which would not arise in the absence of the recreational activity. Such a policy recognizes that an element of expenditure arises irrespective of the presence of recreationalists and would be in line with the financial requirements of the Water Act 1973. To the extent that any part of the identified costs of providing and operating recreational facilities is not recovered from the direct users then such costs fall on the consumers at large.

RECREATIONAL USE OF WATER INDUSTRY FACILITIES

The scope for developing a greater income from water-based recreational facilities in the water industry is significant, particularly when it is borne in mind that some 530 reservoirs exist having a water surface area at top water level of some 21 000 ha. Of this total number of reservoirs, about 340 already support some form of recreational activity either on the water or on surrounding land areas, and are therefore sources of income to the industry.

The largest single activity is fishing, which takes place at 327 reservoirs throughout the country and generates a substantial part of both the income and the expenditure (Table 7.X).

The other major user of water space is sailing, which takes place at 84 reservoirs. Many of the larger reservoirs, of course, can accommodate more than one activity, with the smaller ones being more suited to a single activity, often fishing.

Table 7.VIII illustrates the recreational uses to which reservoirs and their surrounding areas are being made available (some reservoirs, of course, support multiple activities).

TABLE 7.VIII. Types of Recreation Available on Reservoirs and Surroundings

Activity	No. of reservoirs	Percentage of total availability
Fishing-		
coarse	80	16
game	277	56
Sailing	84	17
Canoeing	19	4
Rowing	9	2
Sub-aqua	22	4
Swimming	1	–
Water ski-ing	4	1
	496	100

Source: Brown, K. S., 1978, Water, November (National Water Council), "The personal touch in water recreation".[19]

It can be seen from Table 7.VIII how great a proportion of the recreational activity at reservoirs arises through angling, this being responsible for some 72 per cent of recreational availability. Sailing and canoeing are activities which are gaining in popularity. At most reservoirs where these pursuits are permitted, they are usually organized by a club which then becomes responsible for recruiting members and making satisfactory financial arrangements with the undertaking owning the water. Similarly, rowing and sub-aqua facilities are usually operated through a club with the water space being leased by the owning authority.

A further aspect of recreation to be taken into consideration is whether areas of water and land associated therewith should be made available for more informal recreational pursuits such as picnicking, bird-watching, car-parking, horse-riding, walking, etc. In order to provide for these uses areas need to be set aside, and expenditure incurred in providing paths and footpaths, some of which, if they do not already exist as rights of way, may have to be provided to replace rights lost as a result of reservoir construction. There is effectively no economic way of recovering costs from all persons making use of such facilities, thus highlighting the conflicting responsibilities of making the best use of resources for all recreational users whilst not discriminating between groups of persons as required by Section 30(5) of the Water Act 1973.

AMENITY AND RECREATION—POST 1974

The first year of operation of the water authorities in 1974-75 very much reflected the inherited situation from the former water undertakers particularly in the case of the financing of the recreation and amenity service, when there was no statutory responsibility for recreation and no financial constraint in the form of Section 30 of the Water Act 1973. An examination of water authorities' Recreation and Amenity Accounts for 1974-75 indicates that income from charges for the year financed about 50 per cent of expenditure, with the balance of expenditure being recovered from consumers as a whole through the Environmental Services Charge (known at that time as the Miscellaneous Services Charge). Table 7.IX gives an overall indication of how the situation has changed since the 1973 reorganization became effective.

TABLE 7.IX. Summary of Recreation and Amenity Accounts 1974-75 to 1979-80

Year	(1) Expenditure, £000	(2) Income, £000	(3) Balance, £000	% $\frac{(2)}{(1)}$
1974-75	2024	999	1025	49
1975-76	2989	1064	1925	36
1976-77	2135*	639	1496	30
1977-78	3035	1013	2022	33
1978-79	4094	1518	2576	37
1979-80	5362	2127	3235	40

*Reflects the reallocation of navigation expenditure and charges in the Thames Water Authority to a Navigation Revenue Account.

The 1974-75 average of 49 per cent of total expenditure met from charges to users is derived from figures for individual water authorities ranging from 28 to 130 per cent. The operation of recreation and amenity provisions can be labour intensive and costs have thus been significantly affected by inflation since 1974-75. An element of real growth, however, will also be reflected in the tabulated expenditures since 1974 (Table 7.IX), water authorities having developed their recreational policies by improving and developing new water space. Although the level of income from charges has not kept pace with the increase in expenditure since 1974, there are indications that the industry is making some progress towards financing a greater proportion of expenditure from charges. From Table 7.IX it can be seen that expenditure has increased from £2·135 million in 1976 to £5·362 million in 1979-80, an increase of 151 per cent, whilst over the same period income from charges has increased from £0·639 million to £2·127 million, an increase of 233 per cent.

A detailed summary of all ten regional water authorities' Recreation and Amenity Accounts for 1979-80 is shown in Table 7.X.

If it were thought desirable to progress to a greater degree of self-financing of recreational expenditure it may be that, at the very least, all direct expenditure incurred in providing recreational facilities should be recovered from charges for such recreation. Direct expenditure in this context would include employee costs in respect of recreational staff and expenditure on fish stocking, etc., and would include expenditure sub-totalling to £2·631 million in Table 7.X. If this level of expenditure is compared with the income from charges, then a self-financing rate of 81 per cent is achieved. However, some water authorities have progressed more than others in recovering expenditure directly from users and within the overall recovery rate of 40 per cent in 1979-80 is a range for individual authorities from 20 to 79 per cent.

TABLE 7.X. Summary of Regional Water Authorities'
Recreation and Amenity Accounts 1979-80

	£000	£000
Expenditure		
Recreation and amenity:-		
Fishing	1541	
Other recreation	559	
Supporting facilities	384	
General environmental improvement	147	
Sub-total	(2631)	
Research and development	3	
Technical services control	642	
Policy, management, and administration	1269	
Financing costs	817	
Sub-total	(2731)	
Total expenditure		5362
Income		
Fishing permits	1401	
Other recreational charges	726	
Total income (equivalent to 40 per cent of gross expenditure)		2127
Net expenditure to be financed from the Environmental Services Charge		3235

FISHERIES AND ROD LICENCE FEES

It is relevant to differentiate between the costs of the fisheries service and those arising directly from angling, as a recreation, where this is provided as a "put and take" facility. The main source of fisheries income is rod licence fees issued under the Salmon and Freshwater Fisheries Act 1975, whilst the expenditure incurred in providing for angling as a recreation at specific reservoirs is normally largely recovered from users by the sale of day permits or season tickets. Rod licence fees represented some 93 per cent of all income for fisheries purposes in 1979-80. To the extent that licence duties do not meet the full cost of the service the balance is recovered from the industry's customers generally, through the environmental services charge. Powers of precepting on County Councils no longer apply, since the Water Act 1973, to the fisheries function and now exist only to recover expenditure on land drainage.

An analysis of fisheries income, principally from rod licence fees, compared with expenditure for the period 1974-75 to 1979-80 is shown in Table 7.XI.

TABLE 7.XI. Comparison of Water Authorities' Fisheries
Expenditure and Income 1974-75 to 1979-80

Year	(1) Expenditure, £000	(2) Income, £000	(3) Balance, £000	% $\frac{(2)}{(1)}$
1974-75	1804	816	988	45
1975-76	2538	876	1662	34
1976-77	3213	1667	1546	52
1977-78	3785	1841	1944	49
1978-79	4567	2090	2477	46
1979-80	5488	2622	2866	48

Table 7.XI indicates that some progress was made, particularly in 1976-77, towards increasing the proportion of fisheries income recovered directly. Since then, however, it is evident that the effects of inflation in what is very much a labour intensive service have eroded the progress being made in recovering a greater proportion of expenditure. Another constraint is the lengthy procedure necessary under the Salmon and Freshwater Fisheries Act 1975 in order to increase the level of licence fees. Any proposals must be submitted to the Minister of Agriculture, Fisheries and Food for approval and he has powers to convene a public inquiry before approving the proposals. The procedure does not therefore encourage water authorities to propose changes as often as the effect of increasing costs might otherwise require. Another factor affecting the actual number of licences sold is that, after reorganization in 1974, most authorities introduced regional licences valid throughout each region instead of a licence based on the earlier river authority areas.

There is generally, within the water industry, a multi-tier structure of rod licence fees, i.e. for salmon, other game fishing, and for freshwater or coarse fishing. The following range of adult licence fees applied in 1980 within the water authorities:-

Salmon	£3.00 to £32.40
Trout	£2.50 to £5.00
Freshwater (coarse)	80p to £3.00

The above fees apply for the appropriate season and licences are normally available direct from the regional water authority's offices, or from agents appointed by the authority. The greater part of the income from rod licence fees is derived from the coarse fishing sector where, as can be seen, the fees are relatively low. The low average level of fee for coarse fishing does present a difficulty of enforcement where time and effort spent can far outweigh the cost of the licence. Enforcement procedures are a matter for the individual regional water authority to pursue in the courts, but it is not always evident that the penalty fully fits the crime. The deterrent effect of court action is also reduced by the generally low level of publicity given in the Press to the successful outcome of actions brought against offenders.

TABLE 7.XII Summary of Regional Water Authorities' Fisheries Accounts 1979-80

	£000	£000
Expenditure		
Enforcement and protection	1742	
Fish culture and conservation	817	
Liaison and advisory services	170	
Research and development	90	
Sub-total	(2819)	
Technical services control	769	
Policy, management, and administration	1620	
Financing costs	280	
Sub-total	(2669)	
Total expenditure		5488
Income		
Licence fees	2451	
Other income	171	
Total income		2622
Net expenditure to be financed from the Environmental Services Charge		2866

There is clearly a need for a water authority to weigh the benefits, on the one hand, of maximizing its licence fee income by an effective enforcement policy and, on the other hand, the cost-effectiveness of such a policy.

A detailed summary of regional water authorities' Fisheries Accounts for 1979-80 is shown in Table 7.XII.

The level of income from anglers in 1979-80 was equivalent to 48 per cent of total fisheries expenditure for the year. However, if a comparison is made with "direct" expenditure only, totalling £2·819 million (i.e. excluding central management, technical, and financing costs) then the equivalent recovery figure becomes 93 per cent with the balance (of mainly "indirect" expenditure) being financed through the environmental services charge. The water authorities' recovery rate of total expenditure from fishing interests ranged individually from 15 to 129 per cent, indicating differing policies on recovery of expenditure throughout the industry.

FISHERIES—OTHER SOURCES OF INCOME

Another source of income available to the regional water authorities to finance fisheries expenditure is the power to levy contributions upon owners of fisheries. The power has only been used to date by the Welsh Water Authority who sought the necessary Order in 1976 to levy rates throughout its region. It is something of an anomaly that local authorities levy rates on fisheries but the water industry receives no direct income from rate payments made by owners, other than the environmental services charge on those fisheries having rateable value, although the services of the regional water authorities fisheries staff are available to all fisheries. There is a feeling within the industry that wider powers could usefully be available, enabling contributions to be obtained from owners or occupiers to finance regional water authorities' fisheries expenditure.

A facility also exists, within the financing of the fisheries service, for a general licence to be issued to an owner in respect of his own water so avoiding the necessity of individual anglers on that water having to hold a valid rod licence personally. The payment is normally calculated on an annual basis, being related to a multiple of the rod licence fee and the number of anglers that would be likely to make use of the water at any one time. This arrangement is becoming more popular with water authorities as it can produce income to the fisheries account with the minimum of administrative effort. The general licence facility has been seen by some regional water authorities as a means of reducing the administrative burden in respect of their own recreational angling waters. In effect, the issue of a general licence by an authority means that the cost of the rod licence is included in the cost of the permit issued at the appropriate water.

NAVIGATION

As indicated earlier, some regional water authorities inherited navigation responsibilities from their predecessor river authorities. These responsibilities are defined in the Water Resources Act 1963 "as a duty or power imposed or conferred by or under an enactment to manage or maintain an inland navigation other than a canal, whether natural or artificial and whether tidal or not." It can be seen from the above responsibilities that the main objective of water authorities acting as a navigation authority is to ensure that navigation by boats can take place on the appropriate waters. The main element of expenditure incurred on this function is the maintenance of structures, such as locks and river controls and channels and embankments.

of income from users relate to lock passes which authorize the passage of a vessel through a lock and are normally made available on a daily, weekly, or annual basis.

The Southern Water Authority is responsible for the operation of a harbour at Rye and the navigational responsibilities there are financed by way of mooring fees calculated on the length of the vessel; harbour dues are also payable in respect of both pleasure craft and commercial vessels, the latter also being subject to cargo dues.

FINANCIAL CONTROLS AND PROCEDURES

Having considered how charges may be determined and a balance struck between use and benefit, it remains only to consider how the resultant income calls for procedures to be devised for its safe handling. Cash income arises from the sale of fishing permits, rod licences, navigation tolls and dues, sales from tackle shops, car parking charges and miscellaneous items such as ferry charges. Such income has to be accounted for through procedures followed by those handling the cash and its presence generates the need for measures to protect it alike from petty pilfering and wholesale theft. Credit income arises from the payments for use of facilities made by organized clubs and societies, educational and youth groups, and other block bookings. There may be charges levied annually, seasonally, monthly, weekly, or individually for one-off visits or competitions. Credit income raises correspondingly fewer problems but still requires a system to be in existence (and followed) for the issue and control of accounts. Formal accounts should always be rendered to those who enjoy the facilities.

PROBLEMS IN HANDLING CASH INCOME

During the season, tickets have to be available for sale over a period of perhaps 14 hrs per day, seven days per week; anglers in particular frequently arrive early in the morning. Within a limited level of staffing, enforcement of charges may require some ingenuity especially in the case of fishing permits and rod licences because of the often remote and rural nature of facilities with ease of access.

High levels of manning cannot be justified economically to enforce security and internal checks. An accepted level of risk must be acknowledged and systems designed to be as effective as possible. Independent checks of users are essential. Where carried out by rangers and bailiffs the individuals themselves should not be involved in collecting cash. Bulk cash collection can be made daily, from remote areas by a recognized Security firm if the level of cash justifies it. Alternatively, a safe may be installed at the site or bank night safe facilities can be used. When moving cash for banking, employees need to follow suitable procedures aimed at deterring attempts at theft.

GENERAL CONSIDERATIONS

(a) All income should, where appropriate, be receipted through a cash register and the user supplied with an official dated receipt.

(b) Self-service vending machines on a "trust the user" basis can be used to accommodate early morning anglers, who are then subject to checking procedures as rangers and bailiffs take up their duties.

(c) Automatic barriers, or "pay and display" parking systems, can be used in car parks to minimize staff costs. They introduce a further location from which cash has to be collected for banking and in the case of pay and display systems require regular checks to be carried out of parked vehicles. The costs (in staff time) of bringing evaders to book should not be overlooked.

(d) Seasonal staff can be employed to provide cover in support of full-time staff during the summer season. Whilst such employment can be sought after in a rural area the very remoteness of some recreational sites may present transport difficulties which it may be in the interests of the recreational employer to resolve in securing staff of the right calibre.

CONCLUSIONS

The collection of income from recreational sites must inevitably be a compromise between requirements for enforcement; security; and providing an attractive level of service to the user, whilst minimizing staffing and administrative costs. Provided that systems are laid down, documented to the personnel involved, and are subject to test checking by rangers, bailiffs or other audit staff, a reasonable compromise can be achieved. Those responsible for management of the recreational facilities, however, need to examine from time to time the acceptability of the compromise actually being achieved, because it is unlikely that it will remain at the level originally considered to be acceptable.

7. REFERENCES

1. The Institution of Water Engineers and Scientists, 1979, Water Practice Manuals, Book 1, "The structure and management of the British water industry."
2. Clawson, M., and Knetsch, V. L., 1966, "Economics of outdoor recreation", Johns Hopkins University Press, Baltimore and London.
3. Kaplan, M., 1975, "Leisure: theory and policy", Wiley, New York and Chichester.
4. Cheek, N. H., and Burch, W. R., 1976, "The social organization of leisure in human society", Harper and Row, New York and London.
5. Office of Population Censuses and Surveys (OPCS), "General household survey 1977", HMSO.
6. Birch, F., 1979, *Population Trends,* 17, Autumn, "Leisure patterns 1973 and 1977".
7. Hawes, Douglas K., 1978, *Journ. Leis. Res.,* 10, 247, "Satisfactions derived from leisure-time pursuits: an exploratory nationwide survey".
8. Vickerman, R. W., 1975, "The economics of leisure and recreation". Macmillan, London.
9. Department of Employment, 1978, "Family expenditure surveys 1977", HMSO.
10. Smith, M. A., Parker, S., and Smith, C. S. (ed.), 1973, "Leisure and society in Britain", Allen Lane, Harmondsworth.
11. Central Statistical Office, various years, *National Income and Expenditure,* HMSO.
12. Central Statistical Office, 1979, August, *Monthly Digest of Statistics,* HMSO.
13. Central Statistical Office, 1979, *Social Trends,* HMSO.
14. Central Statistical Office, 1979, *Economic Trends,* September, Annual Supplement, 1979 ed., HMSO.
15. Countryside Commission, 1977-78, 11th Annual Report.
16. Gibson, J., 1978, Recreational Land Use: in Pearce, D. W. (ed.), 1978, "The Valuation of social cost", George Allen and Unwin, London.
17. Ulph, A. M., and Reynolds, I. K., 1979, *Scottish Journ. of Pol. Econ.,* 26, 33, "An activities model of consumer behaviour with special reference to outdoor recreation".
18. Turvey, R. (ed), 1968, "Public enterprise", Penguin, Harmondsworth.
19. Brown, K. S., 1978, *Water,* November (National Water Council), "The personal touch in water recreation".

Chapter 8
PUBLIC RELATIONS
1. INTRODUCTION

ALTHOUGH fishing on reservoirs was taking place as early as the beginning of the century, it is only comparatively recently that it has developed to the intensity of a leisure industry. Certainly, the development of other forms of water recreation on reservoirs is in its infancy, even though, in some parts of the country, sailing was taking place in an organized way in 1947.

Since the Water Act 1973, recreation has become a statutory duty of water authorities and this has no doubt given stimulus to its development. It is possible that the growth would have come about in any case, as the interest in recreation has intensified everywhere over the years, and has now become socially and politically desirable. The use of reservoirs and rivers for recreational purposes is really nothing more than common sense, representing an additional utilization of assets. In the case of reservoirs used primarily for public water supply purposes it is of course essential to ensure that where necessary adequate safeguards are available to protect those sources (*see* Chapter 2).

The growth of recreational activities has brought with it a need for long term planning, specialization, and professional expertise; it has also increased the risk of conflicts between the various user interests. Since the responsibility for water recreation now rests to a considerable extent with the regional water authorities, which are organized as large units, inevitably there has arisen a problem of communication. Public relations is fundamentally no more than communication between an organization and its public, so this particular skill has become increasingly involved in recreational matters.

This chapter deals with some of the areas where public relations are important to the implementation of new ideas, to the efficient running of recreational services, and to the introduction of changes in policy.

2. ANGLERS AND SAILORS

Fishing is frequently quoted as being the fastest expanding sport in the country. Furthermore, the sport is unusual not only in the number of participants, but in their age range[1]. Anglers come from a variety of age groups and socio-economic categories and although they are heterogeneous, they generally have two characteristics in common: a passionate love of the sport and a willingness to fight for its protection. Fishermen are well organized and there are a number of organizations which can present a very influential lobby at national as well as local level. There is no question of anglers as a body being taken for granted.

Other water sportsmen such as yachtsmen and canoeists are currently not so well organized, but the position is changing. Such sportsmen are frequently in dispute with anglers and the recreational manager of a water authority can easily find himself caught in cross-fire between the two. Furthermore, the interests of conservationists are often opposed to both groups.

The aim of public relations in recreation is to get the various interests to accept that what is being done is to everybody's benefit and without favour; to reconcile apparently conflicting priorities; and to try to obtain an acceptance that services must be paid for at realistic levels. This leads on to the contentious question of licence charges.

3. FISHING CHARGES

Over the last few years there has been a hostile reaction to increases in fishing licence charges. This is understandable, for obviously no one likes increased charges of any kind. However, when the cost of a licence is measured against average earnings, and is related to other forms of entertainment, the level of charge is really very modest. It seems illogical that the fishermen will gladly pay very considerable sums for items of equipment, yet begrudge the few pounds that the average licence costs. This is probably because they see the price of the licence and the piece of paper they receive as nothing more than a symptom of administrative overheads, or bureaucratic involvement in their sport. They fail to appreciate that the charging system provides a contribution towards ensuring that their fishing is possible, that fisheries can be restocked, and that pollutions can be monitored and countered. In other words, the very means by which waters are maintained and developed so that fishermen are able to fish at all. They tend to believe that rivers regulate and husband themselves. Until, that is, something goes wrong, when the water authorities will certainly be held to be responsible.

Nevertheless, fishermen will inevitably be faced in the future with considerable percentage increases in licence costs as water authorities move towards the ultimate goal of making fishing and recreational services self-sufficient financially, as they are required to do under the Water Act 1973 and the Water Charges Act 1976. Admittedly in most areas, because of the protracted national procedure for obtaining fishing licence cost increases, the actual progress towards this goal since reorganization in 1974 has been minimal. At present the income from most fishing licences represents no more than some 48 per cent of real costs.

In turn, the hidden subsidy which is represented by this deficiency in income could pose a public relations problem with non-fishermen, i.e. the ordinary ratepayer. Quite rightly, it could be questioned why the ratepayer should be asked to subsidize any particular recreational activity. In the past, this element of subsidy from the general water charges has largely gone unnoticed by the average ratepayer because it was included on a general rates bill; now, with the introduction of direct billing, the cost of environmental services, including fishing, will become clearer to water ratepayers in general. There is little doubt that charges for fishing are likley to be a contentious issue over the next few years, and all licensing authorities will need to carry out painstaking consultation programmes with the fishing organizations.

Normal publicity procedures, such as the production of leaflets explaining charges, are useful, but in practice the only effective way of justifying charges is by personal contact with the various clubs and angling associations. It is a tedious and often thankless task.

4. RESERVOIR RECREATION AND PUBLIC RELATIONS

To fish in a reservoir for a day is likely to cost more than an ordinary annual fishing licence. Yet there is no real problem here, because the rules of economics apply. If fishing charges at a reservoir do not reflect the quality of fishing available, fishermen will not use the facilities and they will go elsewhere. This does not imply that charges can be imposed arbitrarily. There is still a need for explanation and communication in the same way that any service or product must promote for custom in a competitive area.

Reservoir fishing for trout tends to be something of a specialist sport, not in the skill required, it must hastily be said, but simply because it is one of the strange phenomena of fishing that coarse and game fishermen are "different"—neither is more demanding or superior to the other, they are just different. Perhaps this can best be demonstrated by the fact that the game fisherman "fishes for the pot", whereas the coarse angler invariably returns his quarry to the water once caught. In this respect the two categories of fishermen have to be approached differently.

Reservoir exploitation has become of major importance. Not only can it be profitable, and therefore justifiable from the water authorities' point of view, but the amenity and recreational value of reservoirs can be a very significant public relations feature in helping to obtain the necessary planning permission for the development of new water resources. Whereas in the past a reservoir proposal was automatically opposed by amenity societies as an unnecessary intrusion upon nature, today there are balancing factors. It is gradually being appreciated that a reservoir can enhance rather than spoil a landscape. Furthermore, the great surge in leisure activity has in some cases given a considerable public relations asset to development where none existed before.

Although water authorities are likely to continue to argue that they are not in the leisure business, other than incidentally, and that their main responsibility of providing water must be the paramount consideration, it is also true that adequate recreational use is now a prerequisite of any reservoir development, and as such must be taken seriously. Consequently, new reservoirs are being utilized on a scale and with a professionalism undreamed of in the past. Furthermore, this development is an effective public relations aid for the undertakers concerned. Public relations must be in the forefront of any recreational development. Careful consideration needs to be given to the allocation of use between fisheries, sportsmen, and naturalists. This requires tact, patience, and tolerance.

The development of reservoir recreational facilities has another incidental benefit in that it can provide an opportunity to educate the visiting public about the water industry generally. At some sites, the information centre which is now an established feature of new reservoir development has an important role to play. Such centres should not only contain information about the reservoir itself, the facilities available, and advice on the sensible and responsible use of the sites concerned but should also feature general displays on the broader responsibilities of the water authority providing the recreational facilities.

5. STAFFING

In selecting water authority staff who are likely to become involved with the general public, regard should be paid to their friendliness, resilience and tact, for the public can on occasions be trying. The staff should also have a broad knowledge of the workings of the organization, although it is too much to expect that they can have detailed understanding of all the general questions which might be asked. For this reason they should have the ability to obtain information from another source and to provide an answer, if not immediately, then by written reply to the enquirer in a day or so. In practice, it has been found that sportsmen rarely concern themselves with anything other than the pursuit of their own particular interest, while the general public, intent on a pleasant day out, are rarely disposed to raise critical questions on contentious matters. It is interesting that they do not seem to relate charges in water services with the pleasures that they are enjoying.

No matter how reservoir facilities are organized, whether they are operated internally or by franchise, it is important that they should be sensitively managed. Wardens or bailiffs have a most important involvement. They must be firm, for they are there to see that rules and regulations essential to the efficient running of any recreational scheme are observed. But they must also be helpful and polite and project the impression that theirs is a positive role of help, and not merely a negative one of prohibition. Indeed, this philosophy applies to those bailiffs who patrol the rivers and help to maintain them. Such officials are the custodians of the river environment and as such are the friends of the fishermen and sportsmen; on the other hand, since their policing role is important and must be carried out firmly, it is essential that they should command respect.

6. RECREATION DEVELOPMENTS

Apart from angling, the recreational use of reservoirs and other water resources has been mainly confined in the past to sailing and canoeing. In recent years, however, the demand for new facilities has grown considerably. For example, there has been a trend for the use of motor boats to be permitted on some waters and it is not impossible that water skiing could develop on a greater scale in the future. Indeed, the total number of pursuits which can now be enjoyed on the waters and associated land of many sites is quite large. Other chapters in this book are concerned with the needs of these individual activities, and with the safety requirements which are associated with them and with the protection of the primary functions of the sites.

Some see the use of sites being carried even further, with holiday chalets being built in proximity to, or as part of, water resource development to encourage sportsmen, anglers, and others to use reservoir facilities as part of a holiday rather than as an occasional day out. If this particular trend gains momentum, a public relations campaign may well be needed to convince all interested parties that the intention is not to desecrate the environment and spoil the tranquillity of manmade and natural beauty areas, but to pursue the development in a balanced way, so that everyone can enjoy their leisure activities without intruding upon or ruining someone else's.

7. PROMOTIONAL PUBLICATIONS

Water authorities are in the recreational promotional business. They are trying to encourage the use of facilities though with varying degrees of financial commitment. The traditional method of doing this is by the production and effective distribution of literature. The question of whether literature should be free or charged for is a difficult one: it seems that as the main reason for producing literature is to promote use, it is a false economy to curtail drastically the circulation of such literature by charging for it. To be justified at all, charges for literature must be realistic, and if they are significant, they will certainly reduce distribution considerably.

However, the full scale recreational manual is in a different category. It is unreasonable, in view of the high cost of production of such publications, to give them away. Indeed, if such a policy were to be followed fishermen might well be the first to complain that their licence fees were being used irresponsibly. There is no doubt that experience has shown that the marketing of such manuals is a difficult problem.

A local "give away" newsheet circulating among anglers and in some cases other recreational sports is a useful avenue of communication, but here it is important to strike a balance between a professional product and an apparently expensive charge upon resources which might be better spent in other ways. Without some regular

Right. Derwent Water in the Lake District. Although this is a popular tourist area, there are ample opportunities to enjoy the tranquillity of the lakeland scenery. *(British Tourist Authority)*

Below. Family picnic overlooking Llyn Clywedog reservoir in mid-Wales (Welsh Water Authority).

Canals. *Left.* Cruising on the Leeds and Liverpool Canal *(H. McKnight).*
Right. Volunteers restoring the lock on the Basingstoke Canal at Brookwood *(H. McKnight)*

The Lake District in Cumbria. *Above.* Ullswater, showing moorings, sailing club, dinghy park, and camping site. *(H. McKnight).* *Right.* The passenger "steamer" *Raven* of the Ullswater Steamer Service *(H. McKnight)*

. Tree landscaping at the Ferry Meadows
untry Park *(Peterborough Development Corpor-*
n)

ht centre. Horse riding is permitted around
perimeters of many reservoirs.

ht. Birdwatching at Grafham Water (Anglian
ter Authority).

Left. A potentially dangerous situa[ion]
can easily arise if children are allow[ed]
to play unsupervised near wa[ter]
(RoSPA).

Below. Wildfowling on the
marshes *(The British Association [for]
Shooting and Conservation — form[erly]
WAGBI).*

form of communication it is difficult to keep anglers informed about work being undertaken in their interest, as for instance, in fish rearing and biological research, which are important services that are not always apparent to the angler on the bank.

8. LAND DRAINAGE ISSUES

In the past considerable tension has been created between anglers and other users of rivers on the one hand, and farmers, because of the need to drain land for improved agricultural use. Large scale land drainage works have been carried out in certain areas, backed by Ministry of Agriculture, Fisheries and Food grant to maximize agricultural use of land.

There may be a certain justification in the criticism by opponents of land drainage among fishermen and environmentalists that some of this work has been carried out with engineering efficiency as the prime consideration and without enough attention being paid to the effect on the river and on the general environment. The most severe criticism is that rivers have to a greater or lesser extent been canalized, altering their character and natural regime to such a degree that fishing and other interests have sometimes been ruined.

Since 1974 the land drainage function has been incorporated within the broad framework of the regional water authorities (other than in the case of Internal Drainage Boards). One considerable benefit from this arrangement is that liaison arrangements have been increased and a much better climate of understanding has developed. Authorities have drawn up formal rules and regulations relating to land drainage works including a high level of environmental consideration, and schemes are thoroughly discussed with all parties before being finalized.

The important farming interests have been recognized, but so also has the important consideration of environmental effects; both are regarded as equals in the aims and objects of Codes of Practice. The problem, essentially, has been one of building greater confidence and better communication between various parties, and the improvement in relationships represents a considerable public relations achievement.

Two recent publications from the Water Space Amenity Commission may help in this respect. They comprise guidelines[2] and a report[3] on conservation and land drainage which contain the views of a Working Party and are intended to demonstrate how essential works of land drainage and sea defence can be achieved not only with least harm to wildlife and nature conservation but even to enhance them whereever possible.

9. MEDIA

The growth in water recreation generally has been reflected, in turn, in the interest shown in the subject by newspapers and radio and television. Specialist publications dealing with fishing of every description have existed for many years, but now most regional and local, as well as national, papers have fishing correspondents and fishing columns. These media represent the most effective way of reaching the public, and it is therefore important for water authorities to provide them with information on interesting developments and unusual day-to-day events.

Local radio, now augmented in many areas by commercial radio stations, also provides fruitful outlets for news and information on recreational matters and should be used to full effect. Television is rather more difficult; nevertheless, most regional stations will carry occasional items, such as news about open days and other interesting developments. The criterion of use is always whether the information is newsworthy.

The media are extremely important in the recreational sphere, particularly in the case of giving essential publicity to "hard line" stories such as cases of pollution. Good coverage in the media about a particularly bad case of industrial or farm pollution often has very much more effect upon the culprit than the most severe official caution. The same can be said about prosecutions of licence offenders.

In the same way, local media are invaluable in publicizing promotion activities such as fishing competitions, regattas, or canoe slaloms.

10. WATER SPACE AMENITY COMMISSION

The public relations departments of the individual water authorities are concerned, *inter alia*, with the promotion of recreational use on a regional basis. The Water Space Amenity Commission is involved from a national point of view.

The Commission, which is an independent statutory body, was set up under Section 23 of the Water Act 1973. Its function is to advise, after consultation with other parties, the Secretary of State, the National Water Council, and the water authorities on the formulation, promotion and execution of the national policy for water relating to recreation and amenity in England.

The Commission's task is one of co-ordinating and promoting activities in connection with water space within the control of the industry as the amenity arm of the National Water Council, and as the link between the water industry and amenity and recreational interests in general.

The Commission produces a range of promotional and information leaflets, together with a magazine. However, at the time of writing (1981) publication of the magazine has been suspended because of economic constraints. Further information on the Commission is given in Chapter 9, p. 234.

11. CONCLUSION

Recreational activities are increasing everywhere. They are no longer a mere adjunct of other activities, and have developed a personality and importance of their own. They have real potential in economic terms, once the proper financial base for charging has been established.

The present dilemma is that too much promotional activity could encourage a demand for fisheries and recreational facilities from the public that authorities would be unable to meet. This situation would certainly reflect adversely in public relations terms.

A balance is needed in equating demand and provision, but the difficult national financial climate that is likely to prevail for the foreseeable future must to some extent restrict development. Future demand is likely to be met principally in areas that show most financial viability.

There is however little doubt about future demand in the long term, for the era of electronic automation that is gathering momentum must bring with it an increase in leisure time; and nothing is more satisfying or attractive to most people than spending their leisure time in, on, or nearby water.

12. REFERENCES

1. Water Space Amenity Commission, 1980, "National angling survey".
2. Water Space Amenity Commission, 1980, "Conservation and land drainage guidelines".
3. Water Space Amenity Commission, 1980, "Conservation and Land Drainage Working Party Report".

Chapter 9

PARTICIPATING BODIES

1. INTRODUCTION

GENERAL

IN seeking to produce an authoritative text about the use and development of water and associated land for recreational purposes The Institution of Water Engineers and Scientists has appreciated the need to strike a balance in those areas where conflict may arise. Pressures are exerted on public bodies by many groups and organizations. Some advocate the extension and development of existing facilities for recreation while others express apprehension about the effects which recreation, and the human and mechanical pressures which it generates, can exert on the environment and on existing and established activities. In the past the Institution, mindful of the possible effects which the too enthusiastic introduction of recreational facilities would have produced on public water supplies, has advocated caution. Such advocacy may in some quarters have been construed as opposition to the principle of accommodating recreational activity on water supply reservoirs. Chapter 1 in this book is concerned with the historical growth and legal aspects of the demand for greater recreational use. Now that the Water Act 1973 requires Regional Water Authorities and other statutory water undertakers to provide for the recreational use of water and associated land it is fitting that the Institution should draw attention to organizations having responsibilities which are affected in one way or another by the provision of such recreation.

In preparing this chapter therefore an attempt has been made to provide the reader with a knowledge of the broad spectrum of bodies and organizations exerting an influence on proposals to accommodate recreation on water and associated land surfaces. Some of these organizations will, by the very nature of their aims and purposes, be able to assist in turning recreational proposals into reality. Others will, for a variety of reasons, regard less enthusiastically the impact of such recreation on an environment hitherto largely untouched by the presence of the public and the attendant effects of that presence.

Whatever the attitude of the organization concerned, it is important that all associated with the planning, provision, and management of recreational facilities by public bodies should be aware of the existence and role of the organizations with which they may come into contact in the course of recreational development. In compiling this chapter it has been necessary to edit the considerable amount of material which became available at the drafting stage, with the objective of outlining the history and purposes of each organization, only in sufficient detail for the reader to grasp its role. In the process it is inevitable that material, relevant in a general context, has had to be discarded in the interests of brevity. Equally inevitably it will become evident after the book has appeared in print that one or more relevant organizations may have been omitted. This may be because their role has been evolving to a point where it achieves prominence only after the book has appeared. Alternatively, and with a commendable wish to avoid the chapter becoming no more than an index or a shopping list, it may be that exclusion arises because of the very real difficulty of determining whether an individual organization is sufficiently associated with water-related recreation, rather than with recreation in a general sense, to merit inclusion.

A list of each organization's headquarters address has been included (Appendix II, p. 294), so that the reader wishing to get in touch with an organization (either to consult, communicate or to enquire) should be able to pursue matters directly with those most closely associated with the particular field in which their own interests lie.

CONSULTATION

Reference to consultation makes it desirable to emphasize that the promotion and development of a recreational activity often takes part in highly sensitive areas. As a result, full and adequate consultation is a necessary process and one to which ample time must be allotted because adequacy will not be achieved nor will time be saved if an attempt is made to cut short the consultation procedures. Nor does the process cease when generally acceptable proposals have been devised. The operation and management of a water-related recreational function requires that machinery be established to maintain the consultative process through the various forms of committee which are referred to in chapters 6 and 8.

Initially, consultation about proposed recreational developments can be regarded as falling into two general categories:-

(1) *Imperative* consultation with the owners, occupiers, and managers of the land and property which will be affected. Such consultation will also involve approaching public bodies exercising jurisdiction over the uses which it is proposed to make of the land and property and its surroundings.

(2) *Advisable* consultation with bodies and interests affected by the proposals or likely to have views capable of influencing their form and extent and the nature of the activities which they are to accommodate.

The passage of time, and the extent to which the proposals find favour and general acceptance, will remove the distinction between these categories and, once having become involved, individual interests will regard it as imperative that they should continue to feature in the consultation process. To some extent the interests listed in category (1) above become less active and directly involved as the proposals become a reality. However, it must be remembered that the public bodies originally involved because of their powers to authorize, license, or consent will most likely have other powers which call for them to continue to be represented in the consultation procedures. They will, in any case, serve as a forum for the expression of public opinion. Their continued involvement therefore as an informed participant can help in averting apprehensions otherwise likely to arise where individuals or groups feel that they have no "champion" to voice their concerns with a powerful and apparently remote promoting body.

By the very nature of the situation many recreational proposals will be made by the regional water authorities themselves and internal consultation about matters affecting their own divisional or directorate interests will be achieved through their own corporate procedures. This present chapter contains a short summary of the regional water authority functions, but Book 1 in this present series* describes in detail how they are structured and the nature of their functions and responsibilities. Elsewhere, however, other bodies are responsible for some of these same functions and the reader should bear in mind that the relevant bodies (including statutory water

*The Institution of Water Engineers and Scientists, Water Practice Manuals, 1979, Book 1, "The structure and management of the British water industry."

undertakers) exercising "water" functions should be included in the consultation process. Their interests (including the provision of future works) may be affected by recreational proposals. Even where they are not so affected, however, it would be useful at least to make contact with the relevant regional water authority or other "water" body, to ascertain whether comments or advice can be offered in the light of experience gained in the discharge of that body's own functions. With such a situation always in mind the remarks in this chapter about consultation may be construed on the basis that the subject matter on which consultation is sought arises from recreational proposals being made by a regional water authority and therefore that its own internal consultation procedures have been put into motion.

The check list (Appendix A, p. 292) has been compiled on this basis and therefore does not include reference to the areas of responsibility exercised by the regional water authorities, statutory water undertakers, and public bodies exercising similar "water" functions. The list gives an indication of the situations in which the bodies specified as having conservation functions should be involved in any consultation process about recreational developments at as early a stage as is possible. There is no inference that the list should serve as either a maximum or a minimum, nor that the bodies concerned will not have additional functions to those featured in the first column. Such functions could then well extend the immediate area of consultation.

2. BODIES STATUTORILY RESPONSIBLE FOR
ASPECTS OF THE WATER CYCLE

GOVERNMENT'S OVERVIEW OF SPORT AND RECREATION

The simplest forms of physical recreation do not require the provision of either special facilities or assistance from others. But enjoyment of most activities does depend a great deal upon the provision of the appropriate facilities and also upon some measure of organization. Both these aspects are in considerable measure provided for by local voluntary clubs. These are the traditional source of sport and recreation developments in this country and they manage their own affairs under the aegis of their own governing bodies. In competitive sports the governing bodies also fulfil a vital function as the controlling authorities for their particular sports and as providers of the organization without which opportunities for very many participants would not exist. In informal recreation, such as rambling, individuals often enjoy benefits gained through the efforts of voluntary organizations, even if they do not themselves belong formally to any organization.

A large number of people in fact take part in sport and various forms of physical recreation without actually joining a club. The facilities they need are provided either by public bodies — as in the case of many parks and swimming baths — or by commercial undertakings. Local authorities have become the main providers of new facilities, but commercial development of certain facilities such as golf driving ranges, squash courts and marinas, is increasing. Commercial organizations also play an important part in the development of sport by their sponsorship of competitive events. Many national and international sporting events could not take place without such sponsorship.

Facilities for informal outdoor recreation in the towns are mainly provided by public bodies, although there are a number of privately owned parks and squares which have been opened to the public. In the countryside, the majority of recreational facilities have been provided by owners of country estates, and by the

National Trust, who have opened country houses and their adjoining land and grounds to the public. The public also widely enjoy the rights of access to foreshores, cliff tops, commons, fells and footpaths, and many landowners and farmers allow access over their land. Over the last few years, however, local authorities have been increasingly important as providers of country parks and picnic sites.

The Department of the Environment makes certain provision for recreational facilities, mainly through the medium of government agencies. Some agencies are specifically charged with responsibilities relating to recreation, for example; the Sports Council, the Countryside Commission and, to a lesser extent, the Tourist Boards. The Sports Council and the Sports Councils for Wales, Scotland, and Northern Ireland are charged with the promotion of sport and physical recreation and the provision of facilities in their areas. To this end, they give assistance to those bodies which promote and administer the development of particular sports and are known as the "governing bodies" of sport, and also to the local authorities and voluntary clubs. The Countryside Commissions for England and Wales, Scotland, and the Ulster Countryside Committee, have the functions of promoting both the conservation of the countryside and its enjoyment by the public. They assist public and private bodies in the provision of countryside recreational facilities. The English, Wales, Scottish, and Northern Ireland Tourist Boards assist the provision of accommodation and other facilities for tourists in development areas.

Other agencies provide recreational facilities in addition to their main function, for example the Forestry Commission, the British Waterways Board, the Regional Water Authorities, and the Water Companies. The Department of the Environment provides for the enjoyment of the public through its guardianship of ancient monuments and the assistance it gives to the preservation of historic buildings. The Nature Conservancy Council, equally, provides enjoyment through the provision of nature trails in its reserves. In addition, the Agricultural Development Advisory Service of the Ministry of Agriculture, Fisheries, and Food, helps farmers and landowners with the promotion of field sports, tourism, and recreation, especially where farm incomes can be improved from these sources.

Among the governing bodies of sport there is a wide variety of organizations. Some are established on a U.K. basis or on a Great Britain basis, some have a separate organization for each of the home counties, and other variations also exist. These arrangements have usually developed historically in that the governing bodies came into existence long before the Sports Councils were formed and they will doubtless long thrive as independent bodies.

However, it is important to ensure that there is a co-ordinated approach to common problems even though precise uniformity of treatment may be unacceptable or, indeed, impossible to achieve. A United Kingdom Affairs Committee of the four Sports Councils has been established in order to achieve this co-ordination.

While there is a strong concentration of recreational responsibilities vested in the Department of the Environment and the agencies which it sponsors, it is important that in formulating broad recreational policies due account is taken of the objectives, and the problems, of all the departments and agencies involved in England and Wales. The Minister of State consults regularly with his Ministerial colleagues on recreational aspects of the Government's policies. In addition, there are regular meetings of chairmen and directors of the relevant government agencies at what is known as the Chairmen's Policy Group. These arrangements ensure close co-ordination at national level among everyone concerned in the formulation and implementation of broad recreational policies throughout the U.K.

Government departments and agencies concerned with recreation already undertake a good deal of research and the agencies co-ordinate their countryside research programmes through the Countryside Recreation Research Advisory Group. The Government, however, relies upon the Department of the Environment to initiate any research of a strategic nature which cannot appropriately be undertaken by other departments or by particular government agencies. The Department of the Environment is allocated funds for this purpose from its research vote in order to initiate and develop a programme of such research, thus providing the foundation of knowledge and understanding which is needed to support policy.

The historical and traditional demands on water for domestic, industrial and agricultural use have in the recent past gradually expanded to include additional demands for sport and recreation to a degree which has made it necessary for the Government to plan for future developments in these trends. Under the Water Act 1973 it therefore created the Water Space Amenity Commission as an independent advisory body to assist Government on the national policy for the recreational and amenity uses of water in England and to advise the National Water Council, and the water authorities, on the discharge of their functions in this respect.

REGIONAL WATER AUTHORITIES

Regional water authorities, in addition to their responsibilities for, *inter alia*, water supply, sewerage and sewage disposal, have a variety of responsibilities for fisheries and recreation, some inherited from river authorities, others imposed under the Water Act 1973 and subsequent legislation.

An important distinction is drawn between the protection of fisheries — the habitats of salmon and freshwater fish — and the actual activity of fishing, i.e. the recreation or occupation of those who fish. Those statutory duties of water authorities relating to fisheries are concerned not only with the ecological well-being of fisheries, but also with the licensing of both commercial fishing and recreational angling.

It is the duty of the Water Space Amenity Commission to advise the National Water Council and the water authorities in England (it also has, by statute, informal but strong links with the Welsh Water Authority) on the discharge of their recreation and amenity functions, and to collate and publish information and reports.

Revenue to pay for these functions may be raised from the licence fees and charges for the activities concerned, or through the "environmental services charge" which may be levied on all "rateable hereditaments" under the Water Charges Act 1976. Because it is often difficult to recover extra expenditure on these functions from charges made to the users, each water authority has to decide how far to extend the services at the expense of the community. (This particular aspect is referred to in greater detail in Chapter 7.)

Unlike their recreation and amenities functions, the fisheries functions of water authorities have a long tradition dating back to the inception of the Board of Conservators following the Salmon and Freshwater Fisheries Act 1861, through the River Boards to the River Authorities. These functions are subject to general supervision by the Ministry of Agriculture, Fisheries and Food, and the Welsh Office, leaving the water authorities to consult their advisory committees of persons interested in fisheries. Advice on research priorities and technical developments in this field is available from the Joint Freshwater Fisheries Research Advisory Committee.

Water authorities have an interest in water recreation generally, but more specifically in recreation on the water supply reservoirs which they own. The various water undertakers and predecessors of the water authorities were successful in encouraging the use of many reservoirs for fishing and for nature conservation, but the recent rapid growth of recreational activities requires more controls to protect the quality of water supplies and to resolve the clashes of interest between different forms of water recreation. The degree to which direct supply and regulating reservoirs and their associated lands are used for recreational purposes and the supporting requirements and safety provisions are dealt with in earlier chapters of this book. The public health considerations and pollution control aspects are covered in Chapter 2.

Water authorities are less often directly involved in the provision of recreational facilities on rivers, but by the conjunctive operation of river-regulating facilities at a number of water resources it has been possible to develop canoeing to such an extent that at least one site has now been adopted for international canoeing competitions.

The compatibility of some reservoir constructions with nature conservation is demonstrated by the inclusion of a number of water authority and water company reservoirs in the Nature Conservation Review, published by the Nature Conservancy Council (and NERC)*, as biological sites of national importance to nature conservation. The water authorities and the water companies accept the need nowadays for consultation with the Nature Conservancy Council and other interested parties in the formative stages of new projects, and collaboration is extended by County Naturalists Trusts and other voluntary organizations in developing nature reserves at new reservoirs.

Water authorities also have a duty to preserve natural beauty and protect buildings of historic and architectural interest. Such buildings abound throughout the industry — old pumping stations, water mills, treatment works, navigation structures and the like. This legacy is one in which the public is increasingly taking an interest. Water authorities have made substantial contributions towards enhancing public appreciation and enjoyment of old buildings and monuments by restoring pumping plant and buildings, or by leasing historic works to voluntary organizations for restoration and future management.

The interest in navigation of some water authorities is described elsewhere in this book.

WATER COMPANIES

Statutory Water Companies are incorporated by Private Acts of Parliament, some of which date back to the early nineteenth century. There are today 28 such Companies spread throughout the country and they are all long-established or are amalgamations of long-established undertakers. They provide a public water supply on a commercial basis and operate under the various Companies Acts. They each have a Board of Directors, the members of which are chosen in the usual manner by the shareholders. As these water companies are virtually monopolies they have stringent financial constraints imposed on them by way of statutory controls on maximum rates of dividend, the issuing of share capital by auction, limitations on reserve and contingency funds, and a limit on the carrying forward of surpluses to the following year. Such limitations ensure that any financial surpluses are put towards lowering the Companies' charges.

*Ratcliffe, D. (ed.), 1977, "A nature conservation review" (2 vols), Cambridge University Press, London.

Water Companies enter into statutory agreements with their respective Regional Water Authorities to act on behalf of the Authority for the purpose of water supplies and suitable financial arrangements are made between them. The Water Act 1973 (Section 24(2)), gives the Water Authority powers to require the Companies to survey consumption and demand, to formulate proposals for meeting future requirements, and to report to the Water Authority. Some water companies collect various service charges on behalf of the regional water authorities. All Companies are subject to controls in respect of licences, planning, and the development of new resources. They have their own Water Companies Association: most are subscribing members of the Water Research Centre, and all participate fully in the National Water Council's Committee work on manpower, productivity, safety, and quality control. They are also represented on, and are active contributors to the DoE/NWC standing technical committees.

Water Companies also try to ensure that their recreational facilities are self-supporting and, thus, do not become a charge on consumers. In the field of recreation they have, collectively, been "pioneers" in the provision of recreation facilities at reservoirs, and many of the facilities now regarded as standard were introduced by the water companies early this century.

Today, the provision of such facilities is widespread, although it is naturally dependent on the type and size of the reservoir owned. For a number of water companies, their supply of water comes from springs, streams, rivers and boreholes, and because no reservoir is needed water-based recreation is not possible. Otherwise recreational provision at reservoirs is as varied as the reservoirs themselves and can include most if not all the activities referred to elsewhere in this book.

SCOTLAND

Water Authorities

In Scotland water supply is, by virtue of Section 148 of the Local Government (Scotland) Act 1973, a function of the nine Regional and three Islands Councils. In addition, the Central Scotland Water Development Board, established under Section 3 of the Water (Scotland) Act 1967, acts as a developer of large new sources in Central Scotland and as a bulk supplier to its five constituent members (Central, Fife, Lothian, Tayside and Strathclyde Regions).

In terms of Section 63 of the Countryside (Scotland) Act 1967, these authorities are empowered to permit the use, by members of the public for the purposes of any form of recreation, of any waterway or land in which the authorities have an interest. They may also provide, or otherwise make available, facilities for use of any such waterway or land for the purposes of any such form of recreation. Where the water authority does not own the land, these powers are only exercisable with the consent of the owner. Other powers available under the Section are to make reasonable charges for use, to give lettings, and to make byelaws controlling use. Section 65 of the same Act empowers Scottish water authorities to appoint wardens for advising and assisting the public, securing compliance with byelaws, and to perform any other miscellaneous duties.

River Purification Authorities

In Scotland river purification functions in terms of Section 135 of the Local Government (Scotland) Act 1973 are exercised by Islands Councils and by specially constituted *ad hoc* boards (River Purification Boards). The duties of such authorities are laid down in Section 17 of the Rivers (Prevention of Pollution) (Scotland) Act 1951, and are to promote the cleanliness of the rivers and other inland waters and the tidal waters in their areas, to conserve so far as practicable the water resources of their areas, and to exercise for those purposes the functions conferred on them by the 1951 Act.

These authorities have no direct responsibility for recreation, but in terms of Section 25 of the 1951 Act have powers to make byelaws in respect of any stream or part of a stream in their area and in exercising these powers are to have regard to, among other things, its use for fisheries. This power to make byelaws was repealed by the Control of Pollution Act 1974, which substituted a more restrictive form of byelaw-making power but in addition gives the Secretary of State certain powers related to prohibition or restriction of activities likely to lead to water pollution. The 1974 Act (Section 46) gives river purification authorities duties and powers related to operations to remedy or forestall pollution of water which is injurious to the fauna or flora of a stream.

Local Authorities

In terms of Section 61 of the Countryside (Scotland) Act 1967 planning authorities may, as respects any waterway in or adjoining land within their area, carry out such work and do such other things as may appear expedient for facilitating the use of the waterway by the public for sailing, boating, bathing, fishing or other water sport or recreation. In exercising such powers they are bound to take into consideration the disturbance of any fishing rights over the waterway which may be caused thereby. The Section further empowers the authority to enter into agreements for the exercise of such powers and preserves the rights of water authorities. In terms of Sub-section 9, planning authorities are given powers of compulsory acquisition for the purpose of enabling them to exercise powers conferred by this Section. Section 62 of the same Act contains provisions as to the exercise of powers available under Section 61. Section 65 empowers planning authorities within the meaning of the Act to appoint wardens for the same purposes as water authorities as indicated above. Section 78 of the 1967 Act as amended by the Local Government (Scotland) Act 1973 defines the planning authority as meaning a general, regional, or district planning authority within the meaning of Part IX of the Local Government (Scotland) Act 1973.

In terms of Section 91 of the 1973 Act, local authorities have powers to provide social, recreational, and cultural facilities. Section 162 makes it clear that the powers to provide recreational facilities under the Physical Training and Recreation Acts 1937 and 1958 are exercisable by local authority within the meaning of the 1973 Act. This includes explicit powers to provide swimming pools and bathing places and the generality of the powers is such that it would also no doubt extend to other recreational facilities associated with the use of water. Local authorities in this context includes Regional, Islands, and District authorities.

Fisheries

In Scotland, no one body outside of Central Government has overall responsibility for fisheries. Scottish District Salmon Fishery Boards are statutory bodies representing the proprietors of salmon fisheries and authorized by the Salmon Fisheries (Scotland) Acts 1862 and 1868. Although their authorization and constitution is laid down by these statutes, their function is limited to the preservation of salmon fisheries, and they have no general fisheries duties. Despite the limits of their function, District Boards have important statutory rights and duties. The importance of these has been accentuated by the Salmon and Freshwater Fisheries (Protection) (Scotland) Act 1951, because under this Act powers of arrest and search are restricted to police constables, water bailiffs appointed by District Boards and, in special circumstances, persons authorized by the Secretary of State.

Apart from their duties in the enforcement of the Salmon Fisheries Act the Boards have powers to do certain acts for the improvement and preservation of fisheries; these include the removal (by agreement) of obstructions, the purchase of dams or other fixed engines, and the construction of fish passes. Under the Acts 107 Districts were created but only about 50 District Boards are in existence. The Tweed Fisheries Act 1887 details the constitution and powers of the Commissioners of the Tweed Salmon Fisheries. In broad outline, these powers are similar to those of the District Boards. The Secretary of State's Fisheries Committee appointed under Section 5(2) of the Electricity (Scotland) Act 1979, provides advice to the Secretary of State for Scotland and to the two Scottish Electricity Boards on the preservation of fisheries and the stock of fish where waters are affected by electricity developments.

NORTHERN IRELAND

Department of the Environment for Northern Ireland

The Department of the Environment administers a wide range of functions under the general heading of environmental protection. In certain matters the Department is directly responsible for the implementation and enforcement of the relevant legislation. Under the Water Act (Northern Ireland) 1972 the Department is responsible for the conservation of water resources and the control of water pollution.

A continuous water quality monitoring programme was started in 1972 and has been extended to cover 100 stations throughout Northern Ireland. Results to date indicate that over 80 per cent of the major river systems are unpolluted. Surveys of the main estuaries are being carried out to establish a sampling grid for periodic monitoring and to evaluate the effects of major effluent discharges into coastal waters.

The Department of the Environment for Northern Ireland is the sole water and sewerage authority for Northern Ireland. It has a statutory duty to supply and distribute water and to make arrangements for the disposal of sewage, under the Water and Sewerage Services (Northern Ireland) Order 1973. The Water Service operates through Operational Divisions centred in Belfast, Ballymena, Craigavon, and Londonderry, with local offices in most of the provincial towns. A Headquarters unit in Stormont is responsible for policy, finance, engineering co-ordination, resource planning, statistics and operational direction.

One of the most important considerations in determining policy within The Water Service is through the consultative process. In this connection the Northern Ireland Water Council plays a key role. The Water Service seeks the views of the Council in all major policy questions and its advice has been invaluable in a number of issues.

Another important consultative process involves the District Councils. The Divisional Water Managers present their capital works programmes for each year to the District Councils within their Divisional areas. The object of the exercise is to seek the views of the Councils on priorities within their Districts. This process is particularly useful when consideration is being given to extending water and sewerage services in rural areas.

Northern Ireland Water Council

The Water Council's Terms of Reference are to advise the Departments of Agriculture and of the Environment on the exercise of their functions under the Water Act (Northern Ireland) 1972, and the Water and Sewerage Services (Northern Ireland) Order 1973. Membership comprises 14 persons, representing various fields of activity and sectors of the public interest including industry, agriculture and angling. The Departments seek the views of the Council on major policy issues.

The Council is concerned with the progress towards recreational use of property owned by the Department of the Environment and within the limits currently imposed by security and other constraints both Departments maintain a constant interest in this question.

The Council sees that liaison with water interests in Great Britain and in the Irish Republic are continued and strengthened where appropriate. Such problems as pollution, Lough Erne water levels, and the river Foyle have cross-border implications with the Republic of Ireland.

Department of Agriculture for Northern Ireland

The Department of Agriculture acquired certain responsibilities for water recreation under the Water Act 1972. Under Section 16 of this Act the Department may undertake direct work for the purpose of promoting the recreational use of any waterway. The term "waterway" includes rivers and lakes but does not include impounding reservoirs or the sea.

The works which the Department can carry out are generally of a minor nature, for example the provision of footpaths, sign posts and seats, the construction of jetties and the execution of works intended to promote safety on waterways. Numerous projects have been completed and more are underway or planned on various rivers and loughs, including Lough Erne and Lough Neagh, with the aims of improving the recreational amenities, navigation, and safety of waterways.

The Water Act also empowers the Department to regulate by order the use of any waterway for recreational purposes.

3. OTHER STATUTORY AND ADVISORY BODIES

WATER SPACE AMENITY COMMISSION

In England there are about 121,000 hectares of inland waters available for water sports, leisure, and recreation. Anglers, boaters, sailors, canoeists, swimmers, water-skiers, aqua-lung enthusiasts, naturalists, wildfowlers, ornithologists, ramblers, casual walkers, and holidaymakers make up some 40 per cent of all those seeking outdoor recreation. And they are all competing for the use of limited water space and the land adjoining it.

Unlike the areas of land which are available for recreation purposes, most waters are under heavy pressure for many purposes. Water itself is a resource which has many requirements, including potable and industrial use, as a carrier for treated sewage and industrial wastes, and for land drainage and irrigation. It can also be used for river regulation purposes and for hydro-electric power generation. There is, as a result, an inevitable conflict between the different interests wanting to use the same areas of water.

When the water industry was reorganized under the Water Act 1973, a new body — the Water Space Amenity Commission — was created. The Commission is made up of the Chairmen of the ten regional water authorities plus 11 members representing, or linked to, such recreational or conservation bodies as the Countryside Commission, the Sports Council, the Central Council for Physical Recreation, the English Tourist Board, the Nature Conservancy Council, the National Anglers Council, and others.

The Commission has to look at the whole field of water space — lakes, the Broads, rivers, estuaries, canals, reservoirs, and gravel pits. It helps to develop greater recreational and amenity use of existing waters and encourages the development or restoration of unused or derelict areas. The Commission also advises the government on national policies for the recreational use of water in England. It also helps the National Water Council and the water authorities in the promotion of sites and their facilities. The links with the Welsh Water Authority are, by statute, informal but strong.

In the fields of water recreation, nature conservation, and amenity, the Commission maintains a close working relationship with the governing bodies of sport, with youth organizations, water safety committees, and with the many national organizations whose interests lie with the conservation of wildlife, the countryside, fisheries, and a sensitive understanding of the landscape.

Conservation, as far as the water industry is concerned, means keeping a balance between taking water from the countryside for urban use while leaving behind enough for farming, fisheries, and forestry, as well as for the well-being of the landscape. Flood control, land drainage, and irrigation are different but important stages in achieving this balance, and land is as much involved as water.

Wetlands, which include marshes, bogs and land which is frequently flooded, are also important areas. The lands are low in productivity value from the farmer's point of view, but with drainage and flood control this can be improved. However, there is growing pressure from naturalists to preserve these areas, because wetlands are vital habitats for many species of flora and fauna. They are often important staging posts and wintering areas for migratory birds. Nature study and enjoyment of wetland landscapes are valid forms of recreation, quite apart from the basic ecological value of these areas.

The water industry is in something of a cleft stick where recreation is concerned. There is a clear legal duty to provide for recreation but few activities associated with water produce a revenue which is equal to the cost of providing it, unless prohibitive charges are made, and this would be self-defeating. The industry has therefore to consider how far it is justified in meeting a part of the costs from the general water rate. On the whole a fair and acceptable balance is struck between the active recreationalists and those who simply want to enjoy the basic amenities. Today, (1981) over 530 water supply reservoirs — about 85 per cent of the total number — support some form of active recreation.

Gathering grounds of reservoirs occupy about 1 per cent of the land area of England and Wales, but much of this lies in areas of high landscape value. Gathering grounds therefore have considerable attraction for informal recreations such as walking, rambling, pony-trekking, bird watching, rock climbing, and shooting. Because of this the recreation facilities and, even more, the potential provided by reservoirs and their waterside lands is quite considerable, but so is the pressure of use. The ownership by water authorities of many gathering grounds and their reservoirs simplifies the problem of developing recreation. On the other hand, the position for rivers and streams is complicated. Ownership of the banks is usually in the hands of private individuals with riparian rights, and there are questions of pollution, water abstraction, fisheries, and occasionally navigation responsibilities to cope with. In all these matters of conservation, landscape and recreation which are associated with water in England, the Water Space Amenity Commission holds a "watching brief".

The Commission plays an active part in a variety of ways: sometimes through its regular publicity material, research reports, advisory and information leaflets, or through a continuing series of seminars, training sessions and conferences which it organizes throughout the water industry and closely related organizations.

LOCAL AUTHORITIES

The provision of leisure and recreation facilities by local authorities has developed gradually, and at first, imperceptibly, over the centuries. From a "Statute of Labourers" dated 1388 we know, for instance, that some games were *not* allowed by the authorities, such as football, quoits, and tennis and one or two other games not known today, which points to some sort of provision for recreation by the authorities. During the eighteenth and early nineteenth centuries Land Inclosure Acts frequently included allotments of land for recreational use by the local inhabitants, but legislation for recreation and leisure as we think of it today did not really start until the last quarter of the nineteenth century, followed by increasing legislation from the 1930s.

Periods of intensified industrialization would seem to give rise to the need by local authorities to pay attention to the health, via recreation, of the people in their care. The first major item of legislation in this direction came with the Public Health Act 1875, which allowed authorities to provide lands for "public walks and pleasure grounds". This Act did not actually mention the playing of games, but power was given to local authorities in later legislation to provide games areas in their parks. The Commons Act 1876 was the first general law making provision for allotments of land for recreational use.

In the last decade of the nineteenth century the Museums and Gymnasiums Act 1891 and the Libraries Act 1892 gave local authorities the power to provide those facilities. Then, the Small Holdings and Allotments Act 1908 provided the legal machinery to enable the growth of small allotments of land for cultivation by individuals.

The Victorian Acts of the 1870s providing for "public walks and pleasure grounds" were directed towards what has been called "an immobile dweller in an urban environment". A lively departure from this concept came in the Physical Training and Recreation Act 1937 which related to contributions by local authorities towards expenses of providing and maintaining gymnasiums, playing fields, swimming baths, and other facilities. The then Minister of Health and the President of the Board of Education described the 1937 Acts as "the new movement for the improvement of national physique".

In general "out door" terms, the Access to the Mountains Act 1939 and the National Parks and Access to the Countryside Act 1949 were both major steps forward in gaining for the general public greater ease of access to the countryside. The Countryside Act 1968 was a natural extension of this legislation and the outstanding provision of the Act was the power given to local authorities to provide what are known as country parks, which are referred to later.

The powers of local authorities in the sphere of recreation have therefore grown over the years from the somewhat limited nineteenth century recognition in a public health context of the benefits of fresh air and, in the cultural field, an early recognition of the benefits of museums and libraries. A broader view of physical recreation did not really emerge until the 1930s and 1940s and the increasing use of the motor car in particular has led to a consequent increase in desire by the public for visits to the countryside. This is reflected in the countryside legislation of comparatively recent years. It is a situation which has gradually developed and although a corporate identity may be missing, local authorities do now have just about all the powers they need in the field of recreational provision. Some authorities have begun to develop "sports centres" and before the Local Government Act 1972 there were indications of growth in the service of leisure provision.

After the Act, however, there was a definite and marked advance. This service does, however, differ from that of others in that recreation is in the main not mandatory. This division between what is mandatory and what is not can be seen in the Public Libraries and Museums Act 1964 which makes it a duty, i.e. it is mandatory, to provide a free library service, but the provision of museums is only permissive. The Education Act 1944 makes adult education and youth service a duty, but the provision for recreation and entertainment remains permissive under the Local Government (Miscellaneous Provisions) Act 1976, the Local Government Act 1972, and the Countryside Act 1968.

Another important difference from major local government services is that most powers are common to counties and districts and in some instances parish councils.

The economic recession, and restrictions of local government spending since 1974, to which, as a permissive function, the recreation service is particularly vulnerable, have all militated against the development of the service. Nonetheless, there has been a dramatic increase in facilities and the Leisure and Recreation Statistics produced by the Chartered Institute of Public Finance and Accountancy* estimate the expenditure on all aspects of leisure to be well over £500 million in England and Wales. There are more than 320 sports centres in England alone and a further 50 are planned. Provision of country parks has increased and there are now some 120 managed by county and district councils.

The purpose of a country park is to provide opportunities for outdoor recreation of all kinds in a rural setting, but they are generally fairly close to large towns and many can be reached quite easily by public transport. They vary considerably in character according to the part of the country in which they are located and offer a variety of recreational opportunities. Many cater primarily for such casual and informal uses as walking, picnicking, the study of natural history via nature trails, etc. Others have provision for formal activities.

Country parks are all provided with car parking and toilets and some also have refreshment kiosks or similar facilities, picnic sites and information centres. Many of them have wardens to help visitors. The facilities are sometimes offered free of charge, though a fairly usual method is to charge for car parking or for admission to the park itself.

About one half the country parks contain areas of water, while others are adjacent to rivers, lakes, reservoirs, or the sea. This allows for a further range of activities and while some are limited to members of local clubs the general public is often permitted to take part for a small charge. The activities include sailing, rowing, canoeing, and sometimes swimming.

*Chartered Institute of Public Finance and Accountancy, 1980, "Leisure and recreation statistics 1979-80: estimates".

COUNTRYSIDE COMMISSION

The Countryside Commission are the successor to the National Parks Commission which was given powers and duties under the National Parks and Access to the Countryside Act 1949. They became responsible for the preservation and enhancement of areas of natural beauty in England and Wales, primarily in the established National Parks and in Areas of Outstanding Natural Beauty. Under the later Countryside Act 1968, when the Commission changed their title, their responsibilities were widened to cover all parts of the countryside, and they were given additional powers for research and experimentation, and also for financial grant-aiding.

The Secretaries of State for the Environment and for Wales are both responsible for appointing the Commissioners, of which there is no set number, and each Commissioner is appointed in a purely personal capacity. This means that while, individually, the Commissioners are not considered in any way to represent their own organizations, together they cover a formidable range of relevant and related interests.

The Commission are able to offer expertise on all matters relating to the conservation of the landscape, provision of facilities for informal countryside recreation, and on the management, design, and development of countryside information and interpretation services and facilities.

Some activities naturally have a far-reaching effect on the countryside and it is not always possible to obviate difficulties by planning controls alone, as is manifest in the case of forestry or farming land. Both of these activities are of great national importance, but their management has to be reconciled with the need for landscape conservation, ecological balance, and also recreational use. Where land is in private ownership agreements can be reached by negotiations and, in some cases, compensation or payment of a consideration may be necessary to preserve harmony between activities. The position is more difficult where land is in public ownership, but the various managing authorities are, under the Countryside and Water Acts, obliged to pay proper regard to conservation and recreation and they are asked by the Commission to set an example.

Much progress has been made in this direction as far as the National Parks are concerned. There are ten such Parks in England and Wales and around three-quarters of their capital and current costs are met from a block Exchequer grant. For each one a "national park plan" is drawn up to determine the nature and extent of any changes, and the plans include proposals for future management. Priority is given to requirements for conservation over those for recreation whenever there is a conflict between the two requirements. Plans are prepared after widespread and careful consultation with local residents. It is often forgotten that National Parks not only contain some of the loveliest countryside but also have people living and working in them who must be consulted if the Parks are really to benefit everyone concerned.

Attempts are being made to bring about the same kind of involvement in Areas of Outstanding Natural Beauty. There are now over 30 such areas in England and Wales and through them planning authorities are encouraged to protect the smaller and more local areas of beauty. The Countryside Commission can give financial grants to support the work being done and offer advice when needed.

The Countryside Commission also plan routes of long-distance footpaths or bridleways and negotiations with landowners are carried out by local authorities on their behalf in order to secure agreements for any stretches of the routes which may not already be public rights of way. About 12 routes, totalling 2400 km either exist or are planned for opening.

In recent years off-shore prospecting and drilling has drawn urgent attention to the need to preserve as much as possible of the unique coastlines of England and Wales, and under the Commission's "Heritage Coasts Scheme" protection is so far planned for over 1600 km of undeveloped coastline in England and Wales. A wide variety of tasks is undertaken including the clearance of "eyesores" such as redundant wartime defences; landscapes are improved by tree planting where intrusive features need screening; repairs and improvements are carried out to footpaths, stiles and bridges; and protection is given to coastal flora and seabird nesting sites. As far as possible the involvement and co-operation of local farmers and residents is obtained, and the work is carried out by various voluntary groups and, in some cases, under the Job Creation Programme.

Other aspects of the Commission's work include the encouragement of provision of picnic sites and lay-bys for travelling holidaymakers. Grants are also given to Country Parks whether they are privately or publicly owned. These parks are sometimes near to large industrial conurbations and are intended to provide open spaces within easy reach of these built-up areas; they also relieve pressure on the larger National Parks.

In a more general way the Commission advises the Department of the Environment on such things as the design of agricultural buildings, or on the line of a new road to suit the countryside through which it passes. It can also make grants to single projects such as a tree-planting scheme, and it is this flexibility to work on both large and small scales which helps to make the Countryside Commission a positive force in safeguarding the beauties and the ecological values of the countryside.

The Commission publish an Annual Report and a wide range of information leaflets and advisory notes.

COUNTRYSIDE COMMISSION FOR SCOTLAND

The Commission was created by the Countryside (Scotland) Act 1967. It is responsible for advising the Secretary of State for Scotland on all matters relating to the countryside; members of the Commission, usually 14 in number, are appointed by the Secretary of State. The main aims of the Commission are to conserve and enhance the natural beauty of Scotland's countryside and to promote and provide facilities to enable the public to enjoy it. At the same time, the Commission tries to increase awareness of the damage which can be caused by increasing demands on the limited resources of the countryside through lack of care. The Commission is an advisory and promotional organization and co-operates with and gives help to a variety of other statutory and voluntary organizations working in recreation, amenity, and conservation fields.

The Commission is involved in many aspects of access to the countryside. This may vary from proposals for long-distance footpaths and advising local authorities on the development of footpath or access areas, to the provision of large sites or areas such as country parks, of which there are now 22 in Scotland, with several more areas which are now being developed for use. At the other end of the scale is the provision of such things as picnic sites, car parks, toilets, caravan and camp sites, and ranger services. Apart from its co-operation with the appropriate local authorities, the Commission works closely with another three national agencies in Scotland: the Scottish Sports Council, the Scottish Tourist Board, and the Forestry Commission.

The increasing demand for access to the countryside and the need for more
sporting and tourist facilities has made education in conservation of prime
importance, and here the Commission aims to help people of all ages to enjoy the
countryside safely and at the same time develop a positive interest in its
conservation. Ranger services play an important part here and rangers may be met in
any situation where a major use of land is for informal countryside recreation,
including areas of water so that they provide not only information and patrolling
services but also assistance in emergencies.

At a national level, the Commission has undertaken many large-scale studies
which resulted in the publication of its Report, "Scotland's Scenic Heritage". A
total of 98 per cent of Scotland's land and inland waters are classified as
"countryside", and the Commission stresses that it is on the planning authorities
that the main burden of conserving the nation's scenic heritage rests. In its researches
and surveys for the report, the Commission identified some 40 areas in Scotland of
outstanding national scenic significance, and this identification, the Commission
believes, is the first step towards their actual conservation. The areas thus identified
varied from remote parts of the Orkneys and Shetlands to well-known and well-
loved tourist spots.

Because of its widespread knowledge and influence the Commission is now
frequently consulted about new large-scale industrial developments, coastal power
stations and their attendant overhead lines, new roads and reservoirs, and on-shore
oil-related sites. Its research and development services provide a sound basis for
practical advice to local authority and other organizations, and this may take the
form of exploring the problems of planning, surveys, or studies of special topics.
The Commission also publishes a range of leaflets and information booklets, as well
as the larger, more specialist reports. Training courses have also been run by the
Commission since 1969.

ULSTER COUNTRYSIDE COMMITTEE

The Committee is a statutory advisory body set up under the terms of Section 4 of
the Amenity Lands Act (Northern Ireland) 1965 to advise the Department of the
Environment on general questions affecting the natural beauty and amenity of any
area or place in Northern Ireland.

In effect it advises on the general range of matters covered in Great Britain by the
Countryside Commission but has no grant-aiding powers and is purely a statutory
advisory body. Its advice includes consideration of the operation of a number of
country parks by the Department.

NATURE CONSERVANCY COUNCIL

In 1947 the Report of the Wild Life Conservation Special Committee (England and
Wales) was published, and two separate reports for Scotland (1947 and 1949). These
led to the formation by Royal Charter of the Nature Conservancy in 1949. The
Conservancy received its legal powers from the National Parks and Access to the
Countryside Act 1949.

The Conservancy was an independent organization responsible to the Committee
of Privy Council for Nature Conservation. It acquired land and declared National
Nature Reserves (NNRs) but in 1965 it was made a component body of the Department of Education and Science's newly created Natural Environment Research
Council (NERC) to which its legal functions were formally transferred. Further
changes came when the Nature Conservancy Council Act 1973 brought the Nature
Conservancy Council (NCC) into being. However the "main research arm" of the

old Nature Conservancy remained within NERC as the Institute of Terrestrial Ecology.

The NCC is governed by a Council the members of which are appointed by the Secretary of State for the Environment, and is financed through the Department of the Environment. Its Headquarters are in London but there are also separate headquarter offices for England, Scotland, and Wales and 15 regional offices. In addition, Advisory Committees for England, Scotland, and Wales were set up to help the Council in its work.

The principal functions of the NCC are the establishment and management of nature reserves in Great Britain; the provision of advice to Government Ministers and others; the dissemination of information about nature conservation; and the commissioning of relevant research.

To date some 170 NNRs have been declared. They are either owned or leased by the NCC or managed under nature reserve agreements with the owners. They are specially selected in order to represent the most significant types of wildlife habitat in Britain and also those areas of exceptional geological or physiographic importance. They are managed mainly by wardens and estate workers, with help from members of the public who act as voluntary wardens. The management programme for each reserve is designed to maintain or enhance the habitat: for instance, chalk downland rich in plant and insect life may require grazing or mowing to prevent it from being overgrown with hawthorn scrub. NNRs also provide "open-air laboratories" for ecological research and for the monitoring of wildlife communities. It is thus possible to develop practical techniques for habitat management through experimental work.

While the primary function of this network of NNRs is to protect wildlife and important physical features, it also gives the public opportunities to enjoy the country's natural heritage. On many reserves, leaflets, information centres, and nature trails are provided for the visiting public. Reserves are often traditionally used for recreational pursuits such as wildfowling, or by holidaymakers. Because of the popularity of some sites, it has been necessary to restrict access and control certain recreational activities in order to protect fragile vegetation or some species of animals and birds which are sensitive to disturbance.

Nature reserves are, of course, the outward manifestation of the NCC's efforts most familiar to the public, but the Council does valuable work in other directions. It undertakes and commissions surveys of wildlife habitats and geological and physiographic features. The NCC has a duty under the 1949 Act to notify those areas which in its opinion are of special interest—to local planning authorities, and, under the Water Act 1973, to water authorities. There are some 3900 such Sites of Special Scientific Interest covering about 5½ per cent of Britain. In 1977 the NCC and the NERC produced A Nature Conservation Review describing and classifying wildlife habitats and identifying 735 key sites which merit NNR status. In 1980 the NCC announced that more than 50 of these sites had been damaged or destroyed. A parallel Geological Conservation Review is in preparation.

The NCC's powers to declare nature reserves are restricted to land down to the low water mark. Nature Conservation in the Marine Environment, a report of a NCC/NERC Working Party, was published in 1979, and the Government has now accepted the NCC's advice that powers to establish marine nature reserves be included in the wildlife and Countryside Bill. The Bill also extends protection for the otter to Scotland. The otter was already listed as an endangered species in England and Wales, on the evidence provided by the NCC, under the Conservation of Wild Creatures and Wild Plants Act 1975. This Act prohibits the uprooting of wild plants and the picking of 20 species of endangered plants, and protects certain bats, reptiles and insects. One of these, the Large Blue butterfly was declared by the NCC as probably extinct in Britain, after the failure of its last known colony in 1979.

The NCC has predicted that several other species will become extinct by the end of the century if the alarming decline in the extent and quality of our wildlife habitats continues. In evidence to the House of Lords Select Committee on Science and Technology on forestry in 1980, the NCC's chief scientists reported that between 30 and 50 per cent of the ancient primary woodland had been destroyed since 1947 — equalling the losses of the previous four centuries.

The NCC is a licensing authority under the 1975 Act, under the Protection of Birds Acts, the Deer Act 1963 and the Badgers Act 1973. Because of a marked decline in badgers in West Yorkshire, the Home Secretary, on the advice of the NCC, made the county an area of special protection for badgers — the first such area in Britain. The NCC also advises the Government on various international conventions, such as the "Ramsar" convention on wetlands of international importance and the Convention on International Trade in Endangered Species of Wild Fauna and Flora (CITES). In 1980 the NCC published a report on *Wildlife Introductions to Great Britain* and has advised Government on controls and monitoring required for certain species.

The NCC awards grants for projects in the field of nature conservation. The total amount awarded in 1979-80 was £169000, the major part of which went to support the conservation activities of 20 voluntary organizations.

The NCC's research programme includes studies of the ecological effects of tourism and recreation, and of recreational disturbance to waterfowl in co-operation with the Sports Council and the Severn-Trent Water Authority. It issues a code for users of the shores and shallow seas: *The Seashore and You*, and a leaflet: *Visiting National Nature Reserves*. The NCC's project, "Wildlife in the city", encourages the public to take an active interest in their local surroundings, and a report of the wildlife of the West Midlands conurbation, *The Endless Village*, was published in 1978.

In its wider educational and advisory role, the NCC is involved in recreational matters from two main standpoints. It seeks to ensure that any harm to wildlife and geological features arising from recreation and its infrastructure is minimized and that the opportunities to interest and inform people in and about nature conservation through their recreational activities are fully utilized.

CENTRAL COUNCIL OF PHYSICAL RECREATION

The Council (known by the initials CCPR) was founded in 1935 under the title The Central Council of Recreative Physical Training. It grew out of the social, economic, and education needs of the previous decade when unemployment was high, particularly among juveniles, who left school at the age of 14. Those without work when they left school were not eligible for unemployment money until they were 16, and even then the receipt of this pay was conditional on attendance at "Junior Instruction Centres" for handicrafts instruction, games and some physical training — activities which were usually held in make-shift premises.

At the time, despite the growth in the Youth Hostels Association and the activities of the National Playing Fields Association, little outdoor activity was organized specifically for young people, and what there was tended to be provided by such voluntary organizations as the Boy Scouts and Girl Guides. Gradually, greater efforts were made by various bodies to improve facilities for the young which culminated in the formation of the CCPR. In its early years it broke new ground by providing courses for leaders of physical training and it also published leaflets on exercises and general fitness.

A new role came for the Council during the Second World War, teaching munitions and other workers how to handle heavy loads safely and without strain, and providing "keep fit" classes for those sitting at benches all day. In 1944 the Council's name was changed to the Central Council of Physical Recreation (CCPR) and after the War its efforts gradually reverted to the "adventurous, non-competitive" outdoor activities more usually associated with the Council.

In the early 1970s an important change was made. After the establishment of the Sports Council a few years earlier, developments led to the recommendation that the assets of the CCPR should be transferred to the new body. However, the features of the work of the CCPR as a forum of sport and physical recreation, the development of sport at regional and local levels, the management of the centres and the voluntary national fund would be continued. This transfer took place in 1972, and today some 200 governing and representative bodies for sport as well as for many physical recreation activities are members of the CCPR, which now constitutes a standing-forum where all these organizations may be represented and may collectively, or through special groups, formulate and promote measures to improve and develop sport. It supports the work of specialist sports bodies and brings them together with other interested organizations. It also acts as a consultative body to the Sports Council and other representative bodies concerned with sport and physical recreation.

The CCPR has six divisions: games and sports; movement and dance; water recreation; interested organizations; the Major Spectator Sports Division and the Outdoor Pursuits Division; and finally an individual members category which is comprised of people with considerable experience and knowledge of sport and physical recreation.

The regional bodies of sport and recreation have organized themselves into Standing Conferences of Sport and Recreation, or Federations of Sport, to provide an essential advisory service to the Regional Councils for Sport and Recreation and the CCPR.

A scheme introduced in 1974 called "sponsors of sport" enables industrial organizations to be associated with the voluntary and independent nature of British sport. This scheme not only attracts financial support for the CCPR but gives an opportunity for leaders of commerce and industry to get together with sports people to discuss matters which affect them both.

The CCPR's structure ensures that action can be taken on behalf of its members to safeguard their interests, and matters which receive attention include publicity, sponsorship, sport and recreation for the disabled, TV and press, sport and recreation, parliamentary legislation, lotteries, taxation, VAT, etc., the medical aspects of sport and recreation and so on.

The CCPR relates the views of governing bodies to the Government, the Sports Council, local and other authorities, to each other and to the nation, and its "voice" is an influential one for the whole of the U.K.

Sports Councils

Sports Council

The Sports Council is an independent body, established by Royal Charter in 1972 to replace the previous advisory Sports Council, formed in 1965. There are separate

Councils for Scotland, Wales, and Northern Ireland. though all four work closely through the U.K. Affairs Committee to ensure a consistent approach to common problems.

The Council has overall responsibility for British sports matters, as well as domestic affairs in England. It consists of a Chairman, two vice-chairmen and 29 members who are appointed by the Secretary of State for the Environment.

The full Council considers general sports matters, in addition to reports and recommendations from its main committees, which are facilities, sports development, information, research, and finance.

In fulfilment of the objectives of its Charter, the Council receives an annual grant from central Government which it uses to develop sport, and seeks to:-

(1) Promote general understanding of the social importance and value of sport and physical recreation.

(2) Increase provision for new sports facilities and stimulate fuller use of existing facilities.

(3) Encourage wider participation in sport and physical recreation as a means of enjoying leisure.

(4) Raise standards of performance.

Capital grants are made towards the provision of facilities which cater primarily for local community use, as well as national and regional projects. The Council also supports special projects such as prototype schemes, conversions of existing buildings and projects in areas of special need, particularly those which are low cost and provide for participation of youth. Capital grants and loans are available to voluntary clubs for the development of facilities.

Recurrent grants are made to the governing bodies of sport and national organizations of physical recreation to improve administration, develop participation, and improve standards of performance through coaching, preparation training, and international events.

Besides the range of services offered by the Facilities Unit and the Sports Development Unit, the Council has other specialist units at Headquarters offering advice to anyone concerned with sport and physical recreation. The Technical Unit for Sport provides architectural, engineering and quantity surveying advice on the construction of facilities. It also produces design notes and undertakes development projects.

Help and advice is also available from the Research Unit — anything from in-depth data to consumer reaction — and from the Information Centre, a focal point for national and international information. The Centre produces useful reference publications.

The Press and Publications Unit is responsible for the management of Council publications, including the quarterly magazine.

Regional Offices. As described in detail on p. 247 of this Chapter, the staff of the Sports Council in the nine regional offices, have the responsibility of implementing the policies of the Council in developing sport according to regional needs, interests, and conditions.

National Water Sports Centres. The Centre at Holme Pierrepont was established in 1973. It was developed from derelict land as a joint project with Nottinghamshire County Council. The extensive water areas include an international 2000m rowing and canoeing course and separate lagoons for water skiing and angling: all are contained within a Country Park. Lecture, training and conference facilities are also available.

The Cowes National Sailing Centre was established in 1968. It is situated on the river Medina, with direct access to the superb sailing waters of the Solent. Courses in dinghy sailing and racing, dinghy camping, coastal cruising and motor boat handling, navigation and pilotage are provided. It also has a conference and marine study centre.

Sports Council for Wales

The Council was established by Royal Charter in April 1972 and is an autonomous executive body. It took over the duties of the previous advisory Sports Council and also the responsibilities in Wales of the Central Council of Physical Recreation. Its objectives are to foster the knowledge and practice of sport and recreation, to help increase the provision of facilities throughout Wales and to encourage the achievement of high standards in Welsh sport in conjunction with the governing bodies of sport.

The Council uses grant aid, technical service and advice to strengthen the administration, coaching and development of all governing bodies of Welsh sport. It assists Welsh sportsmen and sportswomen to take part in international events as a means of improving standards, and stimulates local authorities to make provision of sporting facilities to meet local, regional and national demands. The financing of new and improved facilities for local sports clubs is an important part of its work, and it also carries out research and assistance for those providing new sports facilities.

In 1973 the Council published a Water Recreation Strategy for Wales in which it listed all the inland waters. Extensive surveys of facilities and consultations with statutory and voluntary agencies had revealed a wealth of information on the existing situation which was adapted to become a strategic blueprint. The document recommended an hierarchical approach, identifying areas of water in national, regional and sub-regional terms and the whole was offered for acceptance to the Welsh Water Authority. Since that time the Council has worked closely with the Authority in the implementation of its survey work.

Scottish Sports Council

The Council was brought into being as an independent body by Royal Charter in December 1971 "with the objects of fostering the knowledge and practice of sport and physical recreation among the public at large, and the provision of facilities therefore, building upon the work in this field of the Scottish Council of Physical Recreation and others...".

The Council has up to 25 members at any one time, including the Chairman and Vice-Chairman, and they are appointed by the Secretary of State for Scotland, normally serving for four years.

The Council works with the governing bodies of sport throughout the country recognizing the important and valuable job they do in helping to foster and develop sport in Scotland, and gives grants where possible to help each sport to develop according to its particular needs. Grants are also made to local voluntary organizations and local clubs, thus harnessing voluntary effort with private finance and the Council's own aid. Special attention is also paid to areas of Scotland where there is unusually high unemployment, particularly among the 16-18 year olds, to introduce people to activities they would not otherwise have experienced. Courses are also held to train and increase the numbers of qualified coaches for those remoter areas such as Orkney, Shetland, and the Western Isles, where staffing is difficult.

The varied countryside and coastline of Scotland make it an ideal country for a wide variety of sports. Scotland has its own Mountain Rescue Committee and a

Scottish Mountain Leader Training Board. As the country has the largest mountaineering areas of the British Isles and because of their remoteness and the vagaries of weather, the Council issues a "Mountain Code for Scotland". Skiing also takes place in these mountainous areas.

Water-based activities include canoeing, sub-aqua diving, sailing, power boating, and angling, and Scotland has its own national bodies for each of these activities with the exception of sailing which comes under the Royal Yachting Association (Scotland), all of which co-operate with the Sports Council. Each water-based sport is geared to the abilities of all its participants whether novice, advanced, or competitive. The Council's national water sports centre on the Island of Great Cumbrae was opened in 1975 and has already built up a sound reputation, particularly in leadership training. The work carried on there has some limitations because of the essentially seasonal nature of its activities and a high staff-pupil ratio is required, but demand for its programmes is increasing, partly in line with the increased coaching and training developments of such organizations as the Royal Yachting Association (Scotland), the Scottish Sub-Aqua Club, and the Scottish Canoe Association.

The Council has two further national sports training centres at Glenmore Lodge, in the Cairngorms, and Inverclyde at Largs. Programmes are aimed primarily at the upper end of ability and at the "training of elitist performers", but courses are available for members of the general public to help them improve their performance or to try out a completely new skill. There are also some "Family activity holidays" available.

The Council publishes a wide range of information leaflets and has established a library for Sport. It co-operates with local authorities and encourages them to produce their own information leaflets covering opportunities for sport in their respective areas. Special studies are also undertaken and results are published by the Council, as well as a summary of each year's activities, in the Annual Report.

Sports Council for Northern Ireland

The Council was established under Statutory Instrument No. 961 (N.I.12) "The Recreation and Youth Service Order 1973", and No. 815 (N.I. 6) "The Recreation (Northern Ireland) Order 1975". It was set up with effect from 1 April 1974 and took over the work of the Central Council of Physical Recreation in Northern Ireland and certain other functions formerly carried out by the Youth and Sports Council and the Ministry of Education.

The object of the Council is the furtherance of sport and physical recreation in Northern Ireland. Its functions are:-

(a) on matters relating to sport and physical recreation, to advise the Department of Education and other Government Departments, Education and Library Boards, District Councils and other bodies interested in sport and physical recreation;

(b) to advise the Department on such applications for grants in respect of facilities for sport and physical recreation as are referred to it by the Department;

(c) to encourage the provision of facilities for, and participation in, sport and physical recreation;

(d) to survey the existing facilities for sport and physical recreation, determine the need for further provision and make recommendations for meeting that need; and

(e) to assist, by financial contributions or otherwise, the provision of administrative services, equipment, coaching and instruction and the organizing of or participating in international or other events, by voluntary organizations providing facilities for sport or physical recreation or organising such activities.

The Council has 23 members including the Chairman and Vice-Chairman. The interests of both practitioners and providers are represented on the Council and assessors from the Departments of Agriculture, Commerce, Education and Environment attend meetings.

Regional Councils for Sport and Recreation

After the creation of the Sports Council in 1965, a number of subcommittees were set up. One of them, under the Chairmanship of Lord Porchester, was the Facilities Committee. Following a meeting with the Central Council for Physical Recreation (CCPR) and the Scottish Council for Physical Recreation (SCPR), Lord Porchester's proposals to set up Regional Sports Councils in England and Sports Councils for Wales and Scotland were accepted. The CCPR and SCPR supplied the Executive Officers for the new Councils, which primarily consisted of representatives of local authorities. The purpose of the new Councils, after undertaking initial surveys and appraisals, was to "facilitate the regional co-ordination and provision of facilities for sport and physical recreation".

In 1976 the Regional Sports Councils in England were replaced by nine Regional Councils for Sport and Recreation, i.e. Northern; North Western; Yorkshire and Humberside; East Midlands; West Midlands; Eastern; London and South East; Southern; and South West. They are concerned with the whole range of sport and outdoor recreational activities in their regions and provide a forum for consultation among local authorities and user and other interested organizations. While they are assisted by relevant government agencies and departments they are not subject to direction by either. Their role is consultative and advisory and does not therefore infringe on the statutory duties of other agencies and authorities, or affect the manner in which local authorities deal directly with such bodies as the Sports Council and the Countryside Commission.

The membership of each Council is carefully balanced between representatives of local council, non-statutory bodies, sports and outdoor recreation organizations and allows of proper representation of conservation, landowning, and farming interests.

The balance of each Council may be varied in the light of particular local needs and circumstances, if necessary, but they must consult with liaison officers appointed by the Countryside Commission and groups of local authorities on the Council on matters of business to be undertaken.

The Regional Councils represent those who plan, provide, and enjoy a wide range of sport and recreation and they are uniquely able to make a considerable contribution to the development of recreation in their regions. For example, during the preparation of strategy documents, wide consultation is important as it both serves the purpose of strategy preparation and is also part of the wider spread of the regional council's influence. Many organizations, besides those already represented in the Councils' membership, often make valuable contributions including the private sector and voluntary organizations. Consultations include discussions to establish common criteria in the light of local and national plans, and the Councils consequently can help or sometimes influence the plans of the Regional Tourist Boards and such bodies as water authorities.

Once regional recreation strategies have been defined, local authorities have the responsibility of formulating and putting into practice individual recreation policies and they achieve this through their statutory plans which are subject to public participation and approval. For the Regional Councils for Sport and Recreation the feedback from this is of considerable importance when reviewing their own strategy, and it enables them to fulfil their role more effectively.

Co-ordination in Wales. — In Wales, as there is no regional council for sport and recreation, much of the responsibility which affects different organizations and specific functions in the whole field of recreational activity lies with the Secretary of State. In this capacity he maintains a continuous oversight of the inter-related activities of the various agencies, including the Sports Council for Wales, in order to secure the development of a coherent strategy. Further, the chairmen and chief officers of agencies having responsibility in the field of recreation meet periodically and discuss the development and co-ordination of their activities. Additionally, the agencies work with local authorities all over Wales and participate directly in the consultation on structure plans. Information and guidance can therefore more effectively flow from the central to the local level and the monitoring of it can be fully maintained. The Advisory Committees for North, West, and South East Wales (which include representatives of the local authorities concerned), consider matters relevant to those parts of the country.

TOURIST BOARDS

English Tourist Board

The English Tourist Board (ETB) was created, together with the British Tourist Authority and the Scottish and Wales Tourist Boards, by the Development of Tourism Act 1969.

The size and nature of tourism at any time is related to the strength of national economies, while the use of the many services which make up the tourist industry reflects the level of disposable income available to people with increased leisure time.

The English Tourist Board has developed a clear identity for England as a holiday destination, and gained strong trade support for its campaigns. At the same time the co-ordination of some 450 Tourist Information Centres, used by nine million tourists annually, has facilitated the special promotions of events and themes aimed at dispersing tourist traffic both seasonally and geographically.

Co-operation with local authorities and the commercial sector in creating 12 regional tourist boards has ensured the more fundamental understanding and implementation of local and national tourism policies. The involvement at this level is one of ETB's notable achievements.

The ETB has acted as the agency of the Department of Trade in handling the Hotel Development Incentives Scheme and latterly the use of Tourist Projects funds to create an improved tourist provision.

From its earliest days, ETB recognized the need for research not only to pre-test and monitor its marketing campaigns, but also to provide the industry with reliable data on year-round demand, and particularly data on accommodation-occupancy. The annual research into holiday intentions and the commissioning of trend forecasts have all served to inform and guide the industry.

A series of region-by-region descriptive studies, supported by economic impact studies and research into resources such as historic buildings, inland waterways, and signposting, and the special needs of young people and the socially disadvantaged, have brought ETB into active partnership with many other organizations responsible for tourism management.

A decision to create a resource development branch, with planning and financial expertise, and a commercial relations department with the task of identifying and informing sources of development finance, has established a firm foundation for ETB's more commercial approach to the tourist industry. Contact with the commercial sector has enabled ETB to give better information to government departments, for whom it has a statutory role to act as adviser on tourism.

The European Conservation Year, and the European Architectural Heritage Year, focused attention on the irreplaceable assets of the English countryside and its cultural heritage, which, as a statutory agency ETB must do all it can to protect, whilst enabling visitors to experience and enjoy them. To this end it has worked closely with the many voluntary and public organizations who have established a national concern for the country's heritage.

In the face of increased energy costs, transportation will need to develop operating economies, and this could lead to even more integration of transport modes to match the expanding leisure needs of the young and old. The country's membership of the European Economic Community will induce a greater leisure provision for the socially disadvantaged, whilst extending the statutory leave entitlement for all.

The English Tourist Board, as advisers on tourism to Government, continues to innovate in the marketing and development of visitor facilities, and seeks to integrate the diverse elements of the increasingly important industry of tourism.

At the regional level the 12 tourist regions correspond reasonably well with those of the water industry. This helps to create and maintain good lines of communication and liaison. The English tourist regions and their approximate water authority counterparts are:-

Tourist Board	Water Authority
Cumbria	North West
North West	North West
Northumbria	Northumbrian
Yorkshire and Humberside	Yorkshire
Heart of England	Severn-Trent
East Midlands	Severn-Trent
East Anglia	Anglian
Thames and Chilterns	Thames
London	Thames
South East England	Southern
Southern	Southern-Wessex
West Country	South West

In Wales, the Wales Tourist Board and the Welsh Water Authority are clearly closely associated, and have many interests in common.

Wales Tourist Board

The Board came into being as a result of the Development of Tourism Act 1969 and it has its Headquarters in Cardiff. The Board has a Chairman, Deputy Chairman and five members; there are also seven management executives who deal with such items as publicity, finance, marketing, development, projects, planning, and research. In addition to this overall structure there are three Regional Tourism Councils which cover, respectively, North, Mid- and South Wales.

Wales is a small country with both assets and problems which are peculiarly its own. It has beautiful, varied countryside with mountains, lakes, and many stretches of unspoilt coastline on the one hand, and, on the other, areas of intense industrialization in which unemployment is steadily increasing as the traditional heavy industries decline or even disappear.

The Board therefore seeks to evolve the policies that are helping to strengthen

Tourism and the Board co-operates closely with the Welsh Office, and with county, district, and local authorities in order to promote Wales' distinctive heritage.

With the rundown of the steel industry in Wales and the consequent loss of jobs, new and ambitious projects are being developed in an effort to offset some of the unemployment. The Board considers that its role complements those of the Welsh Office and the Welsh Development Agency in endeavouring to provide alternative employment and in helping to hold communities together in the affected areas by means of increased tourism attractions. It considers applications from various authorities, individuals, groups and companies for assistance with projects for Wales which would, in the opinion of the Board, improve tourist and amenity features.

A main feature of the Welsh hotel and accommodation business is the smallness of the establishments involved. While this is in itself an attraction, it can lead to a lack of promotional effort on the part of those without the means for large-scale publicity. The Board therefore gives advice on such matters and arranges seminars and conferences for tourist attractions, self-catering, and serviced operations. The Board has also introduced a Self-Catering Award Scheme and a Farmhouse Award Scheme, and holds discussions with the Welsh Office on such subjects as interest relief grant schemes in an attempt to help those individual small-scale enterprises, without much capital behind them, to modernize or extend their accommodation.

The Board has given assistance to fisheries in Wales — via the Welsh Anglers' Council — in order to improve recreation facilities for this sport, a sport which even a few years ago was estimated to generate an income of some £30 million a year in the Welsh Water Authority area.

The Board maintains "working links" with a variety of statutory agencies through the Committee of Statutory Bodies in Wales, and submits formal evidence to committees and working parties on issues which range from EEC rural policy to the tourism potential of historic buildings. One important link of this kind is with the Welsh Water Authority. A reciprocal arrangement exists so that the Board is represented on the Authority's local and regional advisory committees, and in turn the Authority is involved in the activities of the Board, principally through the Development Panels of Regional Tourism Councils and also through their Tourist Attractions Committee. There is close and increasing co-operation between the two bodies on the promotion of such water sports as fishing, sailing, canoeing, etc., with joint participation at major exhibitions.

The Board has in recent years increased the publications side of its work and, with the co-operation of the British Tourist Authority, now sells some 500000 publications throughout the UK and overseas markets. It publishes research reports on a variety of topics and, for the tourist and the general public, a range of guides and booklets.

Scottish Tourist Board

The Board was created by the Development of Tourism Act 1969. In its planning, the Board aims to relate its policies to those for physical and economic planning for Scotland as a whole, taking the view that as tourism has an effect on the life of most people in the country it is equally affected by social, physical, and economic factors. In addition, it recognizes that many local residents can benefit from the widening range of recreation pursuits provided for tourists. The Board therefore works closely with the different regional development organizations, including the Highland and Islands Development Board.

Tourism in Scotland is now a major element in its economy and the country has over 3000 hotels and over 7000 guest houses. This pinpoints one of the Board's objectives, which is to help create new jobs and bring prosperity to those areas in need of help, particularly those small rural communities in remote, but attractive areas, with few job alternatives or opportunities.

Other aims of the Board are to improve local services and to promote conservation. While it is not directly involved in either activity, by concentrating its policies on those types of tourism which maximize the development of facilities, it helps revenue-supporting services such as transport, shops, and recreation, and enhances the environment when steps are taken to conserve tourism's basic resource. In general, tourism provides a stimulus to preservation projects and the conservation of historically/culturally important places. The Board works closely in this respect with the Historic Buildings Council for Scotland, and with many local authorities to identify sites which might be developed as tourist attractions or centres.

In making plans for the future the Board has to take careful note of current difficulties arising out of fuel price increases and the effect these will have not only on airlines and bus companies but also on private motorists. It envisages a "renewed popularity" of centre-based holidays which will enable it to encourage the improvement of accommodation, recreation, and entertainment facilities. It also hopes to attract more holidaymakers by improving facilities for sports holidays, including water sports, trout fishing and sea angling, golf, walking, pony trekking, and riding. The Board operates a discretionary scheme of financial assistance towards development projects of such a nature.

The Board also concentrates on promoting conference facilities throughout Scotland, as research has shown that facilities for small conferences (i.e. for up to 500 persons) are not generally well provided for.

There is an increasing demand for rented accommodation of the chalet/cottage development type, particularly of the sort provided so successfully by the Forestry Commission. It is felt that such schemes should be increased but centred on existing settlements, rather than create yet more settlements deep in the countryside. In the sphere of holidays at a cheaper level, the Board is able to give a certain amount of grant aid to Youth Hostels, when there are indications that new hostels or extensions to existing hostels are clearly required. The Board initiates joint discussions with the Countryside Commission for Scotland, the Scottish Sports Council, and local authorities to improve and develop facilities for such activities as walking, riding, and pony trekking and also on the development of "motor trails" or "scenic routes" for motorists from the main holiday resorts.

More generally, the Board supports the appropriate authorities in the maintenance and improvement of access to the countryside; on the development of catering and accommodation services; the improvement of information services, particularly those in foreign languages; and the improvements in such ancillary items as roadside toilet and litter services. As tourism is labour-intensive, the Board keeps in touch with manpower training schemes and gives assistance itself in training courses in co-operation with universities, colleges, and the Hotel and Catering Industry Training Board, and also through schools careers services.

The Board is conscious of the need, expressed by Government, to switch expenditure to developing untapped potential for tourism in those areas that can readily absorb and benefit from more visitors, particularly in certain parts of the development areas, which in turn will stem pressure on currently congested areas to the greater enhancement of life for the communities in both types of areas and for the visitors using their facilities and resources whether these are scenic or otherwise.

Northern Ireland Tourist Board

The Board was set up under the Development of Tourist Traffic Act (Northern Ireland) 1948. Among other things, the Act aimed at the registration of certain catering establishments and the giving of financial aid towards providing such services and amenities as would help to develop tourism in Northern Ireland and encourage greater tourist traffic. This applied both to visitors from outside Northern Ireland as well as to people actually living there.

More research is being undertaken and overseas tour operators, as well as those from Great Britain, are being reminded of the attractions which await the visitor. However, the general view of the Board is that mass tourism, unless carefully handled, could destroy Northern Ireland's most precious natural tourist asset — the tranquil countryside and freedom from pollution in the uncrowded rural areas.

The country is justly famed for its clean rivers and good fishing. A number of festivals for both the arts and out-door sports are being developed. Emphasis is therefore being placed on "specialist holidays" such as fishing and inland waterway cruising, with financial help going to hire-cruiser operators. There is also much greater provision of marina, slipway, and jetty facilities along with car parks, toilet blocks, and picnic sites. The Sports Council for Northern Ireland has been helping to develop the 640 km footpath known as "The Ulster Way" which loops right around the Province and which has its parallel with the long distance footpaths and bridle-ways in England and Wales, all of which greatly improve the opportunities for enjoying the waterside and the countryside.

The Board is gradually extending its "information units" and is devoting attention to the provision of adequate eating and sleeping accommodation for the tourists which it seeks to attract. For some years grants have been made for the repair and up-grading of existing hotels and guest houses as well as for the provision of new accommodation. Whilst the position is improving, much work needs to be done.

Confidence in the future is nevertheless growing, and increased and better publicity through the press, TV, and trade associations is helping, as is the preparation of attractive tourist literature.

THE INLAND WATERWAYS AMENITY ADVISORY COUNCIL

This Council is a statutory body which was set up under Section 110 of the Transport Act 1968. It represents the interests of all types of users on the 3200 km canal and river network of the British Waterways Board. The members of the Council are appointed by the Secretary of State for the Environment, and they are drawn from all fields of waterway amenity and recreational interest.

In 1979 the Government announced legislation to modify the Transport Act 1968, including the abolition of the Council. In the meantime, its members have been reappointed until the end of 1981.

Under its terms of reference the Council advises the Secretary of State for the Environment and the British Waterways Board on any proposals to add to, or reduce, the cruising waterways. Also, the Council is required to consider and, where thought desirable, to make recommendations to the Board or the Secretary of State, with respect to any other matter affecting the use or development for amenity or recreational purposes, including fishing, of the cruising waterways, or with respect to the provision for those purposes of services or facilities, in connection with those waterways or the commercial waterways.

Under the British Waterways Act 1974 the Council is consulted on any proposed increases in charges for pleasure boat registration.

Matters referred to the Council are dealt with centrally by the Chairman, Secretary, and a small staff in the Council's London office. They liaise with Council members and many interested and related organizations in order to maintain a clear picture of the needs and problems of the system's users. Both the Department of the Environment and the British Waterways Board supply information to enable the Council to form its views on a wide range of issues related to the waterways.

Council members meet regularly and they also visit the Board's system to look at problems on site and discuss proposals at first hand, and offer advice to interested organizations.

As its name implies, the Council is essentially an advisory body with a statutory duty to consider all matters within its terms of reference, referred to it by both government agencies and the many voluntary bodies concerned with waterways recreation resources and restoration, and to this end publishes reports. The Council also establishes working parties in order to consider specific questions.

BRITISH WATERWAYS BOARD

The Board were established by the Transport Act 1962 as one of the successor boards to the former British Transport Commission, and their members are appointed by the Secretary of State for the Environment. Their system is made up of about 3200 km of canals and river navigations — mainly in England, but including several in Scotland and Wales — together with their associated reservoirs, docks, fleets, warehouses, repair yards, workshops, and some waterside land and buildings.

In 1963 the Board began their task of managing the canals and making proposals for their future. Early studies resulted in published reports, in 1963 and 1965, and by Government White Papers in 1966 and 1967. These paved the way for what was described as a new "charter for the waterways", i.e. the Transport Act 1968.

One of the important new provisions of this Act was the classification of 482 km of the Board's waterways as Commercial Waterways and a further 1770 km as Cruising Waterways, all of which were to be maintained in a suitable condition for their respective purposes. The 965 km of Remainder Waterways were to be dealt with in the most economical manner possible consistent with the requirements of public health and the preservation of amenity and safety. Local authorities were given new powers which enabled them to help maintain or improve waterways for amenity purposes.

On the traffic development side, the Board decided that there had to be a radical restructuring of their inherited freight activities. Some needed to develop a new role, but a few proved to have no economic future and therefore ceased to operate. Docks located in the right places could be made to succeed; so could warehouses, skilfully managed and supported by investment in new equipment. The promotional and operational aspects of the Board's freight services are complementary and are combined effectively and economically.

The inland waterways are an integral part of the landscape and are a part of Britain's history. Traversing the countryside, and indeed enhancing it, they bring water with its associated wildlife deep into towns and cities. They also provide many outlets for recreation, including fishing, boating, and walking. They afford opportunities for those who are interested in the voluntary work of the restoration and maintenance of the waterways.

There are opportunities for those who wish to spend holidays on the waterways, and there are many hire cruiser operators ranging from small firms to national companies offering a wide choice of craft and services. Boat owners may use their own craft on the waterways if they are first licensed or registered.

Sailing takes place on river navigations and reservoirs but not, generally, on canals. Moorings are often available from the Board and also at many of the private boatyards and marinas. Water skiing is permitted, with certain controls, on some lengths of river.

If boating is to be enjoyable, shore facilities are essential and many boat owners belong to clubs which provide moorings, a clubhouse and, of course, social events and conviviality. Boatyards and marinas offer services on an increasing scale and the Board, for their part, supply basic waterside facilities of water, refuse disposal points, sanitary stations, casual moorings, bollards at locks and swing bridges, and the canal itself.

Many people get pleasure from canal fishing. In the northwest especially, the Board's waterways are often the only convenient place where coarse fish angling can be pursued. Arrangements for fishing vary and on some of their waterways and reservoirs the Board do not own the fishing rights, which may belong to the adjacent landowners. Where the Board do own the rights they usually operate the fisheries and sell day tickets. A usual arrangement is for the Board to let fishing rights to a club or association who take on the responsibility for controlling the angling on their length, and deal with such problems as litter. Anglers have in recent years benefited from better depth of water following dredging, clearance of weed, and a general improvement in water quality. The Board also improve their fisheries by restocking and by research.

In addition to those actually taking part in water-related activities, many thousands of people use the towing paths and reservoir gathering grounds associated with the Board's waterways system for walking and picnicking.

Of the 965 km of the Board's system classified under the 1968 Act as "remainder waterways", about 560 km had been closed over a period of many years. Some have for long been a source of concern to urban authorities as well as to the Board and their predecessors and, paradoxically, the Act proved to be the solution to the problem. At the end of 1968 ten local authorities met in Manchester to discuss the future of the Ashton and Lower Peak Forest Canals. The response was constructive and immediate and joint working parties were set up to explore possibilities for use and the financial implications. These two canals were soon restored and since then many more have been renovated and improved in order to make them suitable for cruising. In the years since 1968 more than 50 local authorities have become closely involved with the Board in promoting positive action on these remainder waterways, and there has also been a growth in canal societies and other voluntary bodies keen to keep the canals in use.

NAVIGATION AUTHORITIES

About 45 per cent of the inland waterways of Great Britain are not nationalized and under the control of the British Waterways Board but are in the hands of a multitude of different bodies, ranging from Charitable Trusts to regional water authorities. Their histories and background are equally varied.

The canal era started with the Industrial Revolution in the eighteenth century and the great civil engineering works to link up the Mersey, Humber, Severn, and Thames with the industrial Midlands began in 1755 and continued through to about 1840. Many canals came into being as a result of private enterprise. By this time some

6400 km of navigable rivers and artificial canals had been built in Great Britain. These are the bulk of what remains today in spite of enormous competition, first from railways and then roads, as well as great changes in the style of management and administration.

Their survival and, since the Second World War, their restoration, means that public interest has rapidly increased in the recreational use of inland navigations. This is underlined by the fact that over 2 million people annually spend some time boating on them. By definition, most waterways tend to connect the most densely populated areas with the loveliest parts of the countryside so the possibilities for leisure and recreation, though not limitless, are good. There are exceptions. The Norfolk Broads, for example, are a unique area and there is no comparable inland waterway network.

Then there are the Fenland waterways. These fall into three groups. To the north there are the rivers Welland and Nene, in the middle a whole series of navigable drains known as the Middle Levels and to the south, the Great Ouse with its tributaries, the Wissey, Little Ouse, Lark, and the Cam.

The Welland, Nene and Great Ouse (with its tributaries) are controlled by the Anglian Water Authority, but the Middle Levels are all artificial cuts or old streams improved and intended mainly for drainage of the Fens. There are at least 17 separate drains and navigations in the system and except for one which is managed by the Anglian Water Authority, they are controlled by the Middle Level Commissioners — an Internal Drainage Board.

The restoration of the Great Ouse was recently completed by the Anglian Water Authority and the route is open now from King's Lynn to Bedford.

In the area of the Southern Water Authority, there are many historic but little heard-of navigations. The Stour to Canterbury has rights going back to 1514, but thought to be limited to the citizens of Canterbury. The Medway is navigable downstream of Tonbridge, and control of this navigation is shared between the water authority and the Medway Port Authority.

The Royal Military Canal with the rivers Brede and Rother form a small cluster of waterways based on the harbour at Rye. The Royal Military Canal was built as a Napoleonic Wars defence work and was not converted to a navigation until 1807.

Further west along the south coast three rivers, the Sussex Ouse, the Adur, and Arun extend navigation inland from the ports of Newhaven, Shoreham, and Littlehampton respectively. There is some dereliction in their upper reaches but in spite of this there are some good canoeing waters. These are also mainly controlled by the Southern Water Authority.

The Wey and Godalming Navigation operates on the river Wey which joins the Thames at Weybridge. This navigation is now operated by the National Trust. The Basingstoke Canale, an at present derelict branch of this navigation (although restoration work is proceeding), is owned jointly by the Surrey and Hampshire County Councils.

In the Midlands, the Warwickshire Avon has been restored, by voluntary effort, from Tewkesbury to Stratford-on-Avon where it joins with the South Stratford Canal. The South Stratford was restored about the same time by the National Trust and together they form one of the top three waterway "cruising rings" in the country, via the Worcester and Birmingham Canal and the river Severn. The original Avon navigation was created under an Act of 1751 but shortly after the rights were acquired by the old Great Western Railway in 1859 it was allowed to become derelict. It remained in this condition for just over a century. The navigation is controlled by two charitable Trusts. The National Trust owns the South Stratford Canal, the restoration of which in 1964 is still regarded as a watershed in the affairs of waterway enthusiasts.

The non-tidal Thames, upstream of Teddington Weir and now in the hands of the Thames Water Authority, may be described as one of the finest recreational rivers in Europe, perhaps even in the world. It has a long and glittering history and it is said that there are at least 38 Acts relating to navigations on the river between 1423 and 1829. However, the Thames Conservancy was originally incorporated by the Thames Conservancy Act 1857 and its jurisdiction as successor of the Corporation of the City of London extended from Staines to Yantlet Creek in Kent (the tideway). In 1866 the Conservancy took over the river from Staines up to Cricklade. In 1909 the tideway was transferred to the Port of London Authority and remains so to this day. The responsibility of the Thames Water Authority as the navigation authority extends over a distance of about 220 km. The Thames has a quality of its own but it is easy to take its present state for granted, and it must be remembered that it has taken many years to bring the river to its present fine condition.

This brief review of some of the independent waterways does not include some 40 other navigation authorities and their waterways. Many have equally colourful histories of past glories and mid-twentieth century revival.

FORESTRY COMMISSION

The Forestry Commission came into being with the Forestry Act 1919 which was consolidated with other Acts some 50 years later in the Forestry Act 1967. The Commission is responsible for the promotion of forestry interests in Great Britain generally, including afforestation development, the establishment and maintenance of adequate reserves of growing trees and, thus, the production and supply of timber. The work of the Commission therefore falls into two main categories: that of a Forestry Authority, and that of a "Forestry Enterprise".

As a Forestry Authority the Commission's task is to develop and ensure the best use of timber resources, including the promotion of wood-using industries. It combats forest and tree diseases and pests, and undertakes relevant research both on these and on a diversity of other topics which can range from nutrition, drainage and cultivation, to forest genetics, wildlife, and ecological management. Other aims are to advance knowledge and understanding about forestry and trees in the country-side, and to advise and assist with safety and training in forestry work. It also encourages good forestry practice in private woodlands through advice, financial assistance, and by controls on tree-felling. The Commission also publishes a series of technical booklets and other publications.

Under the Forestry Act 1967, the Commission set up three kinds of Committee organization to assist in carrying out its duties. Firstly, the Home Grown Timber Advisory Committee which is the central advisory body on all relevant aspects of forestry in Great Britain; its membership includes mandatory representation of owners of woodlands and timber merchants and its quarterly meetings are attended also by forestry commissioners and representatives of the Department of Industry, Department of Agriculture and Fisheries for Scotland, and the Department of the Environment. The Commission has to consult this Committee before making any regulations with regard to its powers to control the felling of trees.

Secondly, there is the group of national committees for England, Scotland and Wales, which advise the Commission on the exercise of its functions.

Thirdly, there are regional advisory committees with members representing woodland owners, timber merchants, and those concerned with the study and promotion of forestry; other members represent agricultural, local planning, and amenity interests. They advise the Commission on such things as the establishment and maintenance of forests, its powers to control tree-felling, and, in some cases, on the administration of grants.

As the Forestry Enterprise the Commission develops forests for the production of wood for industry and harvests and markets the timber, aiming to obtain the maximum return from its sales. It has a full programme for the extension and development of its forests, mainly in upland areas, but the area of land available for planting in any one year will always depend on government forestry policy. The area of land for tree planting in Great Britain is, compared with many other countries, fairly small but the Commission introduces more productive methods, fresh species of trees, and new fertilizers, wherever possible.

These two aspects of the Forestry Commission's work can be looked on as its business side. There remains the more social aspects of the Commission's work which are concerned with conservation, leisure, amenity and recreation, for which it has statutory powers. Forests are designed to blend with the landscape and care is taken to conserve wildlife habitats.

The ever-increasing demand for outdoor recreational facilities means that the Commission has been developing its forests to provide opportunities for informal recreation and quiet enjoyment, but at the same time it has to ensure that these are in harmony with the forest setting and do not conflict with conservation work.

One of the main needs of visitors — particularly those who come from nearby towns and cities for a day out — is simply somewhere to sit and have a picnic and perhaps take a short walk before returning home. The emphasis is therefore on the provision of day visitor facilities and, with very few exceptions, the Commission welcomes visitors on foot to all its forests. There are over 16000 km of forest roads constructed for timber harvesting and management which, at the same time, provide access to many delightful and remote areas. While a few of these roads may be used as forest drives, motor cars are not generally permitted to use forest roads, except where necessary for access to particular facilities such as car parks, and picnic and camping sites which are actually in the forest. To help visitors understand and appreciate the forests and surrounding countryside information about them is provided in visitor centres and along many forest trails.

In addition to the relatively modest demands of the day visitor, there is a growing need for overnight accommodation and the Commission has in recent years developed into a major operator of camping and caravan sites. It has stipulated, however, that all sites must be financially viable and that there must be a clear demand for a site in a particular area before proceeding with development. The provision is usually for tents and touring caravans, mainly because static caravans can present problems. However, one experiment which proved so popular that it is no longer an experiment, was the creation of self-catering holiday accommodation. This is sometimes provided in houses not required for the Commission's staff or, more usually, in purpose-built forest cabins.

There are forests in nearly every part of Great Britain and they therefore offer the widest possible choice for leisure pursuits. This ranges from the ever-popular fishing, sailing, canoeing, swimming, horse riding, pony trekking, cycling, and moutaineering, to the rather more unexpected pursuits, such as pot holing, skiing, orienteering, and archery. All activities have to be undertaken in such a way as to make them compatible with a forest environment, and the Commissiom works hard to achieve this. A limited number of car rallies are permitted, under strict control and by agreement with the Royal Automobile Club. The Commission usually enters into an agreement with the national representative body of any sport involved, and makes charges for most of the special activities.

In the water industry, many thousands of acres of reservoir gathering grounds, especially in National Parks, are leased to the Forestry Commission. Through the Commission, therefore, vast areas are opened up for public enjoyment without serious risk of harm or pollution to water supplies.

CENTRAL ELECTRICITY GENERATING BOARD

The Electricity Act 1947, which was also the Nationalizing Act, brought the electricity supply industry of England and Wales and Southern Scotland under public ownership, and the existing undertakings, which then numbered 560, were integrated into new statutory area electricity Boards. These Boards (there were 12 in England and Wales, and two in Southern Scotland) shared the responsibility for retail distribution of electricity to customers. Generation and mains transmission, together with central co-ordination and policy direction, were the responsibility of the British Electricity Authority.

In Scotland, the North of Scotland Hydro-Electric Board was formed in 1943 to develop the hydro-electric resources of northern Scotland, although the existing undertakings in that area maintained their responsibilities for distribution. Under the 1947 Act, the North of Scotland Board absorbed these undertakings and became responsible for all public generation, transmission, and distribution throughout northern Scotland. Electricity supply in southern Scotland was again reorganized in 1955 by the formation of a new statutory body — the South of Scotland Electricity Board — to handle generation, main transmission, and distribution. The Board absorbed the British Electricity Authority's power stations and transmission lines in southern Scotland and the distribution systems of the two former Scottish area electricity boards. In England and Wales the British Electricity Authority was renamed the Central Electricity Authority, but its responsibilities and those of the remaining 12 area electricity boards remained unchanged.

The next phase was initiated by the Electricity Act 1957, which reorganized the industry in England and Wales with effect from January 1958. The Central Electricity Authority was replaced by two new statutory bodies, the Electricity Council and the Central Electricity Generating Board (CEGB); in addition, the 12 area boards were given a larger measure of autonomy.

There are unlikely to be further opportunities for the large scale economic production of water power by the classical method of impounding water temporarily behind a dam and allowing it to flow through hydraulic turbines on its way down to the lower reaches of the original water course.

Where hydro-electric stations have been developed in the past, primarily in Scotland and Wales, they have of necessity been sited in mountainous areas which are also highly valued for their scenic beauty and amenity use. With good planning, however, the adverse impact on the environment of such schemes has been much less than is often feared at the outset. It is known, for instance, that large numbers of people actually enjoy visiting dams and the lakes associated with the works and in fact the Rheidol hydro-electric plant has earned a citation from the Wales Tourist Board. Pumped storage power stations can likewise be a popular tourist attraction.

The North of Scotland Hydro-Electric Board collaborates, as far as its powers and duties permit, in the carrying out of measures for the economic development and social improvement of their district. It also has a special obligation, shared with the South of Scotland Electricity Board, to preserve the beauty of the scenery and any object of architectural or historic interest, as well as avoiding, as far as possible, injury to fisheries and stocks of fish arising from its operations.

The CEGB is subject to usual planning regulations as are other industries in the matter of clearing up after their workings, but the recreational work of the Board is entirely voluntary and is considered by them to be part of their "public relations". The Board has in recent years therefore sponsored a variety of conservation schemes, connected with thermal power stations and with substations in association with many outside bodies, including education authorities, local naturalist societies, and ornithologists. These schemes exploit the environmental potential of its land and include nature trails, field study centres, and nature reserves.

INSTITUTE OF FISHERIES MANAGEMENT

The Institute came into being as a result of the efforts of a group of people who felt that a professional body was needed for those engaged in the management of fisheries. The Institute was inaugurated in May 1969. Its affairs are managed by a Council of about 30 members (the majority of whom come from the Water Authorities) and an Executive Committee. There is also a Training Committee and an Annual Study Course Committee.

The principle objects of the Institute are to promote and advance fisheries management in all or any of its branches, and to improve the technical and general knowledge of everyone engaged in fisheries management. This is achieved through a system of correspondence courses, residential field courses, and a series of examinations. For the examinations two Courses are provided: the Certificate Course which provides instruction up to the level expected of a head bailiff or river keeper; it covers such subjects as freshwater biology, fishing methods, fishery maintenance and improvement, fish propagation, water quality and pollution, and legal matters including law enforcement for bailiffs and keepers.

When students have passed the required examinations for the Certificate Course they may then enter for Part II, which is the Diploma Course. This course is divided into two years' work covering fishery law, freshwater biology, fisheries management, and administration, water space recreation and amenity, fish diseases, fish husbandry, and water quality.

More generally, the students can reinforce their correspondence course studies with the events organized by the Institute's regional branches. On a wider scale, the Institute joins with other interested bodies to organize conferences on subjects of mutual concern and interest.

The Institute publishes its own training manuals for students and also a quarterly journal, *Fisheries Management* .

COUNCIL FOR ENVIRONMENTAL CONSERVATION

The Council for Environmental Conservation (CoEnCo) was set up after the third "Countryside in 1970" Conference. The Conferences were concerned with the increasing demands on the countryside and with the pollution of the earth, air, and water, and were supported by numerous organizations who were associated with these problems. CoEnCo was founded to continue the liaison established between these bodies, and its aim is to provide a federal organization which can speak at national level to the government on matters of general principle. Its constituent member bodies include, *inter alia*, the Civic Trust, the National Trusts, the Councils for the Protection of Rural England and Wales, Society for the Protection of Ancient Buildings, Council for British Archaeology, Royal Society for the Protection of Birds, Anglers' Co-operative Association, and the Youth Hostels Association.

PROFESSIONAL INSTITUTIONS COUNCIL FOR CONSERVATION

The Council, known by the initials PICC, was established in 1972 as a forum for inter-professional co-operation on all aspects of conservation. The objectives are to develop an awareness within the professions and elsewhere of the need for a wider knowledge of conservation issues, and to bring environmental problems and their possible solutions to the attention of governments, local authorities, and other public and private organizations.

The governing body is the Council which includes in its membership representatives from most of the professional institutions concerned with the environment. The Council also has a corresponding membership drawn from a wide range of other environmental organizations.

ROYAL LIFE SAVING SOCIETY

The Society was founded in 1891 as the Life Saving Society, following growing concern about the increasing number of deaths caused by drowning which, in Britain at that period, numbered over 2000 each year. Towards the end of the last century, industrial growth and consequent greater prosperity had led to an increased interest in sport and leisure, but when accidents occurred on water few people knew how to help those who got into difficulties. It was this situation which led to the formation of the Society, and it soon attracted widespread attention.

The scope of the Society's work widened gradually. At the outbreak of the Second World War it was able to instruct Civil Defence workers and the National Fire Service in methods of resuscitation. During the War, too, important advances were made following American experience in the Pacific and in Japan which led to a renewed interest in mouth-to-mouth resuscitation; this is the method now most commonly in use.

Today the Society has over 50 U.K. branches and many more overseas; in the Commonwealth alone it has trained over 10 million lifesavers. The Society has teams of volunteers who both teach and practise life saving, and teams of RLSS lifeguards now patrol the most frequented beaches and inland bathing places during the summer with such success that deaths from accidental drowning in this country have been reduced to under 1000 a year, despite the fact that water recreation of all types has increased dramatically over the years.

In order to set and maintain high standards, the Society has a scheme of awards which are given for different levels of proficiency and to individuals ranging from school children to their teachers, and those in specialized groups such as lifeguards, sub-aqua divers, staff in charge of pools, canoeists and lifesavers in open waters. Each award scheme is distinct from the others, but progression between them is possible for those who want to work their way through a series of tests.

The Society provides training under several headings, including water rescue skills, teaching water safety, life saving teachers' guide, resuscitation and first aid. It also produces a special lifeguard manual, a quarterly journal, and smaller information leaflets.

ROYAL SOCIETY FOR THE PREVENTION OF ACCIDENTS

The Society came into being in 1916 following a meeting of about 200 people who got together to discuss traffic accident problems in London. They formed the London "Safety First" Council but widened its scope later to cover public service corporations and industry. A year later an Industrial "Safety First" Committee was formed and from this the British Industrial "Safety First" Association came into being.

In 1924 these and some other local accident-prevention organizations came together under the name National "Safety First" Association and in 1941 the Association was given its present title, which is more frequently referred to by the abbreviation "RoSPA".

From its early days RoSPA tried gradually to widen the scope of its work and influence and today it is a professional body concerned to prevent accidents not only on the road but in the home, on water, and at work. It is a registered charity with an income derived mainly from 20000 subscriptions. Other income is received in the form of Government grants for specific projects and further monies come from fees charged for RoSPA courses and the provision of specialist services, and from the sale of safety materials.

In the field of accident prevention on the roads, the Society operates safety schemes for all kinds of users including child cyclists and "professional" drivers.

RoSPA has a special Occupational Safety Division which may be joined both by individuals and by large organizations such as industrial and commercial under-takings, employers' organizations, trade unions, and educational establishments. The division gives advice to these members both generally and on specific problems, and can arrange for special programmes of accident prevention to be started. The policy of this division is decided by the National Occupational Health and Safety Committee, the members of which come from the Trades Union Congress, the Confederation of British Industry and all sectors of industry and the professions. A wide range of publicity material is published by the division, including an index of some 200 films which can be hired or purchased on occupational health and safety topics.

A Training Centre in Birmingham, with units in Cardiff and Stirling, runs courses for training officers, safety officers, and all levels of workers from apprentices to supervisors. Safety surveys can be carried out on a consultancy basis and an annual Occupational Safety and Health Conference is arranged. Awards are also made annually to those establishments which have achieved the most outstanding success in occupational safety.

A similar division exists for all branches of agriculture, including safety in horti-culture, particularly in parks and gardens and in sports-fields. Because of the holiday-making importance of some farms, particular attention is paid to the safety of children. Training and award schemes with an agricultural bias also exist.

The Society's Home and Leisure Safety Division gives a service which focuses on home accident prevention and works closely with local authorities and area health authorities.

The National Water Safety Committee has a wide membership drawn from water and local authorities, water sports organizations, life-saving, swimming, teaching and rescue organizations, as well as individual bodies such as the Sports Council and the Water Space Amenity Commission. The Committee and its Working Party submit annual programmes of work and discuss such subjects as research into life-saving equipment. Information is gathered on such items as waterside warning notices and the possibilities are considered for legislating specific power for local authorities to promote water safety which could in future become mandatory as opposed to being permissive. Each year a different theme is chosen for a national campaign against drowning accidents.

All these Sections of RoSPA can draw on a number of central services including statistical information, a library, a conference and exhibitions department and a film library.

ROYAL ASSOCIATION FOR DISABILITY AND REHABILITATION

The Royal Association for Disability and Rehabilitation (RADAR) is a voluntary association for all physically disabled people. It was formed in 1977 following the amalgamation of the Central Council for the Disabled and the British Council for Rehabilitation of the Disabled.

RADAR acts as a co-ordinating body and has nearly 400 member organizations. It is particularly active in the areas of access, education (the Preparatory Training Bureau arranges further education courses either by correspondence or personal tuition), holidays, housing, mobility (independent transport), and welfare. There is a also a Travelling Aids Exhibition. A comprehensive publications department exists to supply information and a list of books is provided. Two regular publications are issued — a monthly Bulletin and a quarterly magazine.

RADAR also acts as a pressure group on central and local government to improve the environment for disabled people and it has an active Legal and Parliamentary Committee which liaises closely with the All-Party Disablement Group.

4. REPRESENTATIVE BODIES

(a) Owners and Occupiers

COUNTRY LANDOWNERS' ASSOCIATION

The Country Landowners' Association (CLA) was founded in 1907 in order to protect and promote the interests of the private, individual landowner. Anyone may join the CLA who owns or manages some kind of rural land, whether it is agricultural, a golf course, safari park, market garden, hill farm, or a large landed estate. Membership therefore ranges between those who own quite small areas of land to those who are big landowners letting land to tenant-farmers or who may farm large acreages themselves. Nevertheless, the majority of members are owner-occupiers possessing less than 121 ha.

In addition to landowners, there is a special category of membership for such people as surveyors, bank managers, accountants, and solicitors and whose professional activities give them close connections with rural estates and agricultural land. Members in this category are entitled to use the specialist advisory services provided by the CLA for any client who is also a member of the Association. The present membership is about 49000 and this represents a high proportion of the agricultural and rural estate landowners of England and Wales.

While the CLA is free from party-political ties, its main aim is to make political representations on behalf of the country landowners. It's principal officers have access to Government Ministers and its head office keeps in close touch with government departments.

Representatives of the Association sit on many public bodies involving agricultural and countryside matters and also on the Economic Development Committee for Agriculture. CLA members are frequently interested in, and appointed to, national organizations such as the Countryside Commission, the Forestry Commission, and the Nature Conservancy Council.

The Association's nominees also serve with a number of statutory bodies including, for example, the National Water Council and the Regional Land Drainage Committees of the Regional Water Authorities.

This wide and varied representation means that the Association generates a strong influence throughout England and Wales and its members derive benefits from its strength and initiatives. It helps to maintain agricultural prosperity on the one hand and, on the other, cares for those owners in specially difficult areas such as the uplands or wetlands. It also puts forward to both local and national government possible solutions to the variety of problems and difficulties encountered by its members.

Some of these problems arise out of the constant demand for more land for public works of one kind or another, and the Association seeks to obtain for its members adequate compensation where damage or blighting of land occurs. It seeks protections and safeguards for landowners faced with the laying of pipelines, and cables, the erection of pylons and other wayleaves over or through their land.

Working parties are set from time to time to study certain areas of concern. One example — public access to private land — examined the pressures on rural land for sport and recreation, the nature and sources of that demand, and their implications for landowners. It discussed ways of meeting the demands and put forward recommendations. The Association also publishes information and advisory booklets. It comments on other organization's reports and papers. It issues a journal entitled *Country Landowner*.

The CLA holds an annual Game Fair, and also provides social facilities at many major summer agricultural shows all over the country. Other areas of the Association's service to members includes practical advice on day-to-day matters such as concessionary trading facilities, sickness, farm and motor insurance, as well as legal and technical matters.

COMMONS, OPEN SPACES AND FOOTPATHS PRESERVATION SOCIETY

This is the oldest national amenity body and was founded in 1865 under the title The Commons Preservation Society. The founders were concerned about the effects of the continuing enclosure of commons land, particularly in the London area, which had been increasing throughout the Industrial Revolution. The General Inclosure Act 1845 was passed in an attempt to control enclosure by stipulating that the consent of one-third of the commoners was necessary, and that where commons were situated within five miles of towns with a population of over 10000, the expediency of the proposed enclosure had to be proved, and allotments had to be made for recreation and for field gardens.

From the beginning, therefore, the Society had considerable legal and political fights on its hands and its earliest victory came a year after its foundation, with the passing of the Metropolitan Commons Act 1866, which made the enclosure of London Commons practically impossible.

In its early days the Society was mostly concerned with commons in and around London but over the years it gradually secured for the public such famous areas as Hampstead Heath, Wimbledon, Wandsworth and Berkhampstead Commons, and Epping Forest, in Essex.

Further afield the Society secured Ashdown Forest, Banstead Commons, the Malvern Hills and Epsom Downs. It was also instrumental in securing the New Forest and the Forest of Dean. In 1876 the passing of the Commons Act was achieved, under which adequate provision had to be made for the benefit of the neighbourhood in every case in which a common was to be enclosed. The Society helped to gain a public right by law of access to all commons in urban districts, thus enabling people to enjoy such commons as Helvellyn in the Lake District.

Towards the end of the last century the Society was involved in the work of other kindred organizations and it co-operated with Octavia Hill's Kyrle Society, which had as its aim the placing of objects of beauty within the reach of the poor.

Another organization which owes its existence to the Society and its principles is the National Trust for Places of Historic Interest or Natural Beauty. Because the Society was primarily engaged in legal battles it could neither be incorporated nor hold land and the National Trust came into being because it was felt that there was room for an organization which could steadily set itself to acquire places of special historic interest or natural beauty.

From about 1888 the Society began taking an interest in public footpaths. In 1899 it amalgamated with the National Footpaths Society, and the Society's name was changed to the Commons and Footpaths Preservation Society. In 1910 the words "Open Spaces" were added to the title.

Over the years the Society has been involved in the creation of many Acts of Parliament, including the Law of Property Act 1925; the Road Traffic Acts 1930 and 1960; and the Access Provisions of the National Parks Act 1949.

During the 1950s progress was made with Green Belt schemes, and the Society became a representative body on the Green Belt Council for London. The first complete County Definitive Maps of public rights of way were published during this decade and 1965, the year of the Society's centenary, brought the Commons Registration Act.

Today the Society's main task is that of advising local authorities, commons committees, and voluntary bodies about protecting commons and village greens and similar open spaces, trying, in all its work, to protect the rights of the public. The Society also assists both District and County Councils on the problems of management of areas of common land. It looks at applications for permission to enclose common land, entering objections where necessary and alerting local representatives to enter appropriate objections in their areas. Its work therefore is primarily in the legal field and in the dissemination of information. The Society also publishes a journal and information leaflets and booklets.

But the major and most urgent problem facing the Society today is to obtain legislation on the outstanding recommendations of the 1958 Royal Commission on Common Land, and to try to fill a very serious loophole in the Commons Registration Act 1965. At the time of the Act, thousands of commons were registered but recent legal history has shown that the rights of local people are not, in fact, secure if those rights were not specifically registered at the time the land itself was registered.

NATIONAL FARMERS' UNION

The first attempt to form a Union for farmers came in the 1890s at a time when British agriculture was seriously declining. This began during the Industrial Revolution as the increased export of manufactured goods from this country was paid for by imports of food from other countries. Other factors such as the greater production of foodstuffs by British Empire countries, and the opening-up and

Examples of facilities for the disabled which have been provided at reservoirs by the Welsh Water Authority. *Top*. A woodland trail for blind and visually impaired visitors. Features can include the use of special surfacing materials, timber handrails and earth bunds to guide and protect; braille leaflets and small cassette recorders. *Centre*. Special ramps and platforms enable those confined to wheelchairs to fish safely and independently at the waterside. *Right*. With adequate help and supervision it is possible for the handicapped to get afloat.

Educational opportunities for the young. *Above*. Llyn Brenig reservoir in North Wales. Childr
studying a Bronze Age Cairn with a Welsh Water Authority ranger. *Below*. A nature lesson for a gro
of young enthusiasts. There are many information and interpretation centres throughout the wat
industry and many of these are used to provide practical experience and instruction to suppleme
classroom learning.

development of the North American prairies for grain production, all had the effect of further depressing food production in Britain.

At first small local unions were set up in a number of counties and in 1908 they joined together to form the National Farmers' Union (NFU). Today, the NFU has a membership of some 135000 and represents 85 per cent of all full-time farmers in England and Wales. Its administrative structure includes a policy-forming Council. A total of 49 county branches cover the Union's work throughout England and Wales and within these branches there is a total of 870 local branches.

The basic role of the NFU is described as the provision of circumstances in which British farmers and growers are able to pursue their business effectively, on fair terms, and without undue pressure or interference. It has four main areas for policy:-

Agricultural Land. — To maintain and enhance the production of agricultural land and to minimize the loss of land of value to the farming community by reason of its physical quality, location, or special suitability for local agricultural needs, and to establish conditions in which land in agricultural use can be effectively farmed.

Rural Life. — To seek appropriate administration, housing, employment, and servicing to support viable and better-balanced rural communities, of which the farming community forms a part, and which are essential to an efficient agricultural industry.

The Environment. — To establish the situation in the countryside in which the basic natural resources and requirements of landscape and wildlife conservation are adequately protected, within the context of and essential and changing use of land and resources for agricultural purposes.

Recreation and Tourism. — To establish conditions in the countryside in which the legitimate recreational demands of the urban population can be met without the food-producing capabilities of the agricultural industry being impeded.

To reconcile these conflicting demands on a virtually fixed quantity of land is far from easy, and the impact on agricultural land of non-agricultural demands and activities is considerable. While the NFU recognizes the validity of the different claims, it seeks to minimize the loss of valuable agricultural land by urging that land of "restricted potential" for agriculture is brought into use for non-agricultural purposes. This applies particularly in the case of derelict urban land which, when revitalized and re-used, could improve the environment of inner cities and relieve pressure on the surrounding countryside.

The NFU keeps in close contact with organizations such as the Countryside Commission particularly about "designated areas", that is National Parks, areas of outstanding natural beauty, green and forest belts, etc., which now total about 6.5 million hectares of land in England and Wales. This means that about one-half of this country's agricultural land is "designated" in one way or another and an increase in visitors to these areas can add pressures on agriculutural land and destroy the qualities for which the designated areas are valued. At the same time the NFU tries to establish amongst farmers a wider appreciation of the contributions they can make to the conservation of the countryside and of wildlife and its habitats and to this end supports research projects in order to evolve national policies and give advice to farmers.

SAND AND GRAVEL ASSOCIATION

The Sand and Gravel Association (SAGA) was founded in 1930 to help sand and gravel producers in the U.K. to co-operate with Government and other bodies in formulating policies where these affected the industry and the public generally.

Membership of the Association now represents some 580 quarries and 30 marine landing wharves employing about 10000 people, which produce about 83 million tonnes of aggregate each year. The basic concern of the SAGA is the consideration at both regional and national levels of matters of importance to its members in the fields of technology, legislation, production efficiency, safety, and transport. However, over the last decade or so there has been a dramatic growth of interest in environmental questions and in the problems of restoring worked-out quarries.

Some of the larger quarry sites are internationally famous, but others are quite small. Raw new gravel pits soon become naturalized if the flora and fauna are allowed to establish themselves. Wild flowers take hold and quiet corners may even become home to rare species of plants and animals, but particularly for waterside birds and wildfowl. Opportunities for sailing, fishing, and other water sports are found at many gravel pits; during the past 20 years, for example, the number of sailing clubs at these sites has increased four-fold, with more schools and young people taking to this now popular sport.

For some years SAGA has administered a £1 million Restoration Guarantee Fund to which all Association members must subscribe. It is designed to meet the restoration obligations of its members in the event of bankruptcy or other unforeseen circumstances.

In 1970, European Conservation Year gave rise to the idea of a special award for restoration schemes — the SAGA "Restoration Award". It is presented annually and is highly coveted. The winning sites display a plaque and the firm or group involved receives a certificate. Since the scheme started, 214 awards have been made. In administering the scheme the Association collaborates with other bodies, since the judges for the award must come from outside the sand and gravel industry.

A second, more recent, scheme is the Tree Award. This is run in conjunction with the Tree Council and sprang from SAGA's plan to honour Her Majesty the Queen's Silver Jubilee by planting "Royal Oaks" at sand and gravel quarries all over Britain. More than 8500 trees were planted by member firms and their names were listed in a book which was presented to Her Majesty. Inspired by this success, SAGA decided to make an annual presentation, the owners of the winning entry receiving a £20 contribution to enable them to plant a commemorative tree.

A further aspect of the work of SAGA is in films and publications, including a journal and occasional series of papers of general interest.

Restoration of agricultural land to the highest standards is achieved through constant co-operation with the Ministry of Agriculture, Fisheries and Food. The emphasis today is on "borrowing" as opposed to "consuming" the land, and this approach is making collaboration with environmentalists, local residents, landowners, and planning authorities more fruitful than ever before.

(b) Environmental

BRITISH TRUST FOR CONSERVATION VOLUNTEERS

The Trust promotes practical conservation work throughout Great Britain, and it has its origins in the National Conservation Corps which was founded in 1959 by the Council for Nature. In 1970 the Corps was incorporated into the British Trust for Conservation Volunteers and this is now the largest organization of its type in the country. There are ten regional centres. The stated age limits for membership of the Trust are 16 to 70 years, but most volunteers tend to be between 17 and 25, and many are students who come from all parts of the world, particularly during the summer months.

Within the framework of the Trust are two Corps — one National and one Local. The National Corps organizes the longer, residential work schemes and tasks at a national level and provides the living accommodation for volunteers while they are engaged on schemes. These residential tasks are frequently undertaken on behalf of other organizations and provide the widest possible variety of experience for the volunteers. Assistance has been given to Nature Conservancy reserves, to a re-afforestation project on the Isle of Rhum — here, during a two-week Easter holiday scheme, ten volunteers planted no less than 20000 saplings. Repairs to upland footpaths are frequently undertaken; bird hides are constructed, and maintenance work is carried out on sites of archaeological, industrial archaeological, and geological importance. Work is also undertaken in wetland areas and on canals, and weirs are constructed and sluice gates repaired.

Tasks are also carried out for the National Trust, local authorities and, in certain cases, private landowners with large estates, particularly those which are open to the public. The Trust supplies the transport to the sites, and all necessary tools and equipment. At the last count over 24000 man-days had been worked by volunteers on residential programmes during one year.

Under the local Corps, groups usually undertake tasks within their own neighbourhood to help the community with amenity and conservation work. These tasks are short ones lasting for a day or weekend, some also involving youth or school groups. Man-days worked now number about 35000 a year and the jobs vary from rubbish clearance on common land, to restoration of ponds, footpath repair, tree plantings, hedging, pipe-laying for land drains, and maintenance of buildings of local and historic interest.

There is co-operation with such organizations as the Ramblers' Association which provides information on footpath clearance, and the Inland Waterways Association which advises on canal projects. Parish Councils and Social Service Councils often help with local projects.

Over the years, the Trust's bands of volunteers have developed into what has been called a unique resource of practical experience in the skills of countryside management. Some skills have nearly died out and the Trust renders invaluable service in keeping alive the traditional skills of dry-stone walling, hedging, and others, in all their regional variations.

Volunteers are trained to use different tools and materials, and other courses include tree nursery work, coppicing, fencing, ecology, and management of woodlands. There are also courses for training in leadership and — for fully fledged volunteer leaders — further courses and programme of training in the practical skills of countryside management. Each volunteer group works to a leader, and on every task undertaken the Trust aims at a professional standard of work.

Public awareness of the problems of conservation and the environment generally has been increasing steadily and the Trust provides a valuable service in enlisting the practical and active support of members of the public in conservation work. This is particularly important for the younger members of society who, the Trust hopes, will grow up with a sensitive awareness of their environment and the need for conservation.

COUNCIL FOR THE PROTECTION OF RURAL ENGLAND

The Council for the Protection of Rural England (CPRE) was started in 1926 by a group of eminent gentlemen who were concerned about the sporadic spread of urban ribbon developments, and the effect this would have on the English countryside. Once the idea of a protecting Council was mooted, interested bodies such as the National Trust, the Society for the Protection of Ancient Buildings, and even the RAC and AA were drawn in, and the Council was actually formed from these diverse constituent organizations.

Today the Council has over 200 affiliated bodies, 41 county branches, and a total membership of over 30000. It is now the country's largest independent environmental organization depending on voluntary subscriptions and donations. It is not subsidized by Government in any way, which enables it to retain the freedom necessary for effective criticism.

The major part of the work of the CPRE is to sift through Governmental proposals, debates, and legislation to find anything which may affect the countryside. The Council prepares submissions, reports, or comments for Whitehall and Westminster decision-makers in an attempt to ensure that changes are, wherever possible, for the best.

There is collaboration between the Council's headquarters and the county branches which act as local "watchdogs", keeping a vigilant eye on local developments and planning applications which may threaten the landscape and/or the buildings in their area.

Statistics which constantly worry the CPRE are the 250 km^2 of countryside which every year disappear under housing, factories, reservoirs, and roads — roughly the equivalent of losing a county the size of Berkshire every five years.

The impact on the countryside of major programmes of road construction is a particular concern to the CPRE, but so is the more general erosion of rural calm and quiet caused by a variety of factors. In their work of preserving what is of value and beauty in the English countryside, the CPRE also tries to keep an eye on properly planned caravan parks, on ancient churchyards, agricultural buildings of historical or architectural interest, mineral extraction workings and tree planting.

The Council publishes an annual report, "Countryside Campaigner"—a bulletin of news, views and comments, three times a year—and a number of other reports and leaflets.

NATIONAL TRUST

Despite its name, the National Trust, which was founded in 1895, is not a Government body but owes its existence to a small group of far-sighted and dedicated individuals who set about safeguarding places of natural beauty and historic interest for generations of people in this country. They were concerned about the destructive influence of the industrialization which had been increasing throughout Queen Victoria's reign.

The Trust was formed as a public company not trading for profit. From the beginning a pattern was set for a wide variety and diversity of places to be cared for in this way. In 1907 the Trust was incorporated through an Act of Parliament and received a mandate "to promote the permanent preservation for the benefit of the nation of land and buildings of beauty or historic interest". This Act gave the Trust the unique power to declare its property "inalienable" which thus ensured that none of its properties could be sold or given away without the "express will" of Parliament. This protected the interests of anyone who wanted to give land or property to the Trust.

Over the next 30 years the Trust acquired a number of ancient buildings, areas of countryside, and stretches of coastline. This was all made possible by the generosity and enthusiasm of the donors, by legacies, gifts of money, and by public appeals. But by the 1930s death duties and taxation began to threaten some of England's great country houses, which meant that their contents and surrounding estates were also in danger, and in 1934 attention was drawn to the plight of people trying to preserve their ancestral homes. A further Act of Parliament in 1937 enabled the Trust to hold country houses and their contents. Lord Lothian was the first to take advantage of this Act and bequeathed his own house, Blickling Hall in Norfolk, to the Trust along with its contents and land. Lord Lothian's ideas led to the Country House Scheme under which a country house might be given to the Trust, with or without its contents, but with an endowment fund sufficient for its maintenance "in perpetuity". In return, the donor and his or her descendents may continue to live there rent-free, subject to controls to permit public access and to preserve the original fabric and style of the building.

Some 30 years later another threat was making itself felt, this time to miles of unspoilt and beautiful coastline. Widespread concern led to the launching, in 1965, of Enterprise Neptune with an initial target of £2 million to acquire as much coastline as possible. This target was reached in 1973 and by then the Trust had purchased a total of 628 km of coastline. The scheme is continuing.

The National Trust is today the third largest land-owner in the country, coming second only to the State and the Crown. Among its most priceless assets are the open spaces it owns in such places as the Lake District, Snowdonia, and the Brecon Beacons. On these and other areas the public now have the right to "wander at will", a right which is secure for ever.

Because of the outstanding work done by the Trust, the general public still tends to associate it with great historic buildings and large tracts of countryside, but other aspects of its work concern archaeological sites, woodland, and gardens. In each of these categories are areas which have come into the Trust's possession in a secondary capacity, that is, they happen to lie on land primarily acquired for another purpose. This is frequently true of ancient sites and among the Trust's possessions are hundreds of barrows and over 50 hill-forts. Other antiquities protected by the Trust range from caves occupied during the Palaeolithic period to defended homesteads that awaited and survived the Roman conquest. Some sites of major importance are cared for by the Department of the Environment, while others are maintained out of Trust resources and with voluntary help. This side of the Trust's work is of immense value because it has been estimated that by the end of this century only those field monuments specifically protected will have survived the demands of modern development, including buildings, motorways, and car parks.

Many woodlands are settings for historic houses or gardens in the Trust's possession; others are in more open country, but to each the Trust applies its management policy in such a way as to retain the traditional landscape appearance of the area. Nature conservation is another aspect of the Trust's woodland management, and all this has to be geared to the need to allow public access and yet still preserve the element of tranquillity for which woodland areas are so highly prized. The possession of woods also means a responsibility for the maintenance of footpaths, rides, fences, and gates and the Trust is justly proud of the standards it achieves.

The Trust also owns many important gardens of almost every style, from the sixteenth century through to the present day and each garden has to be considered separately because each has its own history and individuality. Sometimes the Trust has accepted gardens in varying states of care and even dereliction and major and expensive schemes of restoration can be required in these cases.

The Trust policy is decided by the Council, which is its governing body. One-half of its 52 members are the appointments of such national institutions as the British Museum, National Gallery, Ramblers' Association, and the Royal Horticultural Society; the other half are members elected by Trust members themselves.

Today there are some 250 buildings and gardens in the Trust's care which are visited by about 6½ million people annually; an estimated 1 million enjoy the Trust's open spaces every fine summer weekend.

ROYAL SOCIETY FOR THE PROTECTION OF BIRDS

Under its original name of Fur and Feather Group, the Society was formed (in 1889) as a protest against the extensive trade in birds' feathers for the millinery industry, and to try to obtain legislation to curb the importation of plumes from such birds as egrets. The scope of its work soon widened however, and in 1891 the Group's name was changed to the Society for the Protection of Birds. It received its Royal Charter in 1904 by which time the Society had grown rapidly.

By the 1920s a number of problems were coming to light and oil pollution — not a new thing despite present-day publicity and preoccupation with the subject — had become a major problem affecting sea birds. In 1921 the Plumage Act was passed, for which the Society had campaigned since its formation. The need for sanctuaries was becoming widely recognized and the RSPB purchased an area of land at Dungeness, in Kent, for this purpose. As early as 1928 the Society was warning gardeners against the unwise use of toxic chemicals.

By the time of the Second World War the Society's membership had grown to nearly 5000 and although its work was curtailed somewhat during the war years, it managed to continue so that by 1946 its membership had reached 6000. At this time too the Junior Bird Records' Club was started, a Club that still exists under the new name of Young Ornithologists' Club.

During the next few years a number of developments took place. In 1947 it was found that avocets were breeding on marshlands at Minsmere, in Suffolk, and at Havergate and so both areas were made into RSPB reserves. In 1954 an office was established in Edinburgh. This was the first of the Society's regional offices to be opened and quite fortuitously coincided with the discovery that ospreys had been recolonizing in Scotland.

In later years other regional offices were established in Northern Ireland, Wales, and in many areas of England. In 1961 the Society's headquarters moved to Sandy, in Bedfordshire, and this enabled it to expand its work considerably. Today the Society has a membership of over 343000 with some 110000 Young Ornithologists, including over 2000 school groups. There are also Regional Committees for Scotland, Wales, and Northern Ireland and various specialist advisory groups.

The Society is responsible for managing 80 reserves, totalling some 36400 hectares and these are either owned, leased, or held "by agreement" by the Society. All sites are carefully selected and a prime requisite of selection is designation as a Site of Special Scientific Interest or grading at national status level in the Nature Conservancy Council's Nature Conservation Review. The Society prefers to purchase a site outright, but if this is not possible will try to obtain tenure by lease or other agreement. The Society's reserves include examples of all listed habitats in the U.K. It is possible to visit all RSPB sites so long as visiting does not have an adverse effect on the habitat or its wildlife.

Research now plays an important part in the work of the Society. Allied to this work is that of conservation planning and here the Society is constantly on the alert to ensure that legislation, building developments, and land-use practices are not detrimental to birds and their habitats. It also presents to government the case for conservation, as well as co-ordinating advice given to landowners on conservation management. The Society's species protection department investigates alleged offences against the Protection of Birds Acts and works closely with the RSPCA, the Police, and the Customs and Excise Service, dealing with a whole range of matters relating to the protection of rare birds.

In recent years the information and educational side of the Society's work has also grown and courses are held for teachers and YOC members. Projects are organized for schools and assistance is frequently given on educational broadcasts. In addition to its two magazines, *Birds* and the YOC *Bird Life* the Society produces posters, wall charts and books and its film unit works with contract staff to produce 16mm colour films for the RSPB film shows. "Educational versions" are made for schools and there is considerable television demand.

The Society also furthers its work in conjunction with similar societies and organizations both in the U.K. and other parts of the world. In this country the RSPB joined with other organizations to establish the Farming and Wildlife Advisory Group, for example, to help bring about dialogue and understanding between farmers and those interested in the countryside and conservation, and to try to reach solutions which will allow of both efficient modern farming methods and retention of certain features such as hedges, copses, small streams and ponds which provide valuable habitats for wildlife. The Countryside Commission has established a number of demonstration farms to show what can be done with proper planning. The RSPB also joins with other conservationists in objecting to various major land reclamation schemes for agricultural use.

The background and perhaps backbone of much of the Society's work are provided by RSPB Groups all over the country. They are interested bird watchers in the main who arrange outings, raise funds, keep a local eye open for anything which will adversely affect the birdlife of their area, and their local agents arrange film shows. They support the objects of the RSPB in the encouragement of better conservation and protection of wild birds, especially of rare and interesting species, and help in protecting wild birds and their nests and eggs.

ROYAL SOCIETY FOR NATURE CONSERVATION

This is the leading voluntary organization in Britain concerned with all aspects of nature conservation. Originally founded as the Society for the Promotion of Nature Reserves in 1912, by 1916 it had prepared the first list of areas of interest for nature conservation. Its work gradually broadened during the next 25 years and it acquired eight important nature reserves, although some large areas were acquired only gradually.

The Society laid the foundations for Government action in the field of conservation, including the creation of the Nature Conservancy, and it was instrumental in the formation of the International Union for Conservation of Nature (IUCN).

Since 1958 individual county Nature Conservation Trusts have been set up and the importance of the Society as the National Association of these Trusts, of which there are now 42, has been growing ever since. The Trusts in turn strengthen the Society's position and a Royal Charter in 1976 gave the Society wider nature conservation objectives, with specific powers to promote and help the Trusts. When the Charter was granted, the Society took the name Society for the Promotion of Nature

Conservation. The granting of the title Royal early in 1980 resulted in the Society's current title.

Because of the importance of the local Trusts, a major aspect of the Society's work lies in the field of advice and assistance to its member Trusts, the representation of their interests at national level, and encouraging liaison with other voluntary bodies or statutory organizations.

The Society is active in the selection and acquisition of nature reserves and their management, and provision of funds. The reserves provide protected habitats for plant, insect and/or animal species which are being endangered by present-day intensive agricultural methods, forestry, or by urbanization, all of which encroach on and reduce natural habitats yearly. Some reserves are "outdoor laboratories" which are used for research and education, and in all cases astute management is necessary to achieve a proper balance between the conditions for which the reserves are valued, and the enjoyment of visitors. Some types of habitat are rapidly disappearing and those of particular concern to the Society are the many different kinds of wetlands and old meadows. Heaths, downlands and semi-natural features such as copses, hedges, and ponds also claim the Society's attention.

Tourism and recreation now create pressures in some coastal and upland areas and the discovery of north sea oil is another example of modern technology threatening hitherto unspoilt and remote areas. Here local trusts play an important role in bringing attention to such sites and, through the Society, bring pressure to bear on appropriate authorities to safeguard nature conservation.

An important part of the Society's work is found in its publications. The Society also organizes seminars and conferences after which reports are usually published. The Society makes a point of issuing reports or statements on those of other related organizations or government action.

WILDFOWL TRUST

Sir Peter Scott established the Trust at Slimbridge, Gloucestershire, in 1946. It was then known as "The Severn Wildfowl Trust" and retained that name until 1955 when the "Severn" was discontinued in order to underline the significance of the work, particularly that of research, by then being undertaken. Slimbridge remains the headquarters of the Trust, but in the last 30 years six further wildfowl centres have been opened elsewhere in the U.K.

The Trust's main aim is to focus attention on the beauty and wonder of wildfowl and the places they inhabit — the wetlands. The methods pioneered and continued by the Trust at its various centres enable visitors to see at close quarters tame waterfowl from all over the world and, in their natural habitat, wild native species. The centres are now visited by some half a million people every year.

The Trust is well placed by virtue of its world-wide reputation and research programmes to advise on conservation of wildfowl and the best usage of wetland areas. Under its "Noah's Ark" procedure of building up reserve stocks of wildfowl species in captivity, the Trust has been able to repopulate areas where species are in danger of extinction. Of the world's 147 species of ducks, geese, and swans, the Trust possesses 127 species, numbering about 6000 individuals. It also has flocks of each of the world's six species of flamingo.

Ringing plays a vital part in research into breeding areas for wintering wildfowl and in mapping migratory routes. Equally important are bird counts and, since 1949, the Trust has co-ordinated hundreds of amateur bird-watchers in monthly wildfowl counts in Britain during the winter months. In 1967 mid-winter counts were started on an international basis. Information thus gathered enables a check to be kept on numbers so that population declines can be quickly spotted. The data obtained from these counts also helps in planning conservation programmes generally.

The educational work of the Trust is important and the centres are visited by some 200000 children each year. Programmes are provided for those taking "O" or "A" Level examinations in biology, and formal links have been established with education boards. "Post mortems" following bird deaths at the centres have helped build up a fine reference collection of skins, wings, skulls, windpipes, etc.

A great deal of the Trust's scientific work is applied to conservation or agricultural problems.

(c) Water-based Sports and Pastimes

ANGLERS' CO-OPERATIVE ASSOCIATION

The Anglers' Co-operative Association (ACA) was formed in 1948, and arose out of the concern felt for the increasing problem of the industrial pollution of fishing waters. It now has a membership of about 9000 individuals and over 900 clubs, some of which themselves have several thousand members. The Association is run by a Council, and there are a number of local branches which arrange meetings and fund-raising events.

The ACA is probably unique in that it exists solely to fight against the pollution of fishing waters. Under the centuries-old Common Law of this country any private citizen can take legal action against anyone who causes pollution. However, because of the high costs of litigation such action has hardly ever been taken. The formation of the ACA changed this situation dramatically. The Association is able to act on behalf of individual members, and to date has fought hundreds of cases, and it has lost only one. These actions have meant, too, that the Association has been able to recover considerable sums in damages which, in turn, has enabled fisheries to be cleared of pollution and to be re-stocked with healthy fish.

The Association offers help to its members in numerous ways: by advising on the detailed evidence required for a particular legal action. It will also provide a member or club with the legal and scientific advice necessary for preparing a case. The Association and its solicitors then fight the case on behalf of the member or club in the High Court and indemnifies the member or club against the large costs of losing a case.

The Association publishes leaflets about its work generally and, more specifically, the steps to be taken when a stretch or area of polluted fishing water is discovered. It also issues the ACA Review.

NATIONAL ANGLERS' COUNCIL

The National Anglers' Council (NAC) was formed in 1966 out of its four foundation member organizations: The Fishmongers Company, the National Federation of Anglers, the National Federation of Sea Anglers, and the Salmon and Trout Association. It is therefore recognized as the responsible body representing the three angling disciplines of coarse, game, and sea fishing. The NAC represents the whole of England and Wales, although the Welsh Anglers' Council has a degree of autonomy. There is no overall governing body for the sport in Scotland and Ireland but the different branches of it are controlled through various bodies.

The NAC is a non-profit-making body and it promotes and helps the sport of angling generally, and safeguards fisheries of all kinds. It works closely with the

Sports Council in such matters as grant-aid, coaching, and the development of angling facilities, particularly those for the disabled. The NAC also keeps a watch on current or potential legislation generally and will, where appropriate, express its views.

One of the most important aspects of the Council's work is its concern for the protection of fishing waters from pollution and for the stricter enforcement of anti-pollution legislation. To this end it seeks to put pressure on Government Departments. The Council is interested in research into both fishing and fisheries, especially where pollution upsets the balance of nature in rivers and streams.

The research of the Council into fish farming is also of importance and it dates back to 1968 when, with sponsored financial support, a team of scientists and anglers was sent to Holland and Germany to study fish-rearing techniques. As a result a U.K. National Coarse Fish Farm was set up which would concentrate on rearing roach. The NAC takes the view that intensive cultivation of roach and other coarse fish is essential if the fish requirements for stocking purposes and research work are to be met. They also consider that a single national coarse fish farm is no longer necessary and that a series of farms in different regions would help to eliminate the risk of massive fish losses through accident and disease.

During 1980 the National Angling Survey was carried out under the auspices of the Angling Research Working Party of the Water Space Amenity Commission. This Survey, financed partially by the NAC, was carried out by National Opinion Polls and updated the previous Survey of 1970. It did not cover such technical matters as fisheries research, but was concerned among other things with anglers and angling, in order to obtain as accurate a picture as possible of the sport and up-to-date information and statistics, and their possible future trends. As a result of the Survey the Council will consider and make proposals on an improvement of fish stock management, in inland waters, for recreation and will consider the economics of angling, and make recommendations.

Another aspect of the Council's work is its contact, at both national and international levels, with bodies having similar interests. In 1977 the Council introduced its National Angling Coaching Scheme in co-operation with the National Federation of Anglers, the National Federation of Sea Anglers, and the Salmon and Trout Association. The scheme assists experienced anglers to qualify as instructors in coarse, sea, or game assessments, in two grades for each discipline.

The educational side of the Council's work is also furthered by its publication of book lists, information leaflets and film lists on all aspects of angling as a sport, and also on such subjects as fish farms. The NAC also publishes the annual British Record Fish list of all species caught by rod and line.

NATIONAL FEDERATION OF ANGLERS

With nearly one-half million members, the National Federation of Anglers (NFA) is the largest and most important coarse angling "voice" in the country. It was founded in 1903 by a pioneering group who were angling officials concerned even then about the effect on and threat to coarse angling by land drainage schemes and water abstraction, and the problems of pollution.

The NFA has developed into a large organization covering England and Wales through its eight regional councils. In addition, there are five major Committees covering different aspects of the sport, which are regarded as "think tank" forums where information is gathered and sifted to form policies which will benefit coarse fishermen.

Apart from these internal arrangements, NFA officials hold key representative positions in most water authorities and close and constant contact is maintained with such related bodies as the Sports Council, the National Water Council, the Council for the Protection of Rural England, the Water Space Amenity Commission, and the Fisheries, Research and Development Board.

The NFA is concerned with protecting fisheries through the federation rules and it is a founder member of the National Anglers' Council, along with the National Federation of Sea Anglers, the Salmon and Trout Association and the Fishmongers Company, the Council acting as a co-ordinator between the different branches of angling. The NFA is also a member of Confederation International de la Peche Sportive (CIPS) which itself is the only world-wide coarse fishing organization. This membership means that the problems of the British coarse angler can be aired at an international level, and through CIPS membership the NFA enters a team in the world championships.

With the increasing number of problems facing the fisherman, the need for research in all fields is ever present and the NFA now sponsors a bi-annual coarse fish conference at Liverpool University where this need is presented to the various bodies with which the Federation works. The NFA also commissions research projects from time to time, and all aspects of its work are presented to the media and the public by its professional journalists and through its magazine *Coarse Angler*.

SALMON AND TROUT ASSOCIATION

The Association was founded in 1903 to look after the welfare and conservation of game fishing and fisheries, and the interests of game fishermen throughout the U.K. It is the only national body working in this field.

The Association has 70 Branches spread all over the U.K. and its individual membership of over 6000 represents some 190000 game fishermen. A General Council conducts the affairs of the Association and three specialist Standing Committees deal respectively with still waters, migratory fish, and conservation. The Association is a Founder Member of the National Anglers' Council.

The main work of the Association lies in safeguarding and improving the salmon and trout and salmonid stocks and fisheries. This includes the maintenance of adequate supplies of clear water for the fisheries, which is achieved by the sponsorship of research and development, and the study of new legislation in order to protest against, modify, or encourage it and generally to take appropriate action as occasion demands.

Representatives of the Association sit on most of the Regional or Local Fisheries Advisory Committees and Recreation Committees of the Regional Water Authorities, and the work of the Association is recognized by the Ministry of Agriculture, Fisheries and Food to which, for instance, the Association submitted comments on fish farming after political and administrative initiatives had been taken by others on this subject.

The activities of the Association's branches ensure the monitoring of local conditions all over the country so that harmful tendencies by way of discharges into or abstractions from local waters can speedily be opposed. The problem of water abstraction is a recurrent and ever-changing one. The branches also keep an eye on local pollution matters, uncontrolled expansion of fish-farms, which can spread disease, and keep track, by way of counts of sightings, of such pests as the mink which is increasing in numbers and which is an aggressive predator on game birds and fish.

At an international level the Association works closely with such conservation bodies as the International Atlantic Salmon Foundation, the Restoration of Atlantic Salmon in America, and the Atlantic Salmon Trust. Increasing use of monofilament fibres in nets, higher catches of salmon in high seas netting, and coastal and drift netting, combined with increasing poaching activities, are all threatening the survival of the Atlantic Salmon and migratory trout, and the Association adds its voice to urging the need for legislation to conserve salmon stocks.

The Association publishes a magazine *Salmon and Trout* and also a monthly newsletter for branches. It arranges conferences on a wide variety of related subjects and conducts fly fishing courses for "juniors" — 12 to 18 year olds. It also participates with the National Anglers' Council in the examination of candidates for the Salmon and Trout Association/National Anglers' Council Instructor's Certificate, and its staff of honorary consultants advises members on fishery problems.

INLAND WATERWAYS ASSOCIATION

The IWA, a registered charity, was founded in 1946 and is a national organization for all those who are involved in waterways — whether they are interested in boating, fishing or simply walking the towpaths. It has a membership of nearly 20000.

The IWA campaigns for the restoration, retention, and development of inland waterways in the British Isles and for their fullest commercial and recreational use. Most of this work is done voluntarily by members, assisted by a small permanent staff who also deal with the Association's internal affairs.

The Association has been involved in many legal battles, both in the courts and at Westminster. Of particular significance was its opposition to certain clauses in the Transport Act 1968, which classified nationalized waterways into "commercial waterways", "cruiseways", and "remainder waterways". The first two categories were to be maintained and kept in good order by the British Waterways Board (see p. 253). The remainder were given, as a result of IWA influence, a three-year guarantee that nothing prejudicial to restoration would be done to them. The Association is involved in trying to have some of these waterways upgraded to cruiseway status and thus to safeguard their future.

In 1969 the IWA established a National Waterways Restoration and Development Fund which raises, by voluntary contributions, money which is issued in the form of grants to those waterways using voluntary labour for their restoration.

The rapid growth of the voluntary labour movement in waterways is impressive. Spearheaded by the IWA's Waterways Recovery Group, volunteers all over the country are involved in clearing tons of mud and rubbish from derelict canals and repairing and restoring them to good condition.

The Association's Inland Shipping Group was formed to promote commercial carrying on the inland waterways. At present this traffic is confined to those waterways still capable of being navigated by large capacity craft. Nevertheless, about 50 million tons of goods are being carried annually and, following the introduction of barge-carrying ships and push-tugs which offer a direct link with the waterways of Europe and the rest of the world, it is hoped that this will increase. The Group has published three reports.

AMATEUR ROWING ASSOCIATION

The Association was formed in 1879 and the original intention was to draw on the resources of the leading Metropolitan rowing clubs to sponsor "composite" crews in order to meet foreign challenges in rowing competitions. By 1882, however, the membership had extended beyond the Metropolitan area and it was therefore decided to change the name of the body to The Amateur Rowing Association (ARA) to reflect this enlarged membership.

The ARA now consists of over 460 affiliated clubs and 210 regattas in England and Wales. About 230 clubs are associated with universities, colleges, hospitals, and schools. The control of the ARA is in the hands of the Council, and member clubs are organized into 26 territorial divisions which, with minor exceptions, fall within the boundaries of the Sports Council's regional structure. Most divisions are grouped to form regional councils and their function is to develop rowing, discuss matters of common interest, assess requirements, and to maintain contact with local authorities and recreational organizations generally.

Training centres for the National Squad are located at the National Water Sports Centre at Holme Pierrepont, near Nottingham, the ARA headquarters at Hammersmith, in London, and at the Leisure Sport Waterpark at Thorpe. Holme Pierrepont provides facilities for training over 2000m in six lanes — vital preparation for top-class competitions — and can also provide land training facilities. With the opening of the international rowing course at Holme Pierrepont, it became possible to stage the first National Rowing Championships of Great Britain in 1972, and the Championships have already had an impact on the shape of rowing competition in this country. These championships have now become the final aim of many of the country's crews. They also provide those crews with international aspirations a chance to prove themselves before events such as the World Championships or the Olympics, and both the Junior and Lightweight Championships. This is particularly important for women's crews and juniors (those under 18).

Since 1972 the number of people taking part in the National Championships has grown to well over 3000. The whole range of international events is included and, as with other lightweight events, the ARA introduced a lightweight double sculling event in 1977, which is likely to be adopted as an approved class. In 1976 an event for junior women scullers was added to the existing coxed fours, to provide further encouragement for junior women competitors.

In areas where there is no rowing club, especially on new areas of recreational water, the divisional representative and the rowing representative on the Regional Sports Council's "Water recreation committee" supervise the setting up of a steering committee which includes local rowing enthusiasts as well as influential non-rowing people willing to help administer a new club and take part in coaching. They also try to build up a body of local opinion to ensure that provision is made for rowing facilities to be included in development plans for the area.

Such steering committees also arrange publicity for the sport in general. They also try to obtain local authority grants towards premises and co-ordinate the purchase of second-hand equipment, so that an early start can be offered to those who want to participate in the sport.

The ARA has set up a Courses Committee for the purposes of identifying new stretches of water with the potential for use for rowing, and water sports generally. In 1981 it published a booklet on "Developing a rowing course", which is aimed at all those involved in developing and converting water sports.

BRITISH CANOE UNION

The Canoe Club was formed in 1866 by John MacGregor, and after Royal patronage became The Royal Canoe Club in 1873. The following year the club established both the Sailing Challenge Cup and the Paddling Challenge Cup. Events became international in 1886 when the New York Canoe Club, USA, put up the New York Canoe Club International Cup and this in fact is the oldest international cup for single-handed sailing craft in the world.

However, by the turn of the century interest in canoeing began to decline and by the First World War was hardly exercised at all as a sport. Then, in the 1920s interest picked up again, though mainly in Europe, and competition canoeing, particularly racing, gradually revived. The sport improved to such an extent that it was included in the 1936 Berlin Olympic Games.

In Britain, where facilities for outdoor recreation were at the time really quite sparse, the sport of canoeing had only a small number of enthusiasts. They nevertheless kept the sport going in both paddling and sailing, and one canoeist felt sufficiently inspired to enter a British Team for the 1936 Olympics. To achieve this a national governing body had to be formed and it was for this purpose that the British Canoe Union (BCU) was created in March 1936 and through which the first British Team entered the Olympics.

In 1938 the art of slalom arrived from the Continent but at the outbreak of the Second World War canoeing, along with many other things, came almost to a standstill. The sport was revived again after the War with the spirit of the London Olympics, and with great importance for canoeing, the 1948 Henley Regatta.

By 1962 interest in the sport was fairly widespread and a National Coach was created that year so that canoeing finally entered the world of education. Gradually a strong and effective coaching scheme developed and many clubs were started. Large youth organizations such as the Scout and Guide movements developed canoeing sections among their ranks.

As the sport has developed over the last 30 years, new competitions and sections of the sport have come on to the scene: in 1949 slalom became a world championship and wild water racing followed in 1959. Marathon, which was originally known as "long distance racing", was recently recognized as an international event by the International Canoe Federation.

Since the early 1960s a spirit of adventure has led touring canoeists to organize major expeditions round Cape Horn, to North East Greenland, down the Orinocco river in Venezuela, and the Dudh Koshi river in the Hymalayas.

Today the British Canoe Union has some 12000 individual members and over 500 clubs or affiliated groups throughout its regions. Individual canoeists often take BCU proficiency tests which are recognized throughout the world and help to keep up standards of safety and skill.

BRITISH SUB AQUA CLUB

The British Sub Aqua Club (BSAC) was established in 1953 and it is now the recognized governing body for underwater swimming sports in Great Britain. Membership numbers some 25000 and of the 900 branches which have been set up, 150 are overseas. Each branch has its own elected Committee and the branches nominate the members of the Club's National Council. There is, in addition, a special BSAC National Diving Committee which is responsible for all technical matters.

Underwater swimming as a sport grew in popularity in the years immediately after the Second World War. Developments in knowledge and techniques during the War and the invention of the aqua-lung made possible the peace-time use of equipment for the lay as well as the professional diver.

BSAC branches giving training in all aspects of underwater swimming, which is carefully graded to meet the needs of all participants from the complete novice to the more experienced diver. The training programmes begin in swimming pools with the use of mask, fins and snorkel, and trainees gain proficiency in their use before graduating to aqua-lung training which, at this stage, is also undertaken in a swimming pool. Concurrently with practical training, is a programme concerned with the theoretical side of underwater swimming. Novices progress to open water and carry out a number of what are called "qualifying dives" which lead to the BSAC snorkel diver, and the BSAC 3rd class diver qualifications. More advanced courses are available and trainees may proceed to higher qualifications. As the BSAC is a founder member of CMAS (World Underwater Federation), its qualification is also recognized in many countries abroad.

Theoretical studies continue with the higher qualifications and advanced courses are available for those wishing to specialize in a particular underwater activity.

At each stage of the training programme it is stressed that safe diving can only be undertaken as part of a team. The BSAC therefore provides, through its branch clubs, everything needed for the individual who wishes to enter an unusual and taxing sport. Health checks have to be made and people suffering from certain illnesses may not join.

BSAC has also granted official recognition to a number of diving schools who can offer courses of instruction enabling students to gain Club-recognized diving qualifications in a short period of time. Training standards are identical to those used by the British Sub-Aqua Club branches, and all instruction at a recognized diving school is given by BSAC qualified instructors. For those who want to learn to dive quickly, a recognized diving school course is strongly recommended. Students of such schools may then join local BSAC branches to continue their interest in the sport, and to gain higher diving qualifications.

BRITISH WATER SKI FEDERATION

The British Water Ski Federation (BWSF) is now one of the largest in the world and is recognized as the governing authority for the sport in this country. It has a membership of about 9500 individuals and 160 federated clubs. The body had its modest beginnings in 1949 and gradually developed until it became affiliated to the World Water Ski Federation which was formed in 1946 to co-ordinate skiing activities throughout the world and to draw up unified codes and rules for competition. Regional clubs were formed in Scotland in 1956, in Ireland in 1958, and in Wales in 1960.

The BWSF fosters efficient growth and enjoyment of water skiing for family and club groups, and competitive participants alike. It aims at harmonious associations with other water users, and maintains close links with such national organizations as the Central Council for Physical Recreation, the Royal Society for the Prevention of Accidents, and the Royal Yachting Association. It helps individual clubs to organize events by providing technical equipment and data, and also officials and judges. It also arranges coaching courses all over the country and can make available on hire a variety of films about water skiing.

Competitive water skiing now has several forms including tournament, racing, and barefoot. The Federation believes that by the proper grading of proficiency and chanelling of interest and enthusiasm in water skiing, both misbehaviour and accidents on the water can be reduced.

ROYAL YACHTING ASSOCIATION

The Association was founded in 1875 under the title the Yacht Racing Association, and, as the name implies, it aimed at promoting yacht racing and formulating some general rules for the sport. From the beginning the Association attracted the interest of members of the Royal Family and in 1880 the then Prince of Wales became President. The Association changed its name to the Royal Yachting Association (RYA) in 1953.

Today its membership has reached 65000 in some 1400 affiliated member clubs spread throughout 12 regions, which are based on national or regional councils for sport and recreation boundaries. The Association's Council caters for representatives from each region and the head office assistance to the regions covers most matters from the constitution and running of individual clubs and associated legal matters.

Since its formation the aims of the RYA have broadened considerably to keep up with modern developments and it now serves the needs of all pleasure craft users, which includes everyone who "goes afloat" whether under sail or power, on inland waters or on the sea. The Association tries to protect the rights of pleasure craft users and represents their interest in any negotiations with local and national government and with sporting bodies, both national and international. Nowadays, too, many more yachtsmen cruise under power on both coastal and inland waters and their interests and needs tend to be quite distinct from those of the racing fraternity.

More recently the Association has also become the governing body for U.K. sailboarding activities and has created courses of instruction for both beginners and for those more experienced persons who want to become instructors and trainers. The Association also supervises the setting up of schools and teaching establishments for this branch of the sport.

Since the early 1960s the Association has, in agreement with the government, been active in specifying and publishing graduated voluntary standards of competence which are applicable to all branches of pleasure-craft activities. It also promotes and encourages the development of training to required standards and runs a voluntary National Proficiency Scheme through its coaches and instructors. There are over 500 teaching establishments spread throughout the country.

The Association also maintains contact with many other national and regional organizations in order to develop facilities for the new diverse aspects of sailing whether for recreation, racing, or cruising. It also publishes a wide range of books and provides a day-to-day service to the general public on all aspects of their involvement in pleasure craft use.

The Association is affiliated to the International Yachting Racing Union and the Union Internationale Motonautique and is the national authority for yacht racing and power-boating. During the last decade there had been a steadily increasing growth in the number of people taking part in all forms of yachting, both under sail and power. So much so that it has now become one of the great national participant recreations and this in turn has led to an enormous demand for yachts and boats for inland and offshore.

CRUISING ASSOCIATION

Founded in 1908, the aim of the Cruising Association (CA) is to encourage cruising in yachts (power and sail) and to protect the interests of yachtsmen. Its services to members include a regular Bulletin which contains supplements on harbours, anchorages, and navigational notes, and a Year Book listing names and addresses of members and details of their boats.

The Association is represented in ports around the U.K. and all over the world. These representatives give assistance to members, advise on the services of local boatmen, and keep the Association informed of any changes to the information held on the ports for which they are responsible.

The headquarters of the Association is located at St. Katharine Dock, in London. The restoration of this historic dock and associated buildings was completed in 1974 and the Association, with its extensive library containing some 10000 nautical books, is housed in an old warehouse overlooking the river Thames.

Apart from the facilities offered at the Association's headquarters, there are 11 sections based around the country, each of which arranges its own programme of meetings, lectures, and social events.

The Association publishes a Handbook and a pilotage book covering the British Isles and the Continental Coast from the SW Baltic to Gibraltar.

BRITISH SPORTS ASSOCIATION FOR THE DISABLED

The late Sir Ludwig Guttman, of Stoke Mandeville Hospital, first put forward the idea for establishing a sports organization for people with all kinds of disabilities. The British Sports Association for the Disabled (BSAD) was founded in 1961 and in June of that year the first sports week was held. Gradually, more organizations joined the Association and in 1963 the first multi-disabled sports meeting took place, with some 100 competitors. The games continued to be held regularly, and in 1974 there were about 750 competitors.

In that year BSAD took over, on behalf of the International Sports Organization for the Disabled (ISOD), the first world multi-disabled games, when the blind and amputees joined the paraplegics in competitions at international level. In 1979 another world games was held, at which 300 competitors from 19 countries took part. In 1980 the Disabled Olympic Games was held in Arnhem.

The BSAD is recognized by the Sports Council as the co-ordinating body for sport for the disabled, and as such is grant-aided in its work.

The year 1981 has been designated the International Year of Disabled People, when it is hoped that significant progress will be made towards the process of the integration of disabled people within society.

The Water Sports Division of BSAD. Realizing the growing interest in, and the potential of, water sports for the disabled the Sports Council set up, in 1973, an advisory panel comprising representatives of the various organizations and individuals with expertise and experience. In 1981 the panel was merged with BSAD and become known as the Water Sports Division. Its aims are:—

to co-ordinate developments concerning participants in angling, sailing, canoeing, rowing, sub-aqua, water skiing, and power boating;

to provide training programmes for disabled people who wish to become proficient in water sports and to guide instructors in dealing with handicapped trainees;

to initiate research on technical aids and equipment for diabled people to enjoy water sports; and

to act as a clearing house for information and advice.

The Division has its own publication "Water Sports for the Disabled". The Division is also involved in research into the possibility of water sports being undertaken by the mentally handicapped.

(d) Land-based Recreation

BRITISH FIELD SPORTS SOCIETY

The British Field Sports Society (BFSS), which was set up in 1930, is concerned with the promotion of field sports (i.e. game and coarse fishing; shooting; fox, hare and stag hunting; falconry; and coursing) as an integral part of the activities of modern society. Interest and active participation in such sports are increasingly encouraged in universities, schools, and colleges by assistance in the formation of clubs and by lectures and talks, films, and literature. The Society is concerned to put the opposing view to those who seek the abolition of field sports.

The BFSS also makes a positive contribution to the well-being of the countryside. It supports the promotion of legislation which benefits wildlife, e.g. the Deer Act 1963, and seeks to ensure, through publications such as *"The Gun Code"*, a wider understanding of the place of field sports in country life and in the work of conservation. Where finances permit, the Society supports specific research projects.

Advisory committees guide the Society's policy in relation to each sport. They work in close co-operation with the Parliamentary Committee and the Public Affairs Committee.

In 1977 the BFSS was instrumental in setting up and was a founder member of the Federation of Field Sports Associations of the EEC (FACE), and the Society is represented on the U.K. Council, where potential legislation affecting sports is discussed.

BRITISH HORSE SOCIETY

The Society was founded in 1908 as the Institute of the Horse, changing its name to the British Horse Society in 1947. It is the national body for riders and is a registered charity concerned with matters of welfare, training, and competitions.

The Society works on behalf not only of its own members — which now number some 30000 — but also of all riders and horse owners, and aims at improvements in standards of care for horses and ponies and standards of riding; it encourages the wider use of horses and ponies and promotes the interests of horse and pony breeding.

The Pony Club was inaugurated in 1929 and is the junior branch of the Society. In 1977 the Riding Foundation was launched by the Society in order to create a fund which would be used to help the training of promising instructors at all levels, whether professionally qualified or amateur, and potential or established national representatives, both adult and junior.

The Society is run by a Council which co-ordinates the work of various Committees: there is a separate Committee each for England, Scotland, Wales, and Northern Ireland and for such subjects as horse trials, dressage, welfare, royal international horse show, horse and pony breeds, and so on. The four national Committees are supported by Regional and County/District Committees, the membership of which is entirely voluntary.

The Society's work is therefore wide-ranging and ensures the technical competence at professional levels which has made British horsemanship world-famous. The Society also looks after the interests of the amateur rider, and has a system of inspection of registered riding schools/stables to ensure that standards are kept at a high level. There are now well over 3000 licensed riding schools with two-million people riding at least once a week. The growth rate is estimated to be about 10 per cent per annum.

One important aspect of the Society's work today is that concerned with bridleways. The Society has a bridleways executive officer at its Kenilworth headquarters, plus county bridleway officers who, in turn, are responsible to the regional bridleways officers. Bridleways are described as paths over which the public has a right of way on horseback, or leading a horse, or on foot or on a bicycle.

The Society is concerned that every year farmers and other landowners withdraw permission for riding over their land because of requirements for present-day intensive farming methods, or increasing urbanization, and there is thus a greater need to keep open existing bridleways and to seek out new ones. Efforts are made to keep informed of county structure plans and to negotiate for the retention of bridleways or replacements where such retention is not possible.

The Society's Land Policy Subcommittee has recently established through a Divisional Court hearing of a case in connection with planning regulations that the grazing of horses falls within the legislative definition of agriculture and is not, therefore, subject to planning consent. This is of assistance to many owners of one or two horses kept on small grazing areas. The Society provides guidance on the care of such horses and of their grazing areas.

BRITISH MOUNTAINEERING COUNCIL

The British Mountaineering Council (BMC) was constituted to foster and promote the interests of British mountaineers and mountaineering, in all its aspects, in the U.K. and overseas. Jointly with the Mountaineering Council of Scotland (MC of S) it is the representative body of British mountaineers and is recognized by the Sports Councils. The BMC has a membership of clubs, associations, trade organizations, and individuals. It is represented regionally by a number of committees, formed from the regions clubs, who are responsible for BMC matters within that region.

The BMC offers the following services: assistance when necessary to all types of members; working to improve facilities such as guidebooks and reciprocal rights in mountaineering huts; ensuring adequate training for novice mountaineers and helping to improve their skills; negotiating access rights for mountain areas, outcrops and seacliffs; protecting the mountain and upland areas from developments threatening their amenity; and helping expeditions overseas, in co-operation with the Mount Everest Foundation.

The BMC and the other bodies responsible for the various aspects of mountain training in Britain between them offer a mountain walking leader training scheme, a mountain instructor certificate, and a guide certificate.

The Council's Technical Committee organizes the testing, in the interests of safety, of a wide range of mountaineering equipment. The Council produces a wide range of publications.

CAMPING CLUB OF GREAT BRITAIN AND IRELAND

The Club started in 1901 and was originally known as the Association of Cycle Campers. It has the distinction of being the oldest camping club in the world. The name was changed in 1920 to The Camping Club of Great Britain and Ireland and it now has a membership of nearly 200000.

The Club set up its first camping site in 1906 since when it has gradually acquired more sites. At present there are over 70 which are either owned or are managed by the Club. The sites are in a variety of settings, ranging from the remoter countryside, forests and National Parks, to popular seaside resorts and areas close to large cities.

The Club has kept up to date with the developments in modern transportation and now has different "groups" or "sections" to cater for those with specific interests, such as the canoe camping club, the folk dance and song group and the photographic group.

The Club has a full-time headquarters staff in London. A variety of committees and working parties, both national and local, carry out the day-to-day work and planning, and all are responsible to the National Council. There are in addition District Associations known as DAs, which are local organizations of club members covering either a whole or a part of a county. They arrange local weekend "meets" and are able to negotiate special short-term sites on farms, parks, grounds of stately homes, which would not normally be available. Many thousands of members take part in conservation working parties to clear paths, ditches, ponds, weed-out scrub from forest tracts, etc., and some regions now have their own conservation officers.

The Regional Councils have developed into bodies of local camping opinion and have their own representatives on local Sports Councils and similar bodies.

The Club also has a Camping Club Youth section, membership of which is open to young people aged between 12 and 17 years.

The Club offers a number of services, such as insurance cover, foreign touring guides, and technical advice. The Club's magazine "Camping and Caravan" is published monthly, and the "Handbook and Sites List" is issued biennially.

NATIONAL CAVING ASSOCIATION

At first sight caving may not appear to be a form of water recreation, but water plays a large part in the sport. Caving can be dangerous, and it should not be undertaken lightly. In times of flood it can be particularly dangerous, and cavers must be properly equipped to deal with water. Warm clothing and a wet suit should be worn, together with protective headgear; lighting equipment will also be required.

Caving is carried on by special clubs, who often maintain headquarters and run training schemes for novices. Such clubs are to be found in all the main caving areas, and they are usually affiliated to the National Caving Association.

A more dangerous and highly skilled mode of cave exploration is by diving, and this activity is organized by the Cave Diving Group. Cave rescue operations are carried out by experienced cavers organized through the regional Cave Rescue Organizations.

Courses of training in caving are run at Whernside Manor, Dent, North Yorkshire. The scientific aspects of caving are dealt with by the British Cave Research Association, which is concerned with cave exploration, caving equipment, cave hydrology, karstic morphology, biospeleology, etc. There is also an International Union of Speleology, which organizes international conferences every four years.

RAMBLERS' ASSOCIATION

The Association was created in 1935 from the earlier ramblers' "federations" which sprang from the cramped conditions of life in large industrial cities in the earlier part of this century. Membership grew steadily to its present 31500. Some 430 individual clubs and societies are affiliated to the Association and at a national level whole organizations are affiliated such as the Youth Hostels Association of England and Wales, the Holiday Fellowship, the Camping Club of Great Britain and Ireland, and the Anglo-European Tourist Club of the Naturfreunde International.

The aims of the Association are to encourage rambling, to foster a greater knowledge, love, and care of the countryside, and to work for the preservation of natural beauty, the protection of footpaths and the provision of access to open country.

The Association keeps a watchful eye on all legislation and events which are likely to affect the interests of its members. It plays a leading role in fighting to preserve such areas as Exmoor from the plough and resists such proposals as new potash mines on the York Moors and further incursions by limestone quarries in the Peak District and the Yorkshire Dales. It also campaigns against certain motorway proposals, against further water abstraction from some Lake District reservoirs, and against poorly sited or indiscriminate afforestation by mass conifer planting.

Wherever possible the Association seeks to support or amend legislation and was, for example, greatly involved in the Countryside Act 1968. It submits evidence to official committees and to Royal Commissions, and it briefs members of Parliament and Peers for Parliamentary debates. It has had considerable success in opposing clauses in Private Bills that would have meant closure of local bridleways and footpaths and it contributes to legal fees at public inquiries.

At a local level, the Association's volunteers devote time and energy to keeping footpaths defined and open. They also organize many work parties to repair stiles, maintain bridleways, clear overgrown paths and way marking. When the county Definitive Footpath Maps were being prepared, Association members helped with basic survey work and spent considerable sums of money in claiming more than 5000 paths which would have been lost. This type of work continues with the periodic revision of the maps. In addition to their own weekend country rambles, some members act as voluntary wardens in national parks both to help visitors and to protect the countryside.

The Association operates from its London office and has a National Council and an Executive Committee. It covers the whole of Great Britain through its 32 voluntary area organizations within which are some 160 local Groups, usually centred on particular districts or towns. It publishes an illustrated Journal *"Rucksack"* and occasional booklets on certain areas of concern.

The Association actively promotes national and local interest in the restoration and improvement of towing paths and waterside footpaths as well as the provision of access for walkers and riders at many of our new reservoirs.

WILDFOWLERS ASSOCIATION OF GREAT BRITAIN AND IRELAND*

The Wildfowlers Association of Great Britain and Ireland for Shooting and Conservation (WAGBI) was founded in 1908 and incorporated the Game Keepers Association of the United Kingdom which had been formed eight years earlier.

WAGBI recognizes that shooting needs to be carried out in accordance with wildlife management needs. Of particular importance is the impact of the sportsman's harvest on the wild bird populations, as well as the protection of the birds' habitats. WAGBI also believes that the sportsman, having an involvement in

*The name of the Association was changed, in June 1981, to The British Associaton for Shooting and Conservation.

the countryside, should continue to concern himself with environmental conservation in its broadest sense.

WAGBI's *Conservation and Research Division* forms this link between shooting and conservation. It promotes the sportsman's responsibility for the conservation of wildlife and in providing an objective management basis for sporting shooting helps to safeguard a valuable country pursuit in its traditional forms.

The work of the Conservation and Research Division comprises a number of separate work programmes. These are actively promoted by divisional staff aided by conservation and research advisory committees which pool knowledge from a range of professional sources.

The National and International Programme aims to promote a better understanding between the protectionist and sporting interest in wild bird populations. This is based on scientifically collected data yet takes into consideration different cultural viewpoints. The programme is concerned with both national and international policies and legislation relating to the conservation and management of wildlife and its habitat. Of particular importance is the need to manage migratory waterfowl on an international basis.

Through this programme WAGBI works closely with national governmental and non-governmental bodies such as the Nature Conservancy Council, Department of the Environment, the Royal Society for the Protection of Birds, and the Wildfowl Trust. Internationally, WAGBI works with such bodies as the European Commission, Council of Europe, International Council for Game and Wildlife Conservation, Federation of Hunting Association of the EEC, International Waterfowl Research Bureau, and the International Council for Bird Protection.

The Conservation Projects Programme is responsible for protecting and managing such wildlife habitat as falls under the influence and control of the WAGBI membership. This involves the survey and assessment of sites throughout Britain for their nature conservation value, followed by the drawing up of management plans and, where appropriate, the establishment of reserves.

This work, which is grant-aided by the Nature Conservancy Council, involves close co-operation and liaison with the many national, regional, and local conservation organizations, such as the Nature Conservancy Council, the Society for the Promotion of Nature Conservation, the County Naturalists' Trust, together with industry and local planning authorities.

The Conservation Planning Programme seeks to achieve the integration of sporting activities with wildlife interests in areas of recognized nature conservation importance. The work involves assessment of the conservation needs and the identification of measures required on the part of the shooting community. This procedure is undertaken jointly with the appropriate conservation organizations and interests. Action is then taken to ensure that regulated shooting is established or continues through responsible shooting associations acquiring leases and conducting their activities through agreed management plans.

The Research Programme is concerned with evaluating objectively all aspects of sporting shooting and in particular the direct and indirect impact on wildlife and the environment. The programme establishes a sound scientific base for future management policies. The National Shooting Survey provides information on the numbers and distribution of the wild quarry birds shot each year. The development of habitat management techniques and study of their benefits is undertaken on selected sites. Other studies on issues affecting both sporting and conservation interests include research on the national significance of ingested lead shot poisoning carried out jointly by WAGBI, the Royal Society for the Protection of Birds, and the Wildfowl Trust.

With respect to *Scotland and Northern Ireland*, Conservation Working Groups examine and advise on issues of particular relevance to these regions.

(e) Youth Organizations

SCOUT ASSOCIATION

The Scouting movement began modestly enough, in 1907, when Baden-Powell organized an experimental camp for about 20 boys on Brownsea Island, at Poole Harbour in Dorset. The experiment proved successful and the following year he published his "Scouting for Boys" which was an immediate best seller. All over Britain — and, in time, all over the world — boys formed themselves into Scout Troops with adult leaders, to set about the training methods outlined in the book.

In a world where few of what we would now call "facilities" existed for young people, Baden-Powell's simple and direct ideas proved magnetic, in that they appealed to boys' normal desires for fun and adventure and provided them with attractive and interesting activity programmes, giving youthful energy a natural outlet and harnessing it to good purposes. It provided opportunities for developing in young people the qualities that make good citizens — honour, self-discipline, dependability, respect for others and self-reliance.

Whatever age group they belong to, the basis of the Scout method is the Patrol System whereby boys in a Troop divide into small Patrol units of 6 to 8 members from which a Patrol Leader is chosen. There are three Training Sections: Cub Scouts (8-11), Scouts (11-16), and Venture Scouts, which has girl members (16-20).

To the basic activities of the early days of Scouting, of camping, hiking, swimming, pioneering, and nature studies, more ambitious pursuits have gradually been added as, over the years, experience in providing courses and building up funds and equipment have developed. The Scout of today can choose from a range of activities which can include canoeing, sailing, gliding, parascending, caving, mountaineering, and skiing. Water sports constitute an important element in Scouting activities and the Association has its own National Scout Boating Centre at Longridge, at Marlow in Buckinghamshire. Here a variety of craft is provided to cater for each age group and level of ability and experience. Both professional staff and qualified, experienced volunteers are on duty and the Centre has facilities for day and evening visitors. Further "advanced waters" courses are provided at other sites and many courses are geared to RYA and BCU assessments. The Association also has a strong Sea Scout section of about 9000 members, although it is not necessary to have been a Scout before becoming a Sea Scout.

Apart from outdoor activities, Scouts can learn a variety of other skills which can today include car mechanics, amateur radio, model making, or they can make music and take part in stage shows. Life-saving and first-aid are also high on the list and Scouts are renowned for their community work of all kinds.

Within their own ranks, Scouts have members who are handicapped, either mentally or physically, but they are always treated as any other members of their particular group even if their disabilities may well determine the extent to which they can join in some activities. In the mid-1960s the Scout Extension Branch replaced the Handicapped Scout Branch. Advisers support individual leaders and they keep in close touch with medical thought and practice concerned with training handicapped children.

All Scout activities are graded so that from his earliest years a Scout can build up skill and confidence as he passes increasingly difficult tests. The highest award at Scout level is the Chief Scout's Award; and at Venture Scout level, the Queen's Scout Award, the requirements for which must be met before the Scout's 20th birthday.

GIRL GUIDES ASSOCIATION

The Girl Guides Association (GGA) was established in 1910 and members have always taken part in water activities. From the beginning of the movement, swimming and life-saving skills have been taught and encouraged while today many girls take part in rowing, canoeing, and sailing, and some make use of power boats.

Water activities form part of the GGA programme for the girls and in the training of adult leaders and this aspect of the movement's activities has been emphasized here. A number of "county" groups have their own boating centres which are used both for recreation and training.

The Association exercises strict control over all water activities and qualified life savers are always on duty. Members are encouraged to acquire the national qualifications for personal ability from the British Canoe Union and the Royal Yachting Association but they are required in addition to hold the Association's qualification of competency to be in charge of young people.

Training throughout the Girl Guide Association is aimed at and designed for the protection and preservation of the countryside and its amenities and some of the Association's older members participate in conservation projects run by the Inland Waterways Association.

The Association has tests for various boating badges and qualifications which are designed to help members to take part safely in water activities so that they can pass on these skills to others when experience has been gained. The adult qualifications are graded for different types of water, and there has been a great increase in recent years in the numbers taking part in boating activities. Both the BCU and the RYA have a system of graded tests and together with the National School Sailing Association have done much to improve standards.

SEA CADET CORPS

A Corps was in existence as early as 1856 but it was not until 1899 that it was initiated as an organization by the Navy League and the first Navy League Naval Boys' Brigade was formed. The number of Brigades gradually increased over the next 20 years and the League then applied to the Admiralty for official recognition. This was granted but with the proviso that all units had to be inspected annually and be certified as efficient by an officer on the staff of the Admiral Commanding Reserves. The name, Navy League Sea Cadet Corps was then formally adopted, and this was retained until 1942 when the Admiralty gave further recognition to the value of the movement by placing it under the direct control of the Admiral Commanding Reserves and it became known as the Sea Cadet Corps. The Corps later came under the control of the Commander-in-Chief, Naval Home Command. The actual administration remained with the Navy League which itself was renamed the Sea Cadet Association in 1976.

There are now about 400 units — the basic formation of the Corps — with 20000 officers, instructors and cadets in uniform, who are backed by several thousand civilian helpers.

The Corps is a voluntary organization for boys and girls between the ages of 12 and 18. In general, the Corps aims to develop in them qualities of self-discipline and leadership and the desire to be of service to the community. More specifically, the aim is to stimulate an interest in the use and importance of the sea to the nation and to help and encourage those who wish to join one or other of the Sea Services. To achieve these aims the Corps bases its efforts on the high standards of the Royal Navy and Royal Marines, but the Sea Cadet Corps is not a pre-Service organization and there is no compulsion to join the Services.

Much of the cadet's time is spent on the more formal aspects of training. These cover general seamanship, parade training, boatwork, ropework, communications, and a variety of other subjects. The emphasis is on practical rather than classroom instruction. The most important aspect is advancement, particularly towards the higher ratings, when the cadet begins to learn something about responsibility and taking charge. Equally important, however, is activity afloat to impress the association with the sea and the sea services. Though limited by the number available, sea-going billets in HM ships and merchant ships give opportunities to experience life afloat and most units are affiliated to a naval ship or submarine.

Because of the need for sea-going experience, the Corps decided some years ago to build an off-shore sail training vessel. The resulting 80-ton brig Royalist has since proved valuable to hundreds of Cadets, including girls of the Girls' Nautical Training Contingents of the Corps.

In addition to sea-orientated activities, the Corps has such activities as rifle shooting, swimming, camping expeditions and participation in the Duke of Edinburgh's Award Scheme. Cadets may qualify in a number of specialist subjects such as mechanical engineering, seamanship, and cookery. Importance is also attached to moral and spiritual welfare and Chaplains are appointed to give instruction, guidance and to take Prayers on formal occasions.

There are Sea Cadet Corps throughout the country. All units are eligible for registration under the Charities Act 1960. The Corps is also recognized by the Department of Education and Science, the Scottish Education Department, and the Ministry of Education for Northern Ireland as a Voluntary Youth Organization which qualifies units for grant aid from these sources and local education authorities. Additional funds are raised by the units themselves, usually backed by a Parents and Supporters Association.

NATIONAL ASSOCIATION OF YOUTH CLUBS

The Association has its origins in the many clubs which were started in the second half of the last century to meet some of the social needs, particularly among young people, which were brought about by rapid industrialization. In 1861 an organization was formed to care for the "physical and intellectual" needs of girls and in Bristol a club was opened to provide advantages, pleasures and safeguards for young women away from home influence. In Lancashire in 1862 during the cotton famine classes were started for out-of-work girls and in 1880 the Girls' Club Union was founded. In 1911 a National Organization of Girls' Clubs was started to develop the work of the existing girls' clubs. Its first Leaders' Conference was held during the First World War and by 1919 some 203 Clubs and 20 Unions of Clubs were affiliated. The pattern of affiliation to a national body through local organizations was adopted, the first National Members' Conference being held in 1921. The organization changed its name to the National Council of Girls' Clubs in 1926 and a Physical Training Department was set up.

The organization started to attract grants from Trusts and just before the Second World War a circular was issued by the Board of Education and the Service of Youth policy was adopted. The Government encouraged Local Education Authorities to set up Youth Committees and thus created a partnership between voluntary organizations and statutory authorities.

The work continued during the Second World War and recreation centres were provided for transferred "war workers" and, in co-operation with the Ministry of Labour, several Rest Break Houses were set up. In 1944 the Council was renamed the National Association of Girls' Club and Mixed Clubs so that affiliation could be extended to include mixed clubs. This brought the membership up to 1900 clubs and 132000 individuals. The Constitution was then amended several years later to allow for affiliation from overseas. In 1961 the Association changed its name to the present one of the National Association of Youth Clubs (NAYC).

The NAYC is the largest non-uniform voluntary youth organization in the U.K. and it now has a membership of about three-quarters of a million young people who belong to some 6000 affiliated clubs. It is an independent voluntary organization and is registered with the Charity Commission. About two-thirds of its finance comes from voluntary sources but Government recognition brings some money in from official sources, and working relationships have been formed with the Department of Education and Science, Home Office Voluntary Services Unit, the Department of Education, the Department of Health and Social Security, Manpower Services Commission, and the National Youth Bureau. Through membership of the National Council NAYC works closely with other voluntary youth organizations and it has established links with Europe through membership of the organization it helped to bring into being, the European Confederation of Youth Clubs.

The NAYC provides a wide range of services to members which range from training courses and publications, to competitive events — both sporting and recreational. It also provides back-up and encouragement material for its 46 local Associations which cover county and metropolitan areas in England and Wales. Its sports events are organized both at these local levels and at national level. The current sports programme relies heavily on sponsorship and about 70 per cent of the sports budget comes from this source. The Association also organizes "take part in sport" events, mainly at local or regional level, when introductory sessions and coaching enable young people to try their hands at a variety of sports. The Association also takes an active part in developing many forms of water-based activities through its regional organizations and down to individual youth clubs.

Because of its widespread operations through its nine Regional Councils and its co-operation with different agencies throughout the country, NAYC has become recognized as a major pioneering body in new, experimental work with young people. Community Industry is their scheme to employ "unemployable" young people, i.e. those who have left school early without obtaining any qualifications, and Campaign for Rural Youth is an investigatory and action group concerned with rural deprivation. There is also a scheme for literacy where young people help others in their age group to raise their standard of literacy, and a preventive education programme on Homelessness.

It is, however, in the field of recreation and sport and its Sports Festivals that the NAYC is most widely known.

YOUTH HOSTELS ASSOCIATION OF ENGLAND AND WALES

The Youth Hostels movement originated in Germany in the early years of this century and by 1928 it had become firmly established both there and in neighbouring countries. Visitors from England joined the various associations, used the hostels and tried to start a similar movement over here. The British Youth Council was one of the most active organizations. The work came to fruition in 1930 when the National Council of Social Service, at the request of the British Youth Council and the other organizations, arranged a Conference to investigate the possibilities of providing inexpensive hostel accommodation in this country for young people spending walking weekends and holidays. The Youth Hostels Association of Great Britain was formed, but this title was subsequently changed to the Youth Hostels Association of England and Wales (YHA) on the creation of separate Associations for Scotland and Ireland.

During the 1930s the number of hostels rose steadily until, in 1939 at the outbreak of the Second World War, there were 300 and the Association had a membership of 83000. After an international conference in 1932 the International Youth Hostels Federation was formed out of which grew reciprocal arrangements between member-Associations. Voluntary working parties were also started during this period.

Today the YHA has a membership of a quarter of a million and owns over 250 hostels. Apart from wardens and certain officials, the movement is voluntary and is run by the members.

The Association started as an organization for walkers, but it is open to cyclists and all who travel under "their own steam". Minimum age for members is five years, with some rules about accompanying adults for the very young, but there is no upper age restriction on members. The emphasis has always been on individual effort but since the early 1950s adventure holidays have been organized as a means of introducing new members to the movement, or giving present members an opportunity to enjoy the countryside in new ways. Expert tuition and usually basic equipment is provided for sports activities such as sailing, canoeing, and underwater swimming. Pony-trekking and cycling tours are also popular and are sometimes aimed at particular age groups among the younger members.

Built into the whole Youth Hostelling movement of course is a love of and care for the countryside and along with kindred organizations the YHA campaigned for many years for the creation of National Parks. This campaign was intensified after the Second World War and culminated in the National Parks and Access to the Countryside Act 1949. Ten National Parks now exist but the YHA continues to keep a vigilant watch because of undesirable developments within some National Parks which conflict with the basic idea of preserving their natural amenities.

In this connection the National Countryside Committee is the YHA's special watchdog and it operates in partnership with YHA Regions to ensure that the Association's views are made known in debates and public enquiries concerning land usage and development.

APPENDIX A: CONSULTATION CHECK LIST

Suggested consultations check list of bodies (other than those directly concerned with "water" functions) likely to be affected by a proposal for recreational development — *see* section entitled "Consultation", Chapter 9, p. 226.

Area affected	Bodies to be consulted
(a) Any area in respect of which it is considered that the proposed works would have major recreational or environmental impact.	County council, district council, Nature Conservancy Council, local conservation and recreational interests.
(b) National Park.	Park planning authority or committee, district council, local recreational and conservation interests.
(c) "Area of Outstanding Natural Beauty" designated under the National Parks and Access to the Countryside Act 1949.	County council, district council, local recreational and conservation interests.
(d) (i) "Heritage coast" in a National Park.	As in (b) above
(ii) "Heritage coast" not in a National Park.	As in (c) above.
(e) Areas of great landscape, scientific, or historic value designated in local planning authority development plans.	As in (c) above.
(f) "Sites of Special Scientific Interest" (SSSIs) designated under the National Parks and Access to the Countryside Act 1949.	Nature Conservancy Council.
(g) National nature reserve.	Nature Conservancy Council.
(h) Other nature reserves.	Owner or manager.
(i) Bird sanctuary as designated under Protection of Birds Acts 1954 to 1976.	As in (c) above.
(j) Conservation area designated by a local planning authority council.	County council, district council.
(k) Listed building of historical or architectural interest.	As in (c) above.
(l) Ancient monument.	As (c) above, together with the Director of Ancient Monuments.
(m) Footpaths and other public rights of access to area of mountain, moor, heath, down, cliffs or foreshore and other places of natural beauty (i) in a National Park (ii) not in a National Park.	As (b) above. As (c) above.
(n) Any urban area.	County council, district council.

APPENDIX I

SUMMARY OF RECREATIONAL ACTIVITIES AND FACILITIES AT WATER SUPPLY RESERVOIRS
(ENGLAND AND WALES)

Water authority (includes water companies)	No. of reservoirs	Area, hectares	Fishing Game			Fishing Coarse		Sailing		Sub-aqua		Canoeing		Rowing		Water skiing		Bird watching			Country park	Picnic site	Viewing point
			O	*	P	*	P	*	P	*	P	*	P	*	P	*	P	O	*	P			
Anglian	18	3752	—	1	9	2	3	9	2	5	—	2	—	—	—	2	—	1	7	8	—	3	4
Northumbrian	27	1745	—	12	12	—	—	3	1	1	—	—	—	1	—	2	—	15	1	8	1	3	1
North West	161	3044	—	48	24	11	9	10	2	—	—	6	1	1	—	—	—	2	3	35	4	9	2
Severn-Trent	40	2461	—	10	12	6	4	10	—	5	—	2	—	1	—	—	—	5	3	11	—	8	13
Southern	8	766	—	3	7	1	1	4	—	1	—	3	—	1	—	—	—	2	—	6	1	2	1
South West	26	730	2	7	16	1	2	8	1	2	—	3	—	3	—	2	—	3	2	12	—	5	5
Thames	38	1871	—	1	7	16	7	8	1	—	—	—	—	1	—	—	—	3	2	20	—	2	—
Welsh	88	3716	—	40	50	—	5	10	4	5	—	7	2	2	1	—	—	3	5	4	1	23	12
Wessex	17	1000	—	2	9	1	—	4	—	2	—	1	—	—	—	—	—	—	—	8	—	3	4
Yorkshire	109	1996	—	23	11	3	3	14	—	2	—	5	—	1	—	—	—	5	8	44	—	7	8
Totals	532	21081	2	147	157	40	36	80	10	24	—	29	3	11	1	6	—	36	29	156	7	65	50

Notes: 1. **Source:** based on information contained in the Water Space Amenity Commission Annual Report for 1979-80.

2. Natural lakes used for water supply purposes and reservoirs under 2 hectares surface area are excluded.

3. **Key:** O = open to general public; * = access restricted (club, trust, private); and P = permission necessary for public access (permit, ticket, letter of authority).

APPENDIX II

DIRECTORY OF PARTICIPATING BODIES

Body	Address	Telephone No.
THE WATER INDUSTRY		
ENGLAND AND WALES		
Department of the Environment	2 Marsham Street, London	01-212 3434
Ministry of Agriculture, Fisheries and Food	Great Westminster House, Horseferry Road, London SW1P 2AE	01-216 8311
National Water Council	1 Queen Anne's Gate, London SW1H 9BT	01-222 8111
Water Space Amenity Commission	1 Queen Anne's Gate, London SW1H 9BT	01-222 8111
Regional Water Authorities		
Anglian	Ambury Road, Huntingdon, Cambs. PE18 6NZ.	0480 56181
Northumbrian	Northumbria House, Regent Centre, Gosforth, Newcastle upon Tyne NE3 3PX	0632 843151
North West	Dawson House, Great Sankey, Warrington WA5 3LW	092-572 4321
Severn-Trent	Abelson House, 2297 Coventry Road, Sheldon, Birmingham B26 3PU	021-743 4222
Southern	Guildbourne House, Chatsworth Road, Worthing, West Sussex BN11 1LD	0903 205252
South West	3-5 Barnfield Road, Exeter, Devon EX1 1RE	0392 50861-3
Thames	New River Head, Rosebery Avenue, London EC1R 4TP	01-837 3300
Welsh	Cambrian Way, Brecon, Powys LD3 7HP	0874 3181
Wessex	Wessex House, Passage Street, Bristol BS2 0JQ	0272 290611
Yorkshire	West Riding House, 67 Albion Street, Leeds LS1 5AA	0532 448201
Water Companies		
Bournemouth and District Water	Alderney Waterworks, Francis Avenue, Bournemouth BH11 8NB	020-16 2261
Bristol Waterworks	P.O. Box No. 218, Bridgwater Road, Bristol BS99 7AU	0272 665881
Cambridge Water	Rustat Road, Cambridge CB1 3QS	0223 47351
Cheadle Waterworks	43 Chapel Street, Cheadle, Staffs.	05384 2388
Chester Waterworks	Aqua House, 45-51 Boughton, Chester CH3 5AU	0244 20501
Cholderton and District Water	Estate Office, Cholderton, Salisbury, Wilts.	098064 203

Appendix II—*continued*

Body	Address	Telephone No.
Colne Valley Water	Blackwell House, Aldenham Road, Watford, Herts. ED2 2EY	Watford 23333
Corby (Northants) and District Water	Geddington Road, Corby, Northants. NN18 8ES	05366 2331
East Anglian Water	163 High Street, Lowestoft, Suffolk	0502 2406-9
East Surrey Water	London Road, Redhill, Surrey RH1 1LJ	0737 66333
East Worcestershire Waterworks	46 New Road, Bromsgrove, Worcs. B60 2JT	0527 75151
Eastbourne Waterworks	14 Upperton Road, Eastbourne, East Sussex BN21 1EP	0323 21371
Essex Water	342 South Street, Romford, Essex RM1 2AL	0708 46076
Folkestone and District Water	The Cherry Garden, Cherry Garden Lane, Folkestone, Kent CT19 4QB	0303 76951
Hartlepools Water	3 Lancaster Road, Hartlepool, Cleveland TS24 8LW	0429 74405-6
Lee Valley Water	Bishop's Rise, Hatfield, Herts. AL10 9HL	Hatfield 64311
Mid Kent Water	P.O. Box 45, High Street, Snodland, Kent ME6 5AH	0634 240313
Mid Southern Water	Frimley Green, Camberley, Surrey GU16 6HZ	02516 5031-7
Mid-Sussex Water	P.O. Box 129, 1 Church Road, Haywards Heath, West Sussex RH16 4DX	0444 57711
Newcastle and Gateshead Water	P.O. Box 10, Allendale Road, Newcastle upon Tyne NE6 2SW	0632 654144
North Surrey Water	The Causeway, Staines, Middlesex TW18 3BX	Staines 55464
Portsmouth Water	P.O. Box No. 8, West Street, Havant, Hants. PO9 1LG	0705 486333
Rickmansworth and Uxbridge Water	London Road, Rickmansworth, Herts. WD3 1LB	Rickmansworth 76633
South Staffordshire Waterworks	50 Sheepcote Street, Birmingham B16 8AR	021-643 8131
Sunderland and South Shields Water	29 John Street, Sunderland, Tyne and Wear SR1 1JU	0783 57123
Sutton District Water	59 Gander Green Lane, Cheam, Sutton, Surrey SM1 2EW	01-643 8050
Tendring Hundred Waterworks	Mill Hill, Manningtree, Essex CO11 2AZ	020639 2155-7
West Hampshire Water	Knapp Mill, Mill Road, Christchurch, Dorset BH23 2LU	0202 483361
West Kent Water	Cramptons Road, Sevenoaks, Kent TN14 5DG	0732 52307
Wrexham and East Denbighshire Water	21 Egerton Street, Wrexham, Clwyd LL11 1ND	0978 262126

Appendix II—*continued*

Body	Address	Telephone No.
York Waterworks	Lendal Tower, York, North Yorkshire YO1 2DL	0904 22171-2
SCOTLAND		
Scottish Development Department	New St. Andrew's House, Edinburgh EH1 3S7	031-556 8400
Water Authorities		
Borders Regional Council	West Grove, Waverley Road, Melrose, Roxburghshire TD6 9SJ	089-682 2056
Central Regional Council	Viewforth, Stirling FK8 2ET	0786 3111
Dumfries and Galloway Regional Council	Council Offices, Dumfries DG1 2DD	0387 3141-6
Fife Regional Council	Fife House, Glenrothes KQ7 5LT	0592 754411
Grampian Regional Council	Woodhill House, Ashgrove Road West, Aberdeen AB9 2LU	0224 682222
Highland Regional Council	Regional Buildings, Glenurquhart Road, Inverness IV3 5NX	0463 34131
Lothian Regional Council	George IV Bridge, Edinburgh EH1 1UQ	031-229 9292
Strathclyde Regional Council	Strathclyde House, 20 India Street, Glasgow G2 4PF	041-204 2900
Tayside Regional Council	Bullion House, Invergowrie, Dundee DD2 5BB	082-67 581
River Purification Boards		
Clyde	Rivers House, Murray Road, East Kilbride, Glasgow G75 0LA	035-52 38181
Forth	Colinton Dell House, West Mill Road, Colinton, Edinburgh EH13 0PH	031-441 4691
Highland	Strathpeffer Road, Dingwall IV15 9QY	Dingwall 2021-2
North East	Woodside House, Mugiemoss Road, Persley, Aberdeen AB2 2UQ	0224 696647
Solway	39 Castle Street, Dumfries DG1 1DL	0387 63031-2
Tay	3 South Street, Perth PH2 8NJ	0738 27989
Tweed	Burnbrae, Mossilee Road, Galashiels TD1 1NF	0896 2425/4797
NORTHERN IRELAND		
Department of the Environment for N.I.	Parliament Buildings, Stormont, Belfast BT4 3SS	0232 768716
Northern Ireland Water Council	Parliament Buildings, Stormont, Belfast BT4 3SS	0232 768716

Appendix II—*continued*

Body	Address	Telephone No.
Water Service Divisions:— Eastern:	1 Donegall Square North, Belfast BT1 5GE	0232 45541 and 0232 28161
Northern:	Thomas Street, Ballymena, Co. Antrim BT43 6BA	0266 3655
South:	Craigavon House, Bachelor's Walk, Portadown, Craigavon, Co. Armagh BT63 5BH	0762 34221
Western:	P.O. Box 8, Altnagelvin, Londonderry BT47 2LL	0504 46211

STATUTORY, CONSERVATION, AND RECREATIONAL BODIES

Body	Address	Telephone No.
Amateur Rowing Association	6 Lower Mall, Hammersmith, London W6 9DJ	01-748 3632
Anglers' Co-operative Association	Midland Bank Chambers, Westgate, Grantham, Lincs NG31 6LE	0476 61008
Association of District Councils	25 Buckingham Gate, London SW1 6LE	
British Canoe Union	Flexel House, 45 High Street, Addlestone, Weybridge Surrey KT15 1JV	Weybridge 41341
British Field Sports Society	59 Kennington Road, London SE1 7PZ	01-928 4742
British Horse Society	British Equestrian Centre, Stoneleigh, Kenilworth, Warwickshire CV8 2LR	0203 52241
British Orienteering Federation	Matlock, Derbyshire	0629 3661
British Mountaineering Council	Crawford House, Precinct Centre, Booth Street East, Manchester M13 9RZ	061-273 5835
British Sports Association for the Disabled (BSAD)	Sir Ludwig Guttmann Sports Centre for the Disabled—Stoke Mandeville, Harvey Road, Aylesbury, Bucks HP21 8PP	0296 27889
Water Sports Division of BSAD	29 Ironlatch Avenue, St. Leonards-on-Sea, East Sussex TN38 9JE	0424 427931
British Sub-Aqua Club	70 Brompton Road, London SW3 1HA	01-584 7163
British Trust for Conservation Volunteers	10-14 Duke Street, Reading, Berks RG1 4RU	0734 596171
British Water-Ski Federation	70 Brompton Road, London SW3 1EX	01-584 8262
British Waterways Board	Melbury House, Melbury Terrace, London NW1 6JX	01-262 6711
Camping Club of Great Britain and Ireland	11 Lower Grosvenor Place, London SW1	01-828 1012

Appendix II—*continued*

Body	Address	Telephone No.
Central Council for Physical Recreation	Francis House, Francis Street, London SW1P 1DE	01-828 3163
Central Electricity Generating Board	Planning Department, Sudbury House, 15 Newgate Street, London EC1	01-248 1202
Commons Open Spaces and Footpaths Preservation Society	25A Bell Street, Henley-on-Thames, Oxon RG9 2BA	04912 3535
Council for Environmental Protection	Zoological Gardens, Regents Park, London NW1 4RY	01-722 7111
Council for the Protection of Rural England	4 Hobart Place, London SW1W 0HY	01-235 9481
Country Landowners Association	16 Belgrave Square, London SW1X 8PQ	01-235 0511
Countryside Commission	John Dower House, Crescent Place, Cheltenham, Glos GL50 3RA	0242 21381
Countryside Commission for Scotland	Battleby, Redgorton, Perth PH1 3EW	0738 27921
Cruising Association	Ivory House, St. Katharine Dock, London E1 9AT	01-481 0881
English Tourist Board	4 Grosvenor Gardens, London SW1W 0DU	01-730 3400
Forestry Commission	231 Corstorphine Road, Edinburgh EH12 7AT	031-334 0303
Girl Guides Association	17-19 Buckingham Palace Road, London SW1W 0PT	
Inland Waterways Amenity Advisory Council	122 Cleveland Street, London W1P 5DN	01-387 7973
Inland Waterways Association	114 Regent's Park Road, London NW1 8UQ	01-586 2510
Institute of Fisheries Management	Balmaha, Coldwells Road, Holmer, Hereford	
National Angler's Council	5 Cowgate, Peterborough PE1 1LR	0733 54084
National Association of Youth Clubs	70 St. Nicholas Circle, Leicester LE1 5NY	0533 29514
National Caving Association	c/o Department of Geography, University of Birmingham, Birmingham B15 2TT	021-472 1301
British Cave Research Association	9 Grandview Road, Thundersley, Essex SS7 3JE	
Cave Diving Group	Withey House, Withey Close, West Bristol BS9 3SX	
National Farmers Union	Agriculture House, Knightsbridge, London SW1X 7NJ	01-235 5077
National Federation of Anglers	Halliday House, 2 Wilson Street, Derby DE1 1PG	0332 362000
National Trust	42 Queen Anne's Gate, London SW1H 9AS	01-222 9251
Nature Conservancy Council	19/20 Belgrave Square, London SW1X 8PY	01-235 3241

Appendix II—*continued*

Body	Address	Telephone No.
Northern Ireland Tourist Board	River House, 48 High Street, Belfast BT1 2DS	0232 31221
Professional Institutions Council for Conservation	12 Great George Street, Parliament Square, London SW1P 3AD	01-222 7000
Ramblers' Association	1/5 Wandsworth Road, London SW8 2LJ	01-582 6878
Royal Association for Disability and Rehabilitation	25 Mortimer Street, London W1N 8AB	01-637 5400
Royal Life Saving Society	Mountbatten House, Studley, Warwicks. B80 7NN	052-785 3943
Royal Society for Nature Conservation	The Green, Nettleham, Lincoln LN2 2NR	0522 752326
Royal Society for the Prevention of Accidents	Cannon House, The Priory, Queensway, Birmingham B4 6BS	021-233 2461
Royal Society for the Protection of Birds	The Lodge, Sandy, Beds SG19 2DL	Sandy 80551
Royal Yachting Association	Victoria Way, Woking, Surrey GU21 1EQ	048-62 5022
Salmon and Trout Association	Fishmongers' Hall, London Bridge, London EC4R 9EL	01-626 3531
Sand and Gravel Association	48 Park Street, London W1Y 4HE	01-499 8967
Scottish Sports Council	1 St. Colne Street, Edinburgh EH3 6AA	031-225 8411
Scottish Tourist Board	23 Ravelston Terrace, Edinburgh EH4 3EU	031-332 2433
Scout Association	Baden-Powell House, Queen's Gate, London SW7 5JS	01-584 7030
Sea Cadet Corps	Broadway House, Broadway, London SW19 1RL	01-540 8222
Sports Council	70 Brompton Road, London SW3 1EX	01-589 3411
Sports Council for Northern Ireland	49 Malone Road, Belfast BT9 6RZ	0232 663154
Sports Council for Wales	National Sports Centre for Wales, Sophia Gardens, Cardiff CF1 9SW	0222 397571
Ulster Countryside Committee	Parliament Buildings, Stormont, Belfast BT4 3SS	0232 768716
Wales Tourist Board	Brunel House, 2 Fitzalan Road, Cardiff CF2 1UY	
Wildfowl Trust	Slimbridge, Gloucester GL2 7BT	045-389 333
Wildfowlers' Association of Great Britain and Ireland	Marford Mill, Rossett, Nr. Wrexham, Clwyd LL12 0HL	0224 570881
Youth Hostels Association (England and Wales)	National Office, Trevelyan House, St. Albans, Herts AL1 2DY	St. Albans 55215

INDEX